Teacher's Edition

Laboratory Manual:
the
PHYSICAL WORLD

An Introduction to Physical Science
for Christian Schools

Thomas G. Lamb

R. Terrance Egolf

Linda E. Shumate

Bob Jones University Press • Greenville, South Carolina 29614

PLEASE NOTE:

You are legally responsible for the safety of your students in the lab. Insist that they follow safe lab practices. Do not leave them unattended while they are working on any experiment or project in the lab.

The law requires that all permanent containers (not beakers, flasks, etc., that are used for less than one week) be labeled with an HMIS (Hazardous Materials Identification System) label. HMIS labels rank the chemical hazard in terms of health, flammability, reactivity, and contact on a scale from 0 to 4 (0=no hazard; 4=extreme hazard). The information you will need to prepare these labels can be found in the MSDS (Material Safety Data Sheet) obtained from the chemical supplier.

An MSDS must be on file for each chemical you have on hand, and it must be located in an area that is easily accessible to your students. It would be a valuable use of your instructional time to go over the HMIS/MSDS formats with your students.

Your legal responsibilities as a laboratory instructor are covered for the most part by the following groups of regulations:

1. OSHA 29 CFR 1910.1200 Hazard Communication Standard

2. OSHA 29 CFR 1910 Health and Safety Standards: Occupational Exposure to Toxic Substances in Laboratories

3. EPA Summary of Small Quantity Hazardous Waste Generator Rules—Resource Conservation and Recovery Act (40 CFR 261.5, 45 FR 76623, 46 FR 27476)

An excellent book that explains these regulations in plain English is *Managing Safety in the Chemical Laboratory* by James P. Dux and Robert F. Stalzer (1988, Van Nostrand Reinhold).

You may want to consult with your school lawyer to determine whether any local or state regulations should be taken into consideration. Rules regarding laboratory safety and chemical disposal are constantly changing. Safety and disposal procedures in this lab manual should be regarded as only generalized suggestions. You should consult the safety and chemical disposal laws in your own state and community, as well as the most recent OSHA and EPA guidelines.

Although you may resent the intrusion of the government into your classroom, your example will influence the attitude of your students with regard to personal safety, a Christian's responsibility to government, and our responsibility for managing and protecting the environment.

Note:
The fact that materials produced by other publishers may be referred to in this volume does not constitute an endorsement of the content or theological position of materials produced by such publishers. Any references and ancillary materials are listed as an aid to the student or the teacher and in an attempt to maintain the accepted academic standards of the publishing industry.

Laboratory Manual:
THE PHYSICAL WORLD
AN INTRODUCTION TO PHYSICAL SCIENCE for Christian Schools® Teacher's Edition

Thomas Lamb, Ph.D.
R. Terrance Egolf, CDR, USN (Ret.)
Linda Shumate

Editor
Becky J. Smith

Cover Design
Jeremy Jantz

Cover Photo: PhotoDisc, Inc.

Produced in cooperation with the Division of Natural Science
of the Bob Jones University College of Arts and Science.

for Christian Schools is a registered trademark of Bob Jones University Press.

ISBN 1-57924-419-x

20 19 18 17 16 15 14 13 12 11 10 9 8 7 6 5 4

CONTENTS

INTRODUCTION

If science were merely a collection of facts, you would need only an encyclopedia to study science. You could simply research, read, and memorize information that someone else had collected. But science is much more than just a collection of facts. It is a working process, a method of thinking, and a way to solve problems. Science is what scientists do; memorizing a textbook full of facts could not teach you true science.

When it comes to learning, nothing can compare to hands-on experience. The investigations and demonstrations in this book were developed so that you will become genuinely interested in science. Through attention to detail, hard work, and good old-fashioned persistence, you will earn a great appreciation for scientific research and how valuable it is to our present understanding of the physical world.

Purposes

This laboratory manual was developed for the following purposes:

- *To help you understand how science works.* Science is a method of gathering information and solving problems that relate to the physical universe. You will not *imitate* scientists in this course; you will actually *be* a scientist. You will see firsthand how science works, what it can do, and what it cannot do.

- *To help you remember the information in your textbook.* You can remember information more easily when you use it than when you simply memorize it. The applications, investigations, and demonstrations in this laboratory manual allow you to review, apply, and observe the ideas you have encountered in your textbook.

- *To help you develop scientific attitudes.* Are you curious? Do you make decisions based on facts? How do you react when some fact seems to contradict one of your beliefs? A scientific attitude will help you make reasonable decisions in areas as different as buying clothes, forming opinions about ecology, and choosing which courses to take in school.

- *To help you build problem-solving skills.* All your life you will be solving some sort of problem. This laboratory manual will guide you in making accurate observations and sound judgments as you investigate scientific problems.

- *To help you learn laboratory skills.* The activities in this manual will teach you to make accurate measurements and to use common laboratory equipment safely.

Procedures

No book can force you to learn. You are responsible for the benefit you gain from each class period. With the proper attitude and consistent effort, you can succeed. In order to do your best work, follow these procedures as you use this book.

- *Before each class period*

1. Read the entire exercise that your teacher has assigned. Answer the pre-laboratory questions. If you do this, you will be more efficient during lab time because you will know what you are supposed to be doing.

2. Review the textbook material that matches the topic of the investigation. You cannot benefit from an activity if you do not understand what principles it is supposed to teach you.

3. Plan ahead. Organize your work so that you can complete each investigation quickly and efficiently.

4. Bring all necessary supplies with you to class. Besides your lab manual, you will need your textbook, extra paper, and pencils with erasers. For some investigations you may want to bring an apron or an old shirt to protect your school clothes.

- *During the class period*

1. Follow carefully all the instructions given by your teacher as well as all the instructions in your laboratory manual. Do not proceed with the investigation until told to do so.

2. Work efficiently. Restrict your talking to questions that will help you do your work better.

3. Ask questions if you are not sure what to do. The time you spend getting your questions answered will be far less than the time you spend hesitating to begin because of confusion.

4. Record your results accurately. Observations should be recorded as soon as possible after they are made. You may postpone answering some of the questions in the investigation until after class in order to save time.

5. Put each piece of equipment away and clean up your work area when you have completed the investigation.

- *After the class period*

1. Answer all the questions in the investigation. Because the first and most important step to a good grade is completeness, you should do your own work. Although the observations you make will often be the same as your partner's, never copy answers to questions.

2. Answer the questions whenever possible in complete, thoughtful statements. Try to explain why your answer is true using the concepts you have learned.

3. Promptly turn in your report to your teacher.

4. File your work in a three-ring notebook after your teacher has returned it.

Policies

When you walk into a laboratory, you are walking into a potentially dangerous place. What may seem like innocent horseplay could end up seriously hurting you or your classmates or damaging expensive equipment. Obey the following rules and any other guidelines your teacher sets up for your laboratory.

1. Follow closely all written instructions and listen carefully when your teacher gives you instructions.

2. Never perform unauthorized experiments. It is good to be curious, but you should never mix chemicals together to "see what will happen."

3. Wear safety goggles and protective clothing whenever you use chemicals or a heat source.

4. Know where eyewashes, fire blankets, emergency showers, and fire extinguishers are located. Learn how to use them.

5. Avoid touching chemicals. Never taste chemicals or let them touch your eyes. Smell chemicals by fanning their vapors toward your nose with your hand. Never smell chemicals by inhaling deeply.

6. Secure long hair and loose clothing that could interfere with your work.

7. Never heat a closed container. When heating a test tube, flask, or beaker, point the open end away from yourself and any other people in the room.

8. Keep your workspaces neat and uncluttered.

9. Report any accident, however minor it may seem, to the teacher.

10. Keep combustible materials away from open flames.

11. With large amounts of water flush any acids or bases that are spilled on clothing or skin.

We hope that you will have a safe and exciting year studying science, one that will provide you with valuable information and experience. This lab manual will help you to achieve goals that you have set for yourself, but more importantly, it will open doors for you into areas of science you may not have known existed. Even if you don't enter into a career in science, you will undoubtedly face many situations in life in which a basic knowledge of science is crucial. This is the time of your life where you should be walking through open doors, not slamming them shut before you look inside. Who knows—once you walk through the door, you may like what you see!

1A INVESTIGATION
Laboratory Safety

Objectives

The purpose of this exercise is to

1. Familiarize you with the basic rules for laboratory safety.

2. Point out safety equipment in the laboratory.

3. Review basic first aid for common accidents.

4. Identify information on warning labels of common products.

5. Discuss the personal protection and hazard index.

Materials List

Suggested household products
Bleach
Hair spray
Household cleaner
Shaving cream
Paint

Suggested laboratory chemicals
Sodium fluoride
Ammonium nitrate
Mercuric chloride
Lead metal

Introduction

The laboratories that you will perform in this course have been designed with the maximum safety possible. However, even household items can become dangerous if they are not used properly. Before you begin a laboratory investigation, you are expected to have read and understood the procedures. You may not begin the in-class portion of the investigation until directed to do so by your teacher. These rules are for your safety, so follow them at all times.

Introduction

This investigation will include the class period and a homework assignment. The purpose of the investigation is to impress upon the students a serious laboratory attitude and to introduce safety practices that will be used in the remainder of the course. The information for the investigation is primarily found on the bottle label of the chemicals being used in the investigation. By law, the hazard index and personal protection information should be on every bottle stored or used in a laboratory. This information can be obtained from the Material Safety Data Sheet (MSDS), which is available upon request from your chemical supplier. Fully equipped classroom laboratories may have fire extinguishers, eyewash stations, fire blankets, and a shower. These items should be discussed. A suggested list of chemicals for this activity is provided in the materials list. You should plan to use three household products and four lab chemicals. Other substances may be substituted.

Note: Additional chemicals can be evaluated using the blank MSDS information form in the back of the lab manual.

Pre-Laboratory Questions

Read the entire investigation. Answer the following questions prior to class on a separate sheet of paper. Use complete sentences.

1. What is the purpose of this investigation?

2. What should you do if a chemical splashes in your eye?

3. Can household products be dangerous? How can you tell?

4. Give the four items that a label on a container should contain.

5. Give two reasons that household and laboratory chemicals should be stored only in their designated containers.

Basic Laboratory Rules

1. Never perform any experiment without the teacher's permission.
2. Avoid playful, distracting, or boisterous behavior.
3. Work at your own station and do not "visit" with other groups.
4. Never have food or drink in a laboratory.
5. Never taste any chemicals or drink out of any chemical glassware.
6. Place solid trash in the wastebasket and liquid wastes in designated containers.
7. Notify the teacher of any injuries, spills, or breakages.
8. Never leave a flame or heater unattended.

Laboratory Safety Features

A. Eyewash stations (if equipped)
   1. The purpose of the eyewash station is to remove any chemical that gets into your eyes.
   2. Locate the eyewash stations in the room and turn on the water to see how the stations work.

B. Showers (if equipped)
   1. The purpose of the showers is to wash any dangerous chemicals off your clothes or skin.
   2. Locate the shower in the laboratory and observe how it works. **Do not test the shower.**

C. Fire blanket (if equipped)
   1. The purpose of the fire blanket is to wrap up a person if his clothes catch fire.
   2. Locate the fire blanket in the room.

D. Fire extinguishers
  1. There may be several different types of fire extinguishers available that are made for different types of fires.

  2. Locate the fire extinguishers and determine their specific use.

  Location   *Use*

  a. _____   _____

  b. _____   _____

Basic First Aid for Minor Injuries (Notify the lab instructor of all accidents.)

1. Eyes—If any chemical gets into your eyes, remove contact lenses and flush the area with plenty of water for fifteen minutes. Seek medical attention.

2. Minor heat burns—Apply cold water to the affected area.

3. Acid or alkali burns—Flush the area with plenty of water. If irritation persists, seek medical attention.

4. Cuts—Wash the area thoroughly with soap and water.

5. Inhalation of chemical dust or vapors—Remove to fresh air and observe for ten to fifteen minutes. Seek medical attention if breathing distress continues.

Warning Labels

Laboratory chemicals and common household products can be dangerous if they are not used properly. Labels on the containers should specify the hazards, first aid procedures, personal protection information, and the hazard index. Complete the following information about the following chemicals. It may not be possible to complete the information on every product since the labels may not contain all of the information. This investigation can be completed by using products found at home.

1. Hazard index
   Health (e.g., 3—serious hazard)
   Flammability
   Reactivity

2. Personal protection index (e.g., D—face shield, gloves, synthetic apron)

3. Warnings—Warnings may include the following:
   Target organs
   Combustible or explosive
   Strong oxidizer or corrosive
   Storage and disposal instructions

4. First aid

5. Use

NFPA diamond symbol Copyright © 1996, National Fire Protection Association, Qunicy, MA 02269. This warning system is intended to be interpreted and applied only by properly trained individuals to identify fire, health and reactivity hazards of chemicals. The user is referred to certain limited number of chemicals with recommended classifications in NFPA 49 and NFPA 325M which would be used as a guideline only. Whether the chemicals are classified by NFPA or not, anyone using the 704 system to classify chemicals does so at their own risk.

Safety Marking Information

The following material is provided as a reference for helping students to understand the hazard codes they may find on various household and laboratory chemicals. It is not intended to be exhaustive, and the information may change over time. To obtain the most current safety marking information, you should contact the National Fire Protection Association (NFPA) office or visit their web site on the Internet at http://www.nfpa.org.

A common symbol found on many commercial chemicals is the NFPA "hazard diamond" shown below. This information relates to how the substance responds to fires. For a given chemical, the diamond will have a number between 0 (least severe hazard) to 4 (most severe hazard) in each of the spaces named (Health), (Flammability), and (Reactivity).

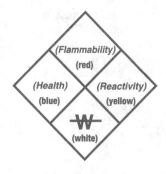

The codes for health hazards vary from 0— "Exposure under fire conditions would offer no hazard beyond that of ordinary combustible materials"—to 4—"Very short exposure could cause death or serious residual injury even though prompt medical attention was given."

A. *Bleach*

1. Hazard index—Health ___3___   Flammability ___0___   Reactivity ___1___

2. Personal protection _B—Safety glasses and gloves_

3. Warnings _Hazardous to humans and domestic animals_

   a. The target organs: ____*skin*____, ____*eyes*____, and ____*stomach*____

   b. Bleach cannot be used with what? _toilet bowl cleaners, rust removers, acids, or ammonia_

   c. What happens if bleach is used with these products? _The combination of chlorine bleach and the above will release hazardous gases._

   d. What will bleach do to metals? _Bleach will pit or discolor metals._

   e. Storage or disposal instructions _Store bleach in a cool, dry place. Rinse empty container and put it in the trash._

4. First Aid—

   a. _Remove contaminated clothing and wash skin thoroughly with water._

   b. _Remove contact lenses and rinse with water for 15 minutes._

   c. _Drink a glass of water._

5. Use _Whitener and sanitizer_

B. _____ (Chemical)

1. Hazard index—Health _____   Flammability _____   Reactivity _____

2. Personal protection _____

3. Warnings _____

   _____

   Target organs _____, _____, and _____

   Storage or disposal instructions _____

4. First aid

   _____

   _____

   _____

5. Use _____

C. _____ (Chemical)

   1. Hazard index—Health _____ Flammability _____ Reactivity _____

   2. Personal protection _____

   3. Warnings _____

   _____

      Target organs _____, _____, and _____

      Storage or disposal instructions _____

   4. First aid

   _____

   _____

   _____

   5. Use _____

The Personal Protection Index is fairly extensive. It consists of eleven iconic symbols representing various protective equipment such as aprons, gloves, protective goggles, and so on. It also includes a series of letters from A through K denoting various combinations of safety equipment to be used with the product. For example, A indicates the use of goggles; B, the use of goggles and gloves; C, the use of goggles, gloves, and apron. Additionally, an X means you must ask your supervisor for special handling instructions.

D. _____ (Chemical)

   1. Hazard index—Health _____ Flammability _____ Reactivity _____

   2. Personal protection _____

   3. Warnings _____

   _____

      Target organs _____, _____, and _____

      Storage or disposal instructions _____

   4. First aid

   _____

   _____

   _____

   5. Use _____

E. _____ (Chemical)

   1. Hazard index—Health _____ Flammability _____ Reactivity _____

   2. Personal protection _____

   3. Warnings _____

   _____

      Target organs _____, _____, and _____

      Storage or disposal instructions _____

   4. First aid

   _____

   _____

   _____

   5. Use _____

F. _____ (Chemical)

  1. Hazard index—Health _____   Flammability _____   Reactivity _____

  2. Personal protection _____

  3. Warnings _____

       _____

      Target organs _____, _____, and _____

      Storage or disposal instructions _____

  4. First aid

       _____

       _____

       _____

  5. Use _____

G. *(Optional)* _____ (Chemical)

  1. Hazard index—Health _____   Flammability _____   Reactivity _____

  2. Personal protection _____

  3. Warnings _____

       _____

      Target organs _____, _____, and _____

      Storage or disposal instructions _____

  4. First aid

       _____

       _____

       _____

  5. Use _____

H. (Optional) _____ (Chemical)

  1. Hazard index—Health _____   Flammability _____   Reactivity _____

  2. Personal protection _____

  3. Warnings _____

       _____

      Target organs _____, _____, and _____

      Storage or disposal instructions _____

  4. First aid

       _____

       _____

       _____

  5. Use _____

Observations and Classification

Name _____

Date _____ Hour _____

Objectives

The purpose of this investigation is to touch you to make objective observations about common items and then to use those observations to classify the items into groups.

Materials

Apple juice
Cola
Cold water
Paper
Penny
Pepper
Rock
Table salt
Wooden block

Equipment

Beaker (250 mL)
Metric ruler
Thermometer

Introduction

A good scientist must make careful and accurate observations so that other scientists can **replicate** (reproduce in a similar way) the results of experiments. To make these observations, the scientist uses his senses. To make the observations more precise, instruments are frequently used. Instruments also make observations more **objective.** An objective observation is one that results from a measurement or the use of descriptive terms that are well defined. **Subjective** observations have limited usefulness in science since they include the observer's personal opinion or use terms that are **ambiguous** (lack precise meaning). For example, a person from Mexico may say that the weather outside is cool, whereas, an Eskimo may say that the weather is warm. These subjective observations can be made objective by stating that the temperature is 65° F. By stating the degrees, personal opinion and ambiguity are avoided.

Scientists do not just make observations. They use these observations to classify data, formulate questions, evaluate ideas, and test theories. The facts or data recorded in observations cannot change, but as scientists identify new information, the interpretations of those facts change, leading to new scientific theories. Scientific principles are continually being modified and retested by different experiments.

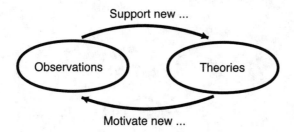

Introduction

The purpose of this investigation is to teach students to make objective observations and then to draw inferences from their observations. Students will not naturally make careful, objective observations. They must be shown what to observe and how to report that observation. It should be pointed out to the students that inferences drawn from facts frequently involve the observer's opinion. Much of what they learn as science will be scientists' opinions that are based on observations. Students can also formulate their own opinions based upon what they observe. That is also science.

There are several terms used in this investigation that may be new to your students. Take time to discuss their definitions and usage.

Pre-Laboratory Questions

Read the entire investigation. Answer the following questions prior to class on a separate sheet of paper. Use complete sentences.

1. Define the following terms.

    a. Replicate

    b. Objective

    c. Subjective

    d. Ambiguous

2. What about science does not change, and what about science is always changing?

Observation Exercise

Selected objects will be given to you for this exercise. For each object, you must write the most accurate descriptive term for each attribute listed on the form that follows. Your teacher may provide suggested descriptions for some of the categories. Some attributes may not be applicable (e.g., flexibility for a liquid). A wooden block will be done as a class example.

Wooden Block

State (solid, liquid, gas)	Odor
Shape	Texture
Size	Hardness
Color	Other observations
Temperature	
Flexibility	

Subjective terms that are very general should be avoided in scientific descriptions whenever possible. To help you distinguish the difference between subjective and objective terms, write a subjective description of the wooden block in the blanks on the next page.

Wooden Block (Subjective description)

Size *Answers will vary (e.g., small).*

Temperature *Answers will vary (e.g., room temperature).*

Hardness *Answers will vary (e.g., fairly hard).*

Rock

State (solid, liquid, gas)		Odor	
Shape		Texture	
Size		Hardness	
Color		Other observatioins	
Temperature			
Flexibility			

Cold Water

State (solid, liquid, gas)		Odor	
Shape		Texture	
Size		Hardness	
Color		Other observations	
Temperature			
Flexibility			

Cola

State (solid, liquid, gas)		Odor	
Shape		Texture	
Size		Hardness	
Color		Other observations	
Temperature			
Flexibility			

Air

State (solid, liquid, gas)		Odor	
Shape		Texture	
Size		Hardness	
Color		Other observations	
Temperature			
Flexibility			

3. *The following list provides some examples of terms you may wish to use in your descriptions. This list is not exhaustive, and you will note that most of these terms are subjective because they are not well defined or involve a personal opinion.*

Shape—regular, irregular, indefinite, cubic, cylindrical, spherical, geometric, box-like

Color—In addition to chromatic colors, you can include pearlescent, mirror-like, etc.

Flexibility—rigid, inflexible, stiff, flexible, flimsy

Odor—flowerlike, burnt, oily, dusty, musty, sweet, burning, acrid, chemical, earthy, decaying flesh, rotten eggs, ammonia, sour

Texture—smooth, satin, matte, coarse, rough, fibrous, dusty, floury, sandy, glassy, leathery, oily, waxy

4. *The Mohs scale of hardness is useful for illustrating a way to make observations more objective. This scale is used to determine the hardness of minerals. It can be found in* Earth Science for Christian Schools, *published by Bob Jones University Press.*

Paper

State (solid, liquid, gas)	Odor
Shape	Texture
Size	Hardness
Color	Other observations
Temperature	
Flexibility	

Table Salt

State (solid, liquid, gas)	Odor
Shape	Texture
Size	Hardness
Color	Other observations
Temperature	
Flexibility	

Pepper

State (solid, liquid, gas)	Odor
Shape	Texture
Size	Hardness
Color	Other observations
Temperature	
Flexibility	

Apple Juice

State (solid, liquid, gas)	Odor
Shape	Texture
Size	Hardness
Color	Other observations
Temperature	
Flexibility	

Penny

State (solid, liquid, gas)	Odor
Shape	Texture
Size	Hardness
Color	Other observations
Temperature	
Flexibility	

_____ (Optional)

State (solid, liquid, gas)	Odor
Shape	Texture
Size	Hardness
Color	Other observations
Temperature	
Flexibility	

Classification Exercise

A collection of observations has little scientific value by itself. The scientist must give meaning to the facts by making an **inference,** that is, deducing something or drawing as a conclusion some new idea. For example, atmospheric information obtained from radar is not useful until a weather forecaster interprets the data and predicts the weather. One way of making an inference is **classification.** To classify means to separate objects into groups that are based on a common characteristic. Establishing a rule based on observable features allows you to make up groups. An example of a rule based on a physical feature would be the color of the object. A rule based upon usefulness would be suitability for a particular use, such as starting a fire.

In this exercise you will classify the observed objects by first establishing a rule. The rule will define two or more different groups in such a way that all objects will fit in one of the groups. The objects in each group will be listed. The objects will be classified two different ways based upon physical characteristics. Do not use the rule given in the example.

Example

Objects observed: wooden block, paper, rock, cold water, table salt, cola, air, pepper, apple juice, penny

	Rule	**Objects**
Group 1	White objects	Table salt, paper
Group 2	Non-white objects	Wooden block, rock, cold water, cola, air, pepper, apple juice, penny

Ideas for Classifications 1 and 2 could include the following:

> *Liquid / nonliquid*
> *Gas / nongas*
> *Room temperature / not room temperature*
> *Definite shape / indefinite shape*

Ideas for Classification 3 could include the following:

> *Edible / nonedible*
> *Satisfies thirst / does not satisfy thirst*
> *Extinguishes fire / does not extinguish fire*

Classification 1 (Physical characteristic) _____

List all the objects that you observed.

	Rule	Objects
Group 1		
Group 2		

Classification 2 (Physical characteristic) _____

List all the objects that you observed.

	Rule	Objects
Group 1		
Group 2		

Classification 3 (Optional—Usefulness) _____

List all the objects that you observed.

	Rule	Objects
Group 1		
Group 2		

Discussion Questions

1. Define the following terms.

   Inference _To make an inference means to draw a conclusion from observations._

   Classification _Classification is separating objects into groups based on a common characteristic._

2. Change the following subjective observations into objective statements.

Subjective	*Objective*
a. Hot	a. *Any reasonable answer is correct (e.g., 90°C).*
b. Cold	b. *Any reasonable answer is correct (e.g., −20°C).*
c. Long	c. *Any reasonable answer is correct (e.g., 100 m).*
d. Heavy	d. *Any reasonable answer is correct (e.g., 900 kg).*
e. Colorful	e. *Any reasonable answer is correct (e.g., bright orange).*

3. Why are inferences necessary in science? *Inferences are necessary to make meaning out of the observations.*

4. Do you think that all objects in nature will neatly fit into the classification systems devised by scientists? Explain your answer. *No, classifying is a human activity seeking to give order to our world. Not everything that was created will fit into man's systems.*

5. Scientists use their *senses* to obtain observations, and *instruments* are used to make their observations more precise and less biased.

6. An objective observation is one that can be *repeated (replicated)* by another scientist.

7. Why is replication important in science? *Humans make errors, and replication is a good way to detect errors. (There are other reasons such as validating experimental procedures, refining results, etc.)*

Name _____

Date _____ Hour _____

Objective

The purpose of this investigation is to solve a problem using scientific methodology.

Materials

Candles
Matches

Equipment

Beakers (250 mL), 2
Metric ruler
Pans for water, 2

Introduction

The **scientific method** is a way of solving problems and is used in all scientific areas. It is not a rigid procedure but rather a set of principles that is followed. It is more accurate to call it *scientific methodology* because the actual steps used for any particular problem may differ from other investigations. To understand how scientific methodology works is equivalent to understanding how scientists work.

The scientific method has a starting point but really no ending point. The first step is to recognize a problem. Then observations are made, data are organized and analyzed, and a solution is chosen. The choice of a solution starts the process again because the solution should be verified by the researcher or other people. Additionally, the initial problem may be evaluated again using different equipment. If the experiment did not verify the original hypothesis, a different hypothesis may be tested. Often, solutions to one problem suggest other questions.

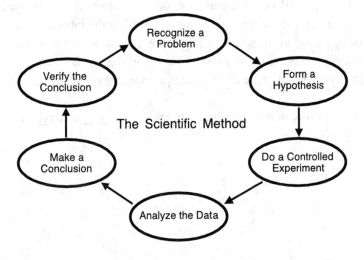

The Scientific Method

Materials and Equipment

Glass jars of sufficient size may be substituted for beakers.

Introduction

This investigation can be done in conjunction with a discussion of the scientific method. Illustrating the scientific method as a cyclical rather than a linear process shows that scientific methodology has the potential to continually increase our understanding of God's physical universe. This process is emphasized in nearly every investigation and forms a basis for teaching critical thinking. The investigation also emphasizes the distinction between observations and inferences. Problems in science and popular literature arise when people fail to make this distinction. The observations that evolutionists and radical ecologists cite may be accurate, but their inferences are frequently questionable.

This investigation emphasizes scientific methodology and not technical accuracy. There are several factors that will affect the results.

- *Some CO_2 gas is produced as the O_2 is consumed.*
- *The solubility of CO_2 is higher than that of O_2.*
- *The flame heats the trapped air, causing it to expand.*
- *Just before the flame dies, it begins producing smoke, which coats the water with soot, interfering with gas absorption.*

The aggregate effect of these factors may produce results that are different from the expected 20% oxygen.

Pre-Laboratory Questions

Read the entire investigation. Answer the following questions prior to class on a separate sheet of paper. Use complete sentences if necessary.

1. What is the scientific method?

2. The scientific method is not a _?_, but rather a set of _?_.

3. Explain why scientific methodology does not have an ending point.

4. What is the first objective in scientific methodology?

Recognize a Problem

Problems in science are frequently stated as questions. A properly formed question is essential for good research. Like a road map, it provides a clear direction to go in solving a problem. A poor question, like a poor map, can result in much wasted time because of wrong turns.

In this investigation we will determine the percentage of oxygen in the air. We will start with the assumption that one of the gases in the atmosphere is oxygen, but we do not know what percentage. From this problem a scientific question can be formed.

Scientific question—What is the percentage of oxygen in the air?

Form a Hypothesis

After stating the research question, all the important information about the topic is obtained and a hypothesis is constructed. A hypothesis is a key feature in science because it formulates the scientific question in a testable form. One test of a valuable scientific idea is whether it can be proved to be true or false. This is why proposing the supposed evolutionary descent of a type of organism from the fossil record is not a part of experimental science. The hypothesized evolution of an extinct organism cannot be tested in the laboratory.

For this investigation, you will formulate a hypothesis by stating your best guess for the percentage of oxygen (0-100%) in the air. For our purposes, it is the testability of the hypothesis that is important and not its correctness.

Hypothesis—I think that the air contains about _____% oxygen.

Do a Controlled Experiment

In this section you will collect data to test your hypothesis.

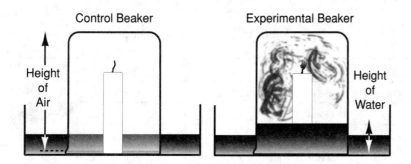

Control Beaker

Experimental Beaker

Height of Air

Height of Water

1. Measure the inside height of the beaker in centimeters.

2. Fasten two candles to the bottoms of pans with hot wax as in the diagram. The beakers must be able to cover the candles without touching the wicks.

3. Pour about 1 cm of water into the pans.

4. Place one of the beakers upside-down over one of the candles.

5. Measure the height of the water inside the beaker from the bottom of the pan. This should be less than 1 cm. Enter this measurement in Table 1, row 1/column 3. Also, subtract the height of water from the measurement you made in step 1, above, and record the difference in Table 1, rows 1-5 in column 2.

The unlit candle is an **experimental control.** The purpose of a control is to provide a comparison. The control is just like the experimental beaker except that it lacks one item, the **experimental variable.** The experimental variable is the factor that the experiment changes to test the hypothesis. In this case, the experimental variable is the presence of the flame.

6. Light the uncovered candle.

7. Quickly place the second beaker over the burning candle.

8. Let the candle burn out, wait about twenty seconds, and then measure the height of the water inside the beaker. Subtract the height of water measurement in step 5, above, from this measurement. Write the difference in Table 1, row 2/column 3. You can assume for the purpose of this investigation that the change of the height of the water column is the same as the amount of air consumed by the candle.

9. Divide the measurement in the third column by that in the second column; then multiply by 100. This gives you the percentage of oxygen that was in the air contained in the beakers. Record this result in Table 1, row 2/column 4.

10. Carefully tip the second beaker to drain the water; then remove it and blow the smoke out of it.

11. Repeat steps 6 through 10 three more times and enter the results in Table 1 for trials 2, 3, and 4.

teachers, although critical thought lies at the heart of science. Some students and teachers may initially feel uncomfortable with this procedure. The initial response of some teachers is not positive when a student points out a problem with a procedure or theory, or identifies a better way to do something. However, such a response indicates that the student is thinking— a goal for all teachers. It should be made clear that critical analysis, although appropriate in science and most areas of human endeavor, is not warranted with respect to God's Word in the sense of attempting to find fault. We accept God's standards as given in the Bible without question. This is a good opportunity to stress that only God is infallible and that the ideas of humans are frequently incorrect.

When removing the beaker from the pan, tip it on one edge to allow the water to drain out before lifting the beaker. If you lift it straight up, the wick may get wet, making repeat trials difficult without a fresh candle.

Analyze the Data

Placing your data in a table allows you to easily retrieve information and make calculations.

Table 1: Experimental Data

Column →	1	2	3	4
Row ↓	Beaker	Height of Air	Height of Water	Percent Oxygen
1	Control	cm	cm	
2	Trial 1	cm	cm	%
3	Trial 2	cm	cm	%
4	Trial 3	cm	cm	%
5	Trial 4	cm	cm	%
6	Average			%

Make a Conclusion

The answer, or solution, to your question is the calculated percent oxygen. However, in this investigation, there are four solutions from which to choose. Instead of selecting the "best" trial (the one that comes closest to your hypothesis), scientists usually average the trials and assume that the average is the best solution. This is a standard principle of scientific methodology since it tends to average out minor factors that are beyond the scientist's control.

To find the average percent of oxygen, add the values of the percent oxygen from trials 1 through 4 and then divide by four.

Average percent oxygen _____%   Record this value in row 6/column 4.

Verify the Conclusion

The verification process checks your procedure to see if your results can be replicated. There are two ways to verify a solution: (1) repeat the experiment and (2) compare your results with another person doing the same experiment. You have repeated your experiment three times (three replications) and now you will compare your results with other groups. Record your average for Group 1 in Table 2 and then obtain the averages from the other groups in your class. Record them in Table 2 as well. Determine the average percentage oxygen for all of the groups in your class and enter this value next to "Average" in the table.

Table 2: Averages

Group	Percent Oxygen (%)
1 (your group)	
2	
3	
4	
Average	

Discussion Questions

Write your answers in complete sentences unless otherwise indicated.

1. Define the following terms.

   a. Experimental variable *It is the item that the experiment alters to test the hypothesis.*

   b. Experimental control *It is a trial that lacks the experimental variable. It provides something with which to compare the experimental trial.*

2. Why is it important to replicate results? *Replication can reveal human, instrument, or procedural errors.*

3. What are the two ways to verify (replicate) results? *You may do the experiment again or compare your results with another person's data.*

4. How was the height of the air and water column made objective? *They were measured with a ruler.*

5. What is the purpose of the hypothesis? *It formulates a testable question.*

6. In the scientific method, why is it necessary to identify a problem first? *A properly stated problem or question provides a clear direction for the investigation.*

Experimental Evaluation

7. What made the water rise in the beaker with the burning candle? *Removal of some of the air caused the water level to rise.*

8. What gas did you assume was burned in the beaker? *We assumed that oxygen was burned.*

9. How did your hypothesis compare with your data? *Answers will vary.*

10. How was your final solution (the percentage of oxygen) chosen? *The average of the results was used.*

11. Do you think this method will always give the best answer? Explain. *Not necessarily, there is a greater chance of the average being closer to correct than any single answer.*

12. Why is it not possible to obtain an exact answer? *Human and experimental errors prevent getting an exact answer.*

13. Why didn't all of your trials come out the same? *Various reasons may be responsible. Many details of the experimental process cannot be exactly duplicated by all investigators.*

14. Why didn't the other groups' averages come out the same? *Same answer as 13.*

15. What observations produced data in this investigation? _The student_
    observed the change in height of the water column.

16. What is the purpose of a control? _The purpose of a control is to provide_
    something to compare to the experimental trial.

17. In this experiment, what was the difference between the control and the
    experimental beaker? _The candle was burned in the experimental beaker._

18. (Optional) What inferences and assumptions were made from these
    observations? _We inferred that the change of air volume in the experimental_
    beaker was due to the consumption of oxygen by the burning candle. We
    assumed that all of the oxygen was consumed, that only oxygen was
    consumed, that no other gases were introduced by the burning process,
    and that no other effects were present that would change the trapped air
    volume (thermal expansion, gas absorption, etc.).

Chapter 2

Name _____

Date _____ Hour _____

Objective

The purpose of this investigation is to introduce the proper form for scientific reports and to illustrate how the scientific method supports this form.

Materials List

Bleach solution
Distilled water
Sugar
Table salt

Equipment List

Alligator clips, 2
Battery (6 V, with binding posts)
Beakers (250 mL), 2
Graduated cylinder (100 mL)
Insulated copper wire
Metal strips (at least 15 cm long), 2
Miniature lamp base
Miniature light bulb
Teaspoon

Introduction

After scientists perform experiments, they publish their work so that other scientists will know what they have done and can verify the results. There are usually four sections in these reports that incorporate the steps of the scientific method: **Introduction, Materials and Procedures, Results,** and **Discussion.** The Introduction states the problem to be tested and gives any related information. The Materials and Procedures section states the equipment to be used, gives the steps to follow, and provides diagrams. The observations are recorded and the data are organized in the Results section. At this point, the investigator often verifies the work by repeating the experiment several times. In the Discussion the investigator states the reasons for the choice of solutions, gives other problems suggested by the research, and further verifies the work by reporting similar experiments performed by other scientists.

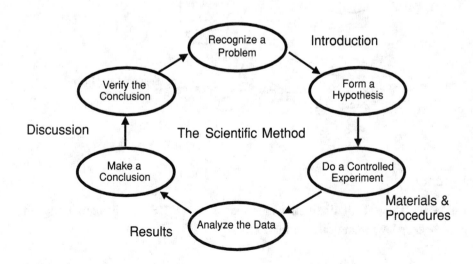

Background

You have probably been told that water does not conduct electricity, yet you have also been told to get out of a swimming pool during a lightning storm. This seems to be a contradiction! An appropriate question for the lifeguard while you are standing on the side of the pool is "Why should I get out of the pool since water does not conduct electricity?" In this investigation you will answer that question. You will use a light bulb to detect electrical current. When the light bulb is not lit, there is no significant current flowing through the water. However, when the bulb is lit, it is as if lightning hit the swimming pool and you "light" up.

Pre-Laboratory Questions

Read the entire investigation. Answer the following questions prior to class on a separate sheet of paper. Use complete sentences.

1. Give the purpose of each of the following parts of a report.

   a. Introduction—

   b. Materials and Procedures—

   c. Results—

   d. Discussion—

2. State your research question.

3. State your hypothesis.

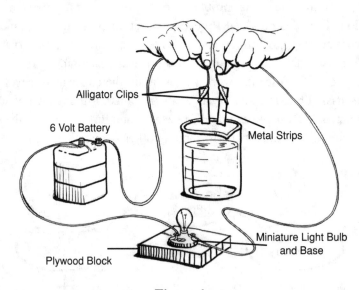

Figure 1

Procedure

1. Pour 150 mL of distilled water into a *clean* 250 mL beaker. Label this beaker **1** with an erasable marker.

2. Place 150 mL of the mixture of bleach and distilled water into a second 250 mL beaker. Label this beaker **2**.

3. Assemble the circuit-testing apparatus according to Figure 1.

4. Touch the metal pieces together to see if the light works. By touching the metal pieces, you create a closed electrical circuit.

   A **closed circuit** means that there is a continuous electrical path, allowing the electricity to make a complete circuit and thus light the light bulb. An **open circuit** means that the electricity cannot follow a complete path because there is an interruption in the path.

5. Place the two metal strips in beaker **1** to determine if the distilled water conducts electricity. Do not let the pieces of metal touch each other in the water. Avoid touching the metal with your fingers. Record your results in the data table under Trial 1 for distilled water.

6. Place the two metal pieces in beaker **2** and observe the light bulb. Record your results in data table.

7. Pour the contents of the beakers down the sink and rinse beaker **2** *thoroughly* in tap water. Rinse the metal strips in tap water.

8. Mix 1 teaspoon of salt and 150 mL distilled water in beaker **1**. Mix 1 teaspoon of sugar and 150 mL distilled water in beaker **2**. Determine the conductivity of each of these solutions using the same procedure as above. Rinse the electrodes between each test. Record your results in the appropriate spaces in the data table under Trial 1.

9. Repeat the experiment if possible and record the results under Trial 2.

10. Record the results from two other groups in the data table under groups 2 and 3.

Attach a third wire to the other screw on the lamp base. Attach the two alligator clips to the two free ends of the wires and insert a metal strip into each clip.

4. A 9 V battery inserted into a battery holder can be used in place of the 6 V battery.

5. Many household items can be substituted for the metal strips. Examples include iron nails, metal paper clips, and stiff aluminum foil. Shine the nails and paper clips with sand paper or steel wool before using.

6. This apparatus will be used in several other investigations, so store the parts in a safe place.

Results

Data Table: Conductivity of Solutions

Solution	Conductive? (Yes or No)			
	Trial 1	Trial 2	Group 2	Group 3
Distilled water				
Water and bleach				
Water and salt				
Water and sugar				

Discussion Questions

Answer the following questions in complete sentences.

1. What information does the background to this investigation give about the conductivity of water? *Water is not supposed to conduct electricity, but swimming pool water does.*

2. What causes water to conduct electricity? *Water will conduct electricity if certain materials are added to the water.*

3. What kind of compound in swimming pools causes the water to conduct?

A compound with chlorine added to swimming pools causes the water to conduct.

4. What are open and closed circuits? *An open circuit has a gap, so the electrons cannot make a complete path from the battery through the circuit and back to the battery. A closed circuit does not have a gap, so the electrons can make the complete circuit.*

Experimental Evaluation

5. State two ways that this experiment was replicated. *Three possible answers are that the students tested the conductivity of different solutions, they may have repeated the trials, and they obtained data from different groups.*

6. Which solution was the control? *The distilled water was the control solution.*

7. What is the purpose of the control? *The control demonstrates that pure water will not conduct electricity.*

8. What is an experimental variable? *An experimental variable is what is being changed.*

9. What was the experimental variable in this experiment? *The experimental variable was the presence of an added substance in the water.*

10. Why was it necessary to touch the metal electrodes together prior to placing them into the solutions? *This test made sure that the light and the rest of the circuit worked.*

11. Is the phrase "one teaspoon" objective or subjective? Explain. *Students should realize that as used in this lab, "teaspoon" is an approximate quantity and is, therefore, subjective. It is a precise volumetric unit in the English measurement system, however.*

12. Did all of the three mixtures conduct electricity? If not, which did not? If not all water solutions conduct electricity, how would you have to modify your hypothesis? *No, the sugar water solution did not conduct electricity. The hypothesis would have to be revised to state that some materials, when added to water, cause it to conduct.*

13. (Optional) The light bulb did not light up when testing the distilled water. Does that prove that distilled water does not conduct any electricity? Explain. *Answers will vary. A very sensitive instrument may detect some current.*

Preparing a Scientific Report

Write a brief scientific report using the information discussed in this investigation. Your teacher will give you the specific guidelines for report length and format. The content should be organized in the following sections: Introduction, Materials and Procedures, Results, and Discussion. You should try to express the problem in your own words, make your own diagrams and tables, and describe the procedure and the results after thinking about the reasons in complete thoughts.

Preparing the Scientific Report

Students at the ninth-grade level generally do not have a lot of experience writing technical papers.

You should provide your students detailed instructions for the written paper.

• Length of paper (no more than two pages, including diagrams)

• Mechanical aspects of paper (handwritten or typed, font, margins, single vs. double-spaced, etc.)

• Detail of diagrams, if included (encourage schematic rather than realistic)

• Data presentation (reproduce the data table in the paper)

• Coordinate with the English teacher several weeks beforehand and make the paper a joint English/science project.

In addition, consider the following:

• Have the students use complete, grammatical sentences.

• Encourage creativity in expression within the limits of the project.

When grading, you should look for an understanding of the basic structure of a scientific report. This experience will be helpful for students considering entering a project in a science fair.

3A APPLICATIONS
Significant Digits/Reading Scales

Objectives

The purpose of this exercise is to

1. Introduce the concept of uncertainty in all measurements.

2, Introduce the use of significant digits and their use in scientific activities.

3. Correctly report the measurements made with common laboratory equipment.

Introduction

Counting

Objects that are counted are reported as exact numbers. When numbering a group of people, for instance, you wouldn't say that there are 12.5 people in the room. A whole number is the only correct way to report such a count. Counting any group of objects is handled the same way. If your teacher gave you a box of paper clips, you could report to him exactly how many paper clips are in that box.

Uncertainty in Measurements

What if you were asked to measure the length of one of the paper clips? This would also appear to be rather simple. If you used a ruler that was calibrated only in centimeters, it would appear to fall somewhere between 3 and 4 centimeters. What would you report? You would probably report an estimate of how far past the 3 cm mark you thought it went, perhaps 3.1 cm.

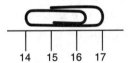

Now, however, your teacher gives you a ruler that is calibrated not only to centimeters but also to millimeters. "Aha," you say. "Now I can give my teacher an exact measurement!" You carefully measure the paperclip and see that the end of the paper clip falls somewhere between 3.1 cm and 3.2 cm. Perhaps with this new ruler you could tell your teacher that the paper clip is 3.13 cm long.

Because you had a measuring device that had greater resolution (i.e., smaller graduations or divisions), you could report the measurement with greater precision. However, because it is not marked with even smaller divisions, you again have had to make an estimate of where between those two measurements the end of the paper clip falls. This example illustrates the uncertainty in making *any* kind of measurement. No matter how small the graduations of your measuring device, you will still have to estimate the last digit that you report. It is for this reason that it is impossible to state that a measurement is exact.

Precision and Accuracy

When you can make a measurement using an instrument with a greater number of subdivisions in its scale, the measurement will be more consistently

Introduction

The first two exercises in Chapter 3 of this lab manual are designed to introduce the student to the meaning and use of significant digits in scientific work. If you do not intend to emphasize significant digits in your course work, it would be best to just skim or even skip Applications 3A and 3B. Students often initially find the use of significant digits confusing until they have had a lot of practice.

Emphasize to your students that significant digits relate to the precision of measurements—they are not just an arbitrary mathematical concept to make life hard for high school science students. Be sure to review the introductory information thoroughly with your students before proceeding with the practical portion of the exercise.

The sequence for presenting this material logically develops the use of significant digits. Students first learn how to make and record measurements, becoming familiar with the uncertainties of measurement in the process. They are then introduced to the rules for making calculations using measurements.

reproduced. In the above example, having ten classmates measure the same paperclip with a millimeter scale will produce ten readings close to 3.1 cm while having the same group make the measurement with a centimeter scale could produce a variety of readings from 3.0 cm to 3.2 cm. *The ability to reproduce a measurement consistently is one definition of* **precision.** The more graduations per unit of measurement an instrument has, the more precise it is. Another term that is often used instead of precision is **accuracy.** *Accuracy refers to how close the instrument can measure to the actual measurement.* Wooden meter sticks can expand and shrink with humidity and metal ruler change length with temperature. Balances get dropped and parts wear. Graduated cylinders are mass-produced and their volumes are not exactly the same. These instruments' accuracies are determined by comparing them against instrument *standards* that are maintained by governments around the world. As you can see, precision and accuracy are two different concepts. For measurements in the laboratory in this course, we will be mainly concerned about the precision of our measurements.

Significant Digits

In any *measurement,* all the digits that are known to be certain (the digits that can be determined from marks on the measuring tool) are reported, plus one that is estimated. This combination of digits is called the **significant digits** of the measurement. When you see a written measurement, you should be able to tell how finely the scale of the measuring device was subdivided (its precision). For instance, a measurement reported as 24.5 g tells you that the balance was only calibrated (marked) with divisions of 1 g and that the last decimal number was estimated. A number reported as 24.506 g indicates that a more sensitive balance was used, one that was calibrated to the nearest 0.01 g and, again, that the last decimal number was estimated. A scientific measurement should never be written with greater or fewer than the permissible number of significant digits. It is important for you to learn how to correctly report the measurements you will be making in future investigations.

Rules

To help you make and report correct scientific measurements, the following list of rules should be followed:

1. All measurements with metric instruments should be reported as decimal numbers, not fractions (0.5 rather than $\frac{1}{2}$).

2. All measurements *must include units* when reported. To report a length of 6.02 is meaningless unless the units used for the measurement are also reported.

3. Measurements must include all digits that are *certain* (based on the markings on the measuring instrument).

4. Measurements must include ONE *estimated digit* to the nearest tenth ($\frac{1}{10}$) of the smallest *decimal* (multiple of 10) calibration marked. This is often called the **least significant digit** of the measurement.

Example: If a balance's smallest calibration marks are 0.1 g, the estimated digit of any measurement will be to the nearest 0.01 g.

Example: If a graduated cylinder's smallest calibration is $\frac{1}{2}$ mL, the estimated digit of any measurement will be to the nearest 0.1 mL (the smallest <u>decimal</u> calibration is 1 mL; $\frac{1}{2}$ is NOT a decimal calibration).

Example: When measuring the length of an object with a ruler calibrated to millimeters, the reading appears to fall exactly on the line 3.4 cm. You would report the measurement as 3.40 cm. Since you are able to estimate to 0.01 cm ($\frac{1}{10}$ mm) with this ruler (see Rules 3 & 4), you must include the final zero to indicate the precision of your measuring device.

Note: When the calibrations are very close together, visually estimating to one-tenth of the interval is impractical. In these cases, estimating to the nearest 0.5 ($\frac{1}{2}$) of the interval is acceptable.

Interpreting Measurements

For each of the following measurements, state the digit that has been estimated and give the smallest calibration of the instrument used to make the measurement.

	Estimated Digit	Calibration
Example: 37.7 mL	7	1 mL
1. 15.02 g	2	0.1 g
2. 7.43 cm	3	0.1 cm
3. −2.9°C	9	1°C

Reading Rulers

On the ruler below, the smallest calibration (marked interval) is 0.1 cm (1 mm). The measurement can be estimated to the nearest 0.01 cm (0.1 mm). Write the measurements for the following points on the ruler. The first two have been done as examples. *Answers ±0.01 cm are acceptable.*

A. 8.13 cm

B. 8.50 cm

C. 8.62 cm

D. 8.80 cm

E. 9.00 cm

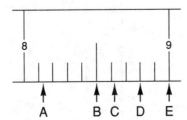

6. The terms markings, divisions, graduations, and calibrations are all synonymous when discussing measuring instruments. "Calibration" often means comparing an instrument's measurements to a reference standard to determine its accuracy.

7. Students generally are not inclined to include units with measurements. Be sure to enforce this practice at this stage in their education so that it becomes a habit. Remind them that a measurement without a unit is meaningless.

8. Emphasize that a decimal graduation is one that is repeated ten times between major graduations. The smallest decimal graduation determines the maximum precision of the instrument.

The answer ranges (±) given for the following problems are guidelines. You may use a wider range of acceptable answers if you feel it is appropriate since the last digit is estimated.

Reading Balances

Below is a portion of the scale of a mass balance that measures in grams. The smallest calibration is ___0.01___ g. Therefore, the measurement can be estimated to one-tenth of the interval, which is ___0.001___ g. Report the measurements at the following points, including the correct units. *Answers ±0.001 g are acceptable.*

A. ___0.715 g___

B. ___0.740 g___

C. ___0.758 g___

D. ___0.773 g___

E. ___0.800 g___

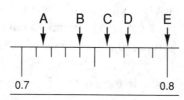

On a less precise balance below, the smallest decimal calibration is ___0.1___ g. The measurement can be estimated to one-tenth of the interval, which is ___0.01___ g. Report the measurements at the following points including the correct units. *Answers ±0.01 g are acceptable.*

A. ___3.15 g___

B. ___3.40 g___

C. ___3.58 g___

D. ___3.73 g___

E. ___4.00 g___

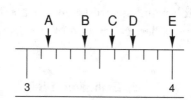

Reading Graduated Cylinders

Measurements made with graduated cylinders follow the same rules as for rulers. The last digit is an estimate of one-tenth of the interval. The smallest marked decimal calibrations on the cylinder below are ___1___ mL. Therefore, the measurement can be estimated to the nearest ___0.1___ mL. Because of the effects of surface tension, the top of the liquid in a cylinder will form a curve called a *meniscus*. The measurement should always be read at the bottom of the meniscus with the eye level with it. Report the measurements at the following points including the correct units. *Answers ±0.1 mL are acceptable.*

A. ___28.5 mL___

B. ___25.0 mL___

C. ___24.0 mL___

D. ___21.3 mL___

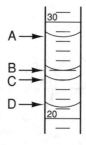

The graduated cylinder below is a small cylinder and is calibrated differently. The smallest decimal calibration is ___1.0___ mL. (Note that there are only five 1/5 mL marks, so these are not *decimal* calibrations.) The measurement can, therefore, be estimated to the nearest ___0.1___ mL (see example 2 under Rule 4 above). Report the measurements at the following points including the correct units. *Answers ±0.1 mL are acceptable.*

A. ___2.9 mL___

B. ___2.5 mL___

C. ___2.4 mL___

D. ___2.2 mL___

Reading Thermometers

The thermometer below is calibrated to ___1___ °C. The measurement can be estimated to the nearest ___0.1___ °C. Report the measurements at the following points including the correct units. *Answers ±0.1 °C are acceptable.*

A. ___24.5 °C___

B. ___28.0 °C___

C. ___30.0 °C___

D. ___33.7 °C___

Reading Beakers

Beakers are not made for volumetric measurements. For example, the beaker below can only approximate measurements up to 80 mL. Answer the following questions for the purpose of practice only. The beaker's smallest decimal calibration is ___10___ mL. The measurement can be estimated to the nearest ___1___ mL. Report the measurements at the following points including the correct units. *Answers ±1 mL are acceptable.*

A. ___85 mL___

B. ___60 mL___

C. ___40 mL___

D. ___23 mL___

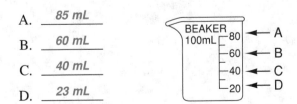

3B APPLICATIONS

Significant Digits in Calculations

Objectives

The purpose of these exercises is to

1. Learn how to identify the number of significant digits in a measurement.

2. Review how to round numbers correctly.

3. Learn the rules for calculations involving significant digits.

Introduction

You learned in Applications 3A that scientists indicate the precision of their measurements by using significant digits (SDs). Recall that *precision* refers to the repeatability of a measurement, which is related to how finely divided the scale of the instrument is. *Accuracy* refers to how close a measurement is to the actual value, which is associated with quality of construction of the instrument and its calibration against a known standard. Scientists regularly have to make calculations using the measurements they have taken in the laboratory. In order to report their results in a way that correctly shows the precision of their measurements, they have developed rules for rounding the results of these calculations. Before you learn these rules, however, you need to know how to determine the number of significant digits in a measurement and review the rules for rounding off numbers.

Determining the Number of Significant Digits

Before we discuss how to perform calculations using measurements, we must first determine the number of SDs in each measurement using the following rules:

1. Significant digits apply *only to measurements*. They do not apply to . . .

   a. Exact numbers obtained from counting (twice, dozen, six students, etc.)

   b. Pure numbers (any real number that is not a measurement: 29, $\frac{1}{2}$, $\sqrt{2}$, etc.)

   c. Definitions (60 seconds per minute, 100 cm per meter, etc.)

2. All non-zero digits are significant. (375.42 cm has 5 SDs)

3. Dealing with zeros

   a. All zeros *between* non-zero digits are significant. (ex.: 208.5 m has 4 SDs)

   b. All zeros in a measurement having a decimal point are significant, except for *leading zeros* (see Figure 1a).

   > example: 65.10 g has 4 SDs
   >
   > example: 0.0651 g has 3 SDs

Introduction

This exercise is the second designed to help your students understand the determination and use of significant digits in scientific calculations. You should have completed Applications 3A before doing this assignment. Review the information thoroughly in this exercise before teaching it.

While the emphasis in this section seems to be determining how many digits are significant, the real intent is to teach students how to determine which digits in a measurement are significant. Both skills are needed to perform scientific calculations.

c. *Trailing zeros* in a measurement *without a decimal point* (see Figure 1b) are *not* significant. If the measurement *has* a decimal point, then all trailing zeros are significant (Figure 1a).

example: 5300 cm has 2 SDs

example: 530.0 cm has 4 SDs

Figure 1

d. To indicate precision of a measurement with significant trailing zeros, use scientific notation. ALL DIGITS IN THE DECIMAL PORTION OF SCIENTIFIC NOTATION ARE SIGNIFICANT.

Example: 380,000 m that was measured to the nearest 1000 meters should be written 3.80×10^5 m. If it was measured to the nearest 100 meters, it should be written 3.800×10^5 m.

Because not all zeros are significant, the number of significant digits is not always the same as the number of digits. Study the following chart to help you learn the rules and complete the exercises below.

Examples

	Measurement	Number of Digits	Number of Significant Digits	Rule
1.	213 m	3	3	2
2.	210 cm	3	2	3c
3.	3.01 g	3	3	3a
4.	5.200 L	4	4	3b, c
5.	0.031 km	4	2	3b
6.	1.7×10^4 mm	2*	2	3d

Adding a zero before the decimal in example 5 is a standard practice to improve clarity.

*In scientific notation, only the digits in the decimal portion are counted.

We will use the following conventions for equalities:

"=" means "exactly equal to with no rounding"

"≐" means "a rounded or truncated calculator result"

"≈" means "an approximate result rounded to the correct number of SDs"

Practice Counting Significant Digits

State the correct number of SDs or write NA if SDs are not applicable. In the equations, look at the underlined portion.

a. 123 cm ___3___

b. 0.012 cm ___2___

c. 2100 cm ___2___

d. 1 gross ___NA___

e. 0.0101 cm ___3___

f. 1 km/h ≐ <u>0.621 mi./h</u> ___3___

g. 2.01 cm ___3___

h. 0.0102 cm ___3___

i. 1020. cm ___4___

j. 1.020 cm ___4___

k. 2,020 ___NA___

l. 1 gal. ≐ <u>3.786 L</u> ___4___

m. 2001 cm ___4___

n. 2000 cm ___1___

o. 1.03 cm ___3___

p. 0.0010 cm ___2___

q. 5.0 cm ___2___

r. 1 min. = 60 s ___NA___

Rounding Numbers

Answers obtained using calculators often have many more decimal places than necessary or permissible. To arrive at the correct answer from calculations involving measurements, we need to round the answer to the correct numerical place. We will use the following familiar rounding rules for our work in this course:

1. Determine the required numerical place to round to in the measurement.

2. If the first digit to the right of the required place is 4 or less, drop it and all remaining digits to the right.

   Note: If the required place is to the left of the (assumed) position of the decimal point, fill in the empty places to the left of the decimal point with zeros.

3. If the first digit to the right of the required place is 5 or greater, add one to the required place, drop all remaining digits to the right, and replace with zeros, if required, as in Rule 2 above.

4. Decimal points should not be added after trailing zeros unless the ones place is significant.

   Examples:

   a. Round 38,462 m to the hundreds place   38,500 m

   b. Round 38,462 m to the thousands place   38,000 m

   c. Round 0.561 m to the tenths place   0.6 m

Practice Rounding Measurements

Round the following measurements to the hundredths place:

a. 10.0944 m _10.09 m_

b. 0.1234 s _0.12 s_

c. 0.0999 km _0.10 km_

d. 1.0149 L _1.01 L_

e. 1.0846 km _1.08 km_

f. 23.095 MHz _23.10 MHz_

Round the following measurements to the tens place:

a. 123 cm _120 cm_

b. 2354 mm _2350 mm_

c. 294.1 m _290 m_

d. 89 s _90 s_

e. 544.9 mL _540 mL_

f. 765.23 m/s _770 m/s_

Rules for Calculations Using Significant Digits

Rules for calculations have been developed to ensure that results reported correctly show the precision of the measurements made in the laboratory. Let's say that you measured the edge of one side of a rectangle to be 2.38 cm and the other to be 5.79 cm using a metric ruler marked in millimeters (0.1 cm). What area would you report for this rectangle? The calculator answer for this product is 2.38 cm $\times$ 5.79 cm = 13.7802 cm^2. Let us analyze this answer. In the expanded multiplication problem shown, all circled digits are either estimated or result from operations performed with estimated digits.

$$
\begin{array}{r}
5.79 \text{ cm} \\
\times\ 2.38 \text{ cm} \\
\hline
46\ 32 \\
1\ 73\ 7 \\
11\ 58 \\
\hline
13.78\ 02 \text{ cm}^2
\end{array}
$$

The results of calculations must follow the same rules as the original measurements—they may have only one estimated digit. Allowing more than this would indicate your original measurements were more precise than they actually were. This would not be honest reporting. All workers, and Christians in particular, must be honest when reporting their results. In this example, the answer must be rounded to the tenths place, 13.8 cm^2. It is important to know how many significant digits to use when reporting your results. Study the following rules and answer the problems below.

Basic Rules for Operations with Significant Digits

1. *Multiplication and Division*—Answers to problems resulting from **multiplying** or **dividing** two or more measurements can have no more significant figures than the factor, divisor, or dividend with the fewest SDs. Round the result to correct.

   Example: 2 cm $\times$ 4.55 cm = 9.10 cm^2

   Since only one SD is allowed, the answer $\approx$ 9 cm^2.

2. *Addition and Subtraction*—Answers to problems resulting from **addition** or **subtraction** of two or more measurements can be no more precise than the least precise addend, minuend, or subtrahend.

   Example: 30 g + 22.5 g = 52.5 g

   The least precise measurement or the highest-placed estimated digit in any addend is the tens place in 30 g. Therefore, the answer $\approx$ 50 g.

Advanced Rules for Operations with Significant Digits (Optional)

3. The **multiplication** or **division** of a measurement by a *pure* number should not produce a result that is less precise or more precise than the original measurement. Round the result to a number having the same precision as the original measurement (that is, the least significant digit is in the same place as the original measurement).

   Example:

   Compute the radius of a circle given that the diameter is 1.35 cm. $d = \dfrac{r}{2}$, therefore, r = 1.35 cm $\div$ 2 = 0.675 cm.

   Due to the precision of the original measurement, you must round the result to 0.68 cm.

Example:

Compute the surface area of a cube if one face (B) is 2.25 cm². $A = 6B$, therefore $6 \times 2.25 \text{ cm}^2 = 13.5 \text{ cm}^2$. Because the original face area was precise to hundredths of a cm², the final result must reflect this precision: $A = 13.50 \text{ cm}^2$.

Recall that multiplying by a pure number is just repetitive addition, so the basic addition rules apply.

4. In any given problem, all similar, simultaneous operations that must be performed should be calculated in one step before rounding to proper SDs. Rounding after each step of a multiple-step problem introduces unnecessary errors.

> *Example:* Find the volume of a rectangular solid 4 cm $\times$ 1.10 cm $\times$ 2.1 cm. The product by calculator is 9.24 cm³. This product is allowed one SD (Rule 1), so the result is rounded to $V \approx 9 \text{ cm}^3$.

But if you find 4 cm $\times$ 1.10 cm = 4.40 cm² this is rounded to 4 cm² (1 SD). If you then multiply 4 cm² by 2.1 cm, the answer is 8.4 cm³. When you round this result to one SD your final answer is 8 cm³. Compared to 9 cm³, this has an 11% error!

5. When performing a connected series of multiplication/division and addition/subtraction operations, be sure to apply the appropriate SD rules to the applicable steps before going on to a different type of operation. In other words, do not apply multiplication/division rules to the results of addition/subtraction, and vice versa.

Practice Calculating with Significant Digits

Report the results of the following calculations in raw form and using the appropriate number of SDs. Give the operations rule number that applies to the calculation.

	Raw Answer	Rounded Answer	Rule Number
1. 6.3 cm $\times$ 8.05 cm	50.715 cm	51 cm	1
2. 40.2 mL + 27 mL	67.2 mL	67 mL	2
3. 6 mL − 2.5 mL	3.5 mL	4 mL	2
4. 17.0 mm $\times$ 5.4 mm	91.8 mm²	92 mm²	1
5. 19.80 g − 7.3 g	12.50 g	12.5 g	2
6. (See word problem below)	5 cm³	5.0 cm³	1, 4 (Advanced rule)
7. (See word problem below)	122.1 mL	122.1 mL	2
8. 16.5 mm ÷ 2	8.25 mm	8.3 mm	3 (Advanced rule)
9. 5.5 mL $\times$ 3	16.5 mL	16.5 mL	3 (Advanced rule)
10. 7.2 cm $\times$ 5 cm $\times$ 1.25 cm	45 cm³	50 cm³	1, 4 (Advanced rule)
11. (See word problem below)	2.725 km	2.7 km	3 (Advanced rule)
12. (See word problem below)	102.4 m²	1.0×10^2 m²	5 (Advanced rule)

Definitions:

factor—a number multiplied by another number

divisor—a number by which another number is divided

dividend—a number that is being divided

addend—a number that is added to another number

minuend—a number from which another number is subtracted

subtrahend—a number which is subtracted from another

Word Problems (Show your work.)

6. Mr. Rodriguez, the science teacher, needs to determine the volume of a block of wood. Its dimensions are length—2.5 cm, width—2.00 cm, height—1.0 cm. What is the volume of the cube? *V = 2.5 cm × 2.00 cm × 1.0 cm*

7. Dr. Dickson added 63.7 mL of water to 58.4 mL of sodium hydroxide solution. What is the volume of the new solution? *V = 58.4 mL + 63.7 mL*

11. The route that Shane jogs every day is 10.9 km long. Shane's little brother wants to run a distance one-fourth as long. What distance will Shane have to measure for his brother? *d = 10.9 km ÷ 4*

12. A missionary is going to carpet three classrooms in his school. The rooms measure 3.3 m × 3.95 m, 5.4 m × 6 m, and 7.35 m × 8.08 m. What is the total area of carpet he must buy? *A = (3.3 m × 3.95 m) + (5.4 m × 6 m) + (7.35 m × 8.08 m) ≈ 13 m² + 30 m² + 59.4 m² Note: Each product must be rounded to SDs before adding (see Rule 5). In practice, the missionary would need more than 103 m² of carpet, but this problem is adequate to illustrate Rule 5.*

3C INVESTIGATION
Measuring

Objectives

The purposes of this investigation are to

1. Become familiar with the use of basic laboratory instruments.

2. Verify that exact measurements are not possible.

Equipment

Mass balance
Metal specific gravity cylinder or other solid object
Metric ruler (1 per student)
Thermometers (Celsius/Fahrenheit scales), 4

Introduction

Scientists use many different instruments to aid their senses. These instruments help make their observations more objective. For example, instead of saying that the water is hot (subjective), a person can measure the temperature of the water with a thermometer and say it is 110 °F (objective). This appears to settle the question of the water temperature, but does it really? Did that person mean that the temperature is exactly 110 °F or approximately 110 °F? Can a person assert that the temperature is exactly 110 °F? In this investigation, we are going to answer the question "Is it possible to make exact measurements?"

Pre-Laboratory Questions

Read the entire investigation. Answer the following questions prior to class on a separate sheet of paper. Use complete sentences.

1. What do scientists use to aid their senses in making observations?

2. What is an objective observation?

3. What is a subjective observation?

4. Which is more desirable when making scientific observations, objectivity or subjectivity? Explain.

5. State your research question.

6. State your hypothesis.

Procedure

You will be performing a series of measurements using three different common laboratory instruments. In addition to gaining practice obtaining accurate measurements, you will practice recording data using the correct number of significant digits. Review the rules for recording measurements in Applications 3A and 3B, if necessary.

Introduction

This investigation is a good supplement to the discussion of significant digits (SDs). Accurate recording of SDs is critical to the meaning of every measurement in science. The main objective here is to show the student that no measurement is exact.

Answers to Pre-Laboratory Questions

1. Scientists use instruments to aid their senses.

2. An objective observation is one that results from a measurement or the use of descriptive terms that are well defined.

3. A subjective observation is one that uses ambiguous terms that include the observer's personal opinion or bias.

4. Objectivity is more desirable; subjectively reported observations are not easily replicated.

5. Research Question—"Is it possible to obtain perfectly accurate measurements?"

6. Hypothesis—Answers will vary. Students should provide something like "Measurements cannot be exact, only approximated."

---

1. Divide your class into teams of three to six students.

2. Prior to actually taking data, review how to use each instrument. Demonstrate how parallax affects each.

3. The mass balance must be zeroed (by the teacher) before beginning. Correct use of the balance must be discussed to prevent damage.

4. Non-mercury thermometers are preferable for use in the classroom.

5. The thicker the ruler, the better the parallax demonstration.

6. Make sure each student returns the balance weights to the zero position when finished finding the mass of the cylinder or other object.

7. Verify that each student actually makes his own measurements and that the data is being recorded to the correct number of SDs.

A. Balances

1. Measure the mass of the cylinder or another object. Do not reveal this measurement to your team members until they have made their measurements. Record your measurement in Table 1.

2. Return all of the balance sliders to the zero position.

3. After the other people on your team have measured the same object, record their results in Table 1.

4. Average the values for the mass of the object (add the values and divide by the number of readings).

B. Rulers

1. Draw a line on the side of this page 10 inches long. Try to make your line exactly 10 inches.

2. Measure the line in centimeters as precisely as possible, using the measurement rules you have learned.

   10 inches = _____ cm

   Calculate the length of one inch in centimeters.

   1 inch = _____ cm

Parallax Error

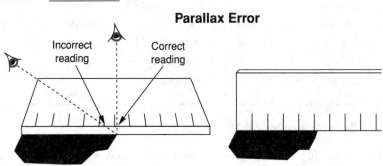

Parallax error occurs when the scale on the ruler and your line of sight to the object being measured are not correctly aligned. When placing the ruler flat on the page, the scale you are reading should be placed directly in front of you so that your line of sight is perpendicular to the edge of the ruler at the point of measurement. If the scale is placed to the right of your eye, the reading will appear to be farther to the left on the scale than the correct reading. This error can also be avoided by placing the ruler on its edge so that the scale directly contacts the line or object being measured. Parallax error is one of the most common measurement errors experienced in the laboratory. Always be alert for it.

3. Draw a line on your paper 11.20 cm long.

4. Place the ruler flat on the paper. Read the measurement of the line you drew in step 3 perpendicular to the ruler. Without moving the ruler, alter your line of sight to the scale so that you are reading it from far to the left. Observe how the apparent measurement differs as you alter your line of sight. Record your measurement from this position. _____ How does this compare with the original length? _____

_____

5. Place the ruler on edge as in the diagram on the right, above. Again, as you measure the line, alter your line of sight to the scale. It should not affect the reading. This is a more reliable way to measure something.

6. Measure the length and width of your lab manual to hundredths of a centimeter and record the measurements in Table 2.

7. After the other people on your team have measured the same manual, obtain their measurements and write them in Table 2.

8. Average the measurements of the lab manual in Table 2.

C. Thermometers

1. Measure the room temperature in °C with four thermometers and record this value in Table 3. (Be sure to use the correct significant digits as discussed in Applications 3A and 3B.)

2. Obtain four room temperature readings from each of two other teams and write these in Table 3.

3. Average the values from each team and determine the average of the averages (grand mean).

4. (Optional) Measure room temperature in °F. _____ °F

Results

Table 1: Object Mass

Team Member	Mass (g)
Average	

Table 2: Book Measurements

Team Member	Length (cm)	Width (cm)
Average		

Table 3: Room Temperature

Thermometer	Yours (°C)	Other #1 (°C)	Other #2 (°C)
#1			
#2			
#3			
#4			
Average			
Grand Mean			

Discussion Questions

Write your answers in complete sentences. Try to explain your answers.

1. Were all the object and book measurements the same? If not, give some reasons. *No, differences in instruments and human errors can cause measurements to vary.*

2. When you measured the room temperature with different thermometers, were all the values the same? If not, what are some sources of error? *No, they may vary because of slight differences in calibration. The thermometer accuracies are different. Also, human error can cause differences.*

3. In Table 3, how far apart are the averages of the three sets of readings compared to the spread of the individual measurements? *The averages should be closer together than individual measurements.*

4. Why is it sometimes necessary to measure something more than once and then take an average? *Averaging the results will normally eliminate random human errors from a set of readings.*

5. When a person says that the temperature is 110 °F, is this an exact value or an approximation? Explain. *It is an approximation. It is impossible to measure anything exactly, and different people and different instruments will obtain different measurements of the same quantity.*

6. Explain parallax error. *Parallax error occurs when your line of sight to the mark on the measuring instrument is not correctly aligned.*

Experimental Evaluation

7. Did this investigation answer the research question? Explain. *Yes, most of the measurements differed slightly, so it appears improbable that a measurement can be made exactly.*

8. Give two ways that the measurement of room temperature was replicated.

   a. *The student used several different thermometers to take the same measurements.*

   b. *The student obtained data from other teams.*

9. (Optional) Having established the difficulty of obtaining exact measurements, give two other research questions suggested by this investigation. *Several questions include "Can human error be minimized?"; "What kinds of human errors are there?"; "What kinds of instrument errors are there?"; "Can all instrument errors be eliminated?" Other answers are acceptable.*

3D INVESTIGATION
Density

Objectives

The purpose of this investigation is to

1. Gain experience in the use of laboratory equipment.

2. Calculate the density of several objects.

3. Apply the principles of significant digits to calculations.

Introduction

The purpose of this investigation is to help the students understand density by actually calculating densities. The difference between objective and subjective observations is reviewed, and the students gain experience in correctly making measurements.

Materials

Rectangular wooden block
Sewing thread

Equipment

Beaker (250 mL)
Eyedropper
Graduated cylinder (100 mL)
Mass balance
Metal specific gravity cylinder or other
    metal object
Metric ruler
Overflow can

Introduction

If you had a chance to play with a professional football team, the members of that team would probably consider you a fairly light player. Suppose that after the football game, if you were still alive, you looked after your neighbor's six-year-old darling. The six-year-old would think you were a big, heavy person. The terms *heavy* and *light* are subjective terms that represent personal opinions. The ideas of heaviness and lightness are scientifically useful, but they must be described objectively. For example, a block of lead is heavy for its size and will, consequently, sink in water. However, the same size block of cork is light and will float. To make the relative heaviness of an object quantifiable, we use the concept of **density.** The density of an object or substance is the amount of mass in each unit of its volume. Since mass and volume are measurable, objectivity is gained.

Pre-Laboratory Questions

Read the entire investigation. Answer the following questions prior to class on a separate sheet of paper. Use complete sentences if necessary.

1. Which two properties of an object do you have to measure to calculate the density of an object?

2. Describe the two different ways volume will be determined in this investigation.

3. What is the accepted density for water?

4. Give the formula for the volume of

   a. a cylinder.

   b. a rectangular block.

5. How do you find the percent difference between two numbers?

Procedures

A. The Density of Water

1. Volume

a. Measure 50.0 mL of water into your graduated cylinder. (Note that this measurement must be precise to one-tenth of a milliliter.) You may find that using an eyedropper is helpful to make any final adjustments in level.

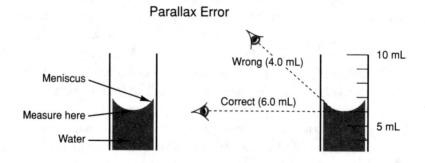

Parallax Error

To avoid parallax error in reading a graduated cylinder, you must place your eye so that it is level with the bottom of the meniscus. If you read the level at an angle (either from above or below), your recorded value will not be correct. The above diagram illustrates this problem.

b. Record 50.0 mL in the data table on page 50 in the "Volume" column and set the water-filled graduated cylinder aside.

2. Mass

a. Find the mass of a dry beaker using a balance. Record this value in ❶ below. Why is it important that the beaker be dry? _The extra weight_ _from water clinging to the beaker would alter the measured mass of the_ _beaker._

b. Carefully pour the 50.0 mL of water from the graduated cylinder into the beaker. How would spilling some water or leaving water in the cylinder affect the results? _If you spill or omit any water, the volume of water_ _assumed to be present from the previous measurement would not be_ _correct._

c. Find the mass of the beaker and water together. Record this value in ❷.

d. Subtract ❶ from ❷ and record this value in ❸. This is the mass of the water. Record this value in the data table in the "Mass" column.

    ❷ Mass of water and beaker   _____ g

    ❶ Mass of beaker   − _____ g

    ❸ Mass of water   = _____ g

3. Density

Density is the ratio of the mass of a substance to its volume. It is obtained by dividing the mass by the volume.

a. Divide the water's mass by its volume to calculate the density. Record this value in the data table under the "Density" column. Include the proper units (g/mL).

b. The density of pure water is 1.00 g/mL. If the density is not within the range 0.95 g/mL − 1.05 g/mL, repeat the steps above.

B. *The Density of a Metal Cylinder*

1. **Volume by Water Displacement**

a. Measure 50.0 mL of water into the graduated cylinder. Record this value in ❶ below.

b. Tie a piece of thread to the metal cylinder and carefully lower it into the water in the graduated cylinder. **Caution:** Do not drop the metal object into the cylinder. Doing so can break glass cylinders.

c. Measure the combined volume of the water and metal cylinder. Record this value in ❷ below.

d. Subtract ❶ from ❷ and record this value in ❸. If you cannot perform step 2 because your metal object is not a cylinder, record the value from ❸ in the data table under the "Volume" column and skip to step 3.

    ❷ Volume of water and metal   _____ mL

    ❶ Volume of water   − _____ mL

    ❸ Volume of metal (V_D)   = _____ mL

3. In high school laboratory investigations, a result that varies up to 5% from a known standard is considered acceptable. When calculating a result using two different methods, 5% difference is also considered acceptable.

4. An overflow can may be constructed from household materials. Drill a hole in a coffee can a few inches from the top, insert a short length of wide bore, Tygon hose ($\frac{3}{8}-\frac{1}{2}$ in.) and apply caulk to create a watertight seal. The hose should incline downward slightly. Similarly, you could use a 2-liter soda bottle whose top has been cut off, inserting a wide plastic straw into a hole a few inches down from the rim. Because you are trying to make a precise measurement of the water displaced, you must ensure that you don't lose any water through leakage around the insertion hole. Using a wide straw or hose ensures that all of the water that flows out of the container enters the graduated cylinder and does not remain in the spout.

5. Obtaining accurate results using the overflow can be a little tricky when measuring an object that floats. Make sure that the block is submerged only once and allowed to resurface slowly, without bobbing up and down.

2. **Volume by Measurement**

   If you are using standard cylindrical metal specific gravity samples, you can calculate their volume from their dimensions.

   a. Measure the cylinder's diameter (d) to one-hundredth of a centimeter. $d =$ _____ cm

   b. Measure the cylinder's length (geometrically equal to its height [h]) to the same precision. $h =$ _____ cm

   c. The formula for the volume of a cylinder is $V = \pi r^2 h$. You must find the radius (r) of the cylinder before you can use this formula.

   d. Calculate the radius: $r = \dfrac{d}{2} = \dfrac{cm}{2} =$ _____ cm. Recall from Applications 3B that this result cannot have greater precision than your original measurement.

   e. Compute the volume of the cylinder from measurements: $V_M =$ _____ cm^3. If you are not observing SDs, round to hundredths of a cubic centimeter. Record this value in the "Volume" column in the data table.

   f. Calculate the percent difference in the volumes found by displacement and by calculation. Divide the difference in the volumes by the average of the two volumes (v_{avg}). Multiply this result by 100%.

   $$\text{Percent difference} = \frac{|V_M - V_D|}{V_{avg}} \times 100\% = \underline{\hspace{2cm}}\%$$

   If the difference is greater than 5%, review your calculations in step 2f. If these are accurate, repeat steps 1 and 2 in this section.

3. **Mass**

   Measure the mass of the dry metal cylinder using a balance and record this value in the data table under the "Mass" column.

4. **Density**

   Calculate the density of the cylinder by dividing the mass by the volume recorded in the data table. Record this value in the data table under the "Density" column.

C. The Density of Wood (Optional)

1. **Volume by Measurement**

   a. Measure the length, width, and height of a wooden block in cm. (Estimate dimensions to hundredths of a cm.)

      Length _____ Width _____ Height _____

   The allowed SDs depends on the size of the block. The volume calculation cannot have more digits than the dimension with the least number of digits.

   b. Calculate the volume of the block by multiplying the three measurements. If you are observing proper significant digits, how many are allowed? _____ cm

      If you are not observing significant digits, round the volume to two decimal places.

   c. Record the resulting value in the data table under the "Volume" column.

2. Volume by Water Displacement

a. Measure the mass of the wooden block according to step 3 below *before* determining the volume by water displacement. Why is this necessary?
The block may soak up water that would add to its measured mass.

b. Fill the overflow can with water. Overfill it slightly so that some water pours out the spout.

c. When the water has stopped dripping from the spout, place a dry graduated cylinder under the spout of the can.

d. Float the wooden block in the can. Using three fingers to steady the block, slowly push it under the water until its upper face is just level with the water's surface. Be careful that your fingertips do not go under water. You do not want to include the volume of your fingers in the measurement. Once it has been fully submerged, wait until the water stops dripping out of the spout. Remove the graduated cylinder before releasing the block.

e. The volume of the water that has spilled into the graduated cylinder is the volume of the wooden block.

Volume by water displacement: V_D = _____

Volume by calculation of measurements: V_M = _____

f. Calculate the percent difference in the volumes. Divide the difference in the volumes by the average of V_M and V_D. Multiply this by 100%.

$$\text{Percent difference} = \frac{|V_M - V_D|}{V_{avg.}} \times 100\% = \text{_____}\%$$

If the difference is greater than 5%, review your calculations in step 2f. If these are accurate, repeat steps 1 and 2 in this section.

3. Mass

Find the mass of the wooden block and record this value in the data table under the "Mass" column.

4. Density

a. Calculate the density of the wooden block and record this value in the data table under the "Density" column.

b. If the value is greater than 1.00 g/mL, you need to repeat the measurements for the mass and the density of the wooden block. Why?
Since wood floats, its density must be less than that of water. Therefore,

its density must be less than 1.00 g/mL.

Results

Data Table: Densities

Object	Mass (g)	Volume (mL)	Density (g/mL)
Water			
Metal			
Wood			

Discussion Questions

1. The density of a substance is the ratio of its ___*mass*___ and its ___*volume*___ .

2. What is the unit for density? *g/mL (g/cm³ is also acceptable.)*

3. The density indicates the number of grams in one mL of a substance. Complete the following statements.

   a. A density of 3.0 g/mL means that there are 3.0 grams in 1 mL.

   b. A density of 5.1 g/mL means that there are ___*5.1 g*___ in ___*1 mL*___ .

   c. A density of 0.9 g/mL means that there are ___*0.9 g*___ in ___*1 mL*___ .

4. Which substance in question 3 (a, b, or c) is the least dense? Explain the reason for your choice. *C is the least dense because it has the fewest grams in 1 mL.*

5. Assume that the density of water is 1 g/mL. 30 mL of water will have a mass of *30 g* .

6. Since the ratio of cubic centimeters (cm³) to milliliters is 1, 40 cm³ is another way of saying *40* mL.

7. A piece of metal has a mass of 120 g and a volume of 30 mL. What is its density? *4 g/mL (or 4 g/cm³)*

8. A piece of wood has a volume of 200 mL and a mass of 100 g. What is its density? *0.5 g/mL (or 0.5 g/cm³)*

Experimental Evaluation

9. Which of the materials in this investigation is the most dense? Why? *The metal is the most dense because it has the most mass per unit volume.*

10. What appears to be the relationship between density and the ability to float in water? *Objects with densities greater than 1 g/mL tend to sink, while objects with densities less than 1 g/mL tend to float.*

11. Describe the method of finding the volume of an object by water displacement in a graduated cylinder. *Pour some water into a graduated cylinder and read the volume. Place the object into the water so that it is completely covered and measure the new volume. The volume of the object is the difference between the two volumes.*

12. (Optional) Of the two methods you used to find the volume of the metal cylinder, which do you think is the more precise? *The volume by* *measurement should be more precise because direct measurement of* *dimensions has more precision than volumetric measurement.*

13. (Optional) When would it be preferable to find the volume of an object by water displacement rather than by measuring its dimensions? Give an example. *It would be easier to use the water displacement method when* *the object has an irregular shape. Examples will vary. Students may* *recall finding the density of minerals in an earth science course by water* *displacement.*

14. (Optional) What are some difficulties with using the overflow displacement method to find the volume of small objects? *Students may* *mention that it is hard to hold buoyant objects just under water without* *including the fingertips. Also, the high surface tension of water may cause* *it to stick to the object, affecting the amount of water that flows out.*

Density

4A INVESTIGATION
Chemical and Physical Changes

Name _____

Date _____ Hour _____

Objectives

The purpose of this investigation is to

1. Learn the difference between chemical and physical changes.

2. Learn the difference between evidence and proof that a chemical change has occurred.

Materials

Aluminum foil
Ammonia
Baking soda
Epsom salts
Sugar
Table salt
Vinegar

Equipment

Beaker (250 mL)
Beakers (100 mL), 2
Bunsen burner
Bunsen burner lighter
Graduated cylinder (100 mL)
Large rubber band
Teaspoon
Tripod
Wire gauze

Introduction

Chemistry is primarily the study of chemical and physical changes of matter, while physics focuses on physical processes involving matter. A **physical change** occurs when a substance simply changes shape, form, or state (gas, liquid, or solid)—its identity is not altered. Examples of physical changes include boiling, evaporation, melting, bending, tearing, and dissolving. A **chemical change** results when a new substance is formed that is different from the original material(s). The research question is "Is it possible to distinguish between physical and chemical changes?" Physical changes can frequently be easily "undone" or reversed. Ice can be melted and refrozen. Clay can be formed into a different shape. However, chemical changes are often very difficult to reverse. The appearing of a new and different substance is **proof** that a chemical change has occurred. There are some common **evidences** that often accompany chemical reactions. They are summarized as follows:

Evidence	Proof
A solid separates from a liquid.	The appearance of a new and different
A gas is produced.	substance is established by analytical tests.
The colors of the chemicals change permanently.	
The temperature of the substances changes.	
Light or sound is produced.	

These **evidences** alone do not prove that a chemical change has occurred. Some of these also accompany certain physical changes. For example, boiling water

Introduction

This investigation emphasizes the difference between observations and inferences. Color change can be observed, but the occurrence of a chemical reaction is an inference. A key concept to convey to your students is summarized in the answer to Discussion Question 4: Evidence from which inferences are made may be ambiguous—more than one phenomenon can produce the same evidence. Proof results from observations that can be associated with only one phenomenon. In science there are very few facts that have been unequivocally proved.

Preparation

Red cabbage extract

1. Cut $\frac{1}{4}$ of a small head of purple cabbage into small pieces and place them in a cooking pot.

2. Add about 500 mL (2 cups) of distilled water.

3. Boil for five minutes. Allow the mixture to cool to room temperature.

4. Pour the cabbage juice through a strainer and discard the leaves. Refrigerate in a capped jar or bottle until needed.

5. Dilute the juice with an equal amount of water before using. This will yield approximately 1 L of cabbage juice.

Saturated Epsom Salts Solution

1. Add Epsom salts to about 500 mL of warm water and stir until no more salt will

dissolve. You will know you have reached this point when after several minutes of stirring there are crystals of salt remaining on the bottom of the container.

2. Allow the crystals to settle and carefully pour off the saturated solution into a clean capped bottle or jar.

Answers to Pre-Laboratory Questions

1. A physical change is a change that does not alter the identity of the material.

2. A chemical change occurs when the identity (not appearance) of a substance is changed.

3. Evidences of a chemical change include separation of a solid from a liquid, gas production, color change, temperature change, and light or sound production.

4. A chemical change can be confirmed by further analytical tests that a different substance has formed.

5. The research question is "Is it possible to distinguish between physical and chemical changes?"

6. Since these are hypotheses, it is not necessary for them to be correct. The correct answers are included here for reference.
a. chemical
b. physical
c. chemical
d. physical
e. chemical
f. chemical

Expected Results

Procedure A: Burned sugar will look like a brownish-black molten mass. Water vapor is released.

produces gas and sound during a phase change—a physical change. The appearance of solid crystalline salt in a slowly evaporating salt solution is another example of a physical change. In order to prove that a chemical change has taken place, the suspected new substance must be chemically analyzed in the laboratory to determine its identity. We will discuss chemical changes in greater detail in Chapter 9.

Pre-Laboratory Questions

Read the entire investigation. Answer the following questions prior to class on a separate sheet of paper. Use complete sentences.

1. What is a physical change?

2. What is a chemical change?

3. What are the evidences that a chemical change has occurred?

4. How can you prove that a chemical change has occurred?

5. State the research question.

6. For your hypothesis, state whether the following procedures will result in a chemical or a physical change:

   a. Burning sugar

   b. Mixing salt and water

   c. Mixing baking soda and vinegar

   d. Stretching a rubber band

   e. Mixing red cabbage juice and ammonia

   f. Mixing Epsom salts and ammonia

Procedures

A. Burning Sugar

1. Obtain a 15 × 15 cm (approximate) piece of aluminum foil.

2. Make a spoonlike instrument from the foil with a handle and a bowl to hold the sugar.

3. Write a description of the sugar in the first column of Table 1 in the Results section.

4. Light the Bunsen burner. Your teacher can show you how to use the burner and the lighter.

5. Place about 3 cm^3 ($\frac{1}{2}$ tsp.) of sugar in the "bowl" at the end of the foil.

6. Hold the foil bowl over the flame. Tip the Bunsen burner slightly to make sure the sugar comes in direct contact with the flame. Make sure you don't spill any grains of sugar into the barrel of the burner. **Caution:** If the burner flares up, immediately put the burner down and ask for assistance.

7. When the sugar starts to burn, remove it from the flame.

8. After the flame dies, allow the sugar and foil to cool (about one minute).

9. Record your observations in Table 1. Include observations such as the production of heat, light, gas, or smoke, and any color changes and other physical changes. Then determine whether this was a chemical or a physical change.

10. Place the cooled foil and burned sugar residue in the trash.

B. Mixing Salt and Water

Procedure B: No reaction is expected.

1. Write a description of the salt in the table.

2. Pour about 25 mL of tap water into the 250 mL beaker.

3. Add about 5 cm^3 (1 tsp.) of salt to the water and stir until dissolved.

4. Is there any evidence of a chemical change? Record your observations.

5. Place the beaker on the wire gauze on the tripod over the Bunsen burner.

6. Light the burner and boil the solution until all the water is gone (about 10-15 min.). Perform Section C of the investigation while the water is heating.

7. After the water has boiled away, turn off the Bunsen burner and observe what is left in the beaker.

8. Rinse the beaker with water in the sink.

C. Mixing Baking Soda and Vinegar

Procedure C: Rapid fizzing will occur, and the baking soda will disappear. Students may detect a slight warming.

1. Write a description of the baking soda and vinegar in the table.

2. Pour about 25 mL of vinegar into a beaker.

3. Add about 5 cm^3 (1 tsp.) of baking soda to the vinegar.

4. Touch the base of the beaker with the back of your hand and note any temperature change. Record your observations and determination of the type of change in the table.

5. Discard the contents down the drain.

D. Stretching a Rubber Band

Procedure D: The rubber band will become noticeably warmer with repeated stretching. A balloon works well also.

1. Write a description of the rubber band in the table.

2. Place the rubber band against your skin just under your lower lip. Notice the temperature of the rubber band.

3. Rapidly stretch the rubber band several times to its full extension. While it is fully extended, place it against your lower lip. Note any temperature change.

4. Record your observations and determination of type of change in the table.

E. Mixing Red Cabbage Extract and Ammonia

Procedure E: Red cabbage extract turns to a color between green and yellow with the addition of a base (ammonia); it turns reddish with addition of an acid (vinegar).

1. Write a description of the cabbage extract and ammonia in the table.

2. Place about 25 mL of cabbage extract in a 100 mL beaker.

3. Rinse the graduated cylinder with tap water and then add about 5 mL of ammonia to the cabbage extract. Record your observations in the table.

4. Flush the mixture down the drain with plenty of water and thoroughly rinse the beaker.

5. (Optional) Repeat steps 2 through 4 using 10 mL of vinegar in place of the ammonia.

F. Mixing Epsom Salts and Ammonia

1. Write a description of the saturated Epsom salts solution in the table.

2. Pour about 25 mL of the Epsom salts solution in a 100 mL beaker.

3. Add about 10 mL of ammonia to the Epsom salts solution. Record your observations and determination of type of change in the table.

4. Flush the mixture down the sink with plenty of water. Thoroughly rinse the beaker and dry it.

G. Cleanup

Unless your teacher directs otherwise, wash and dry all glassware thoroughly. Place all similar equipment together in one place. Return all chemicals and solutions to their designated locations. Be sure all bottle caps are tight. Lab cleanup should be considered part of every laboratory exercise.

Results

Table 1: Chemical and Physical Changes

	Describe Original Substances	New Substance (Yes/No)	Color Change (Yes/No)	Temp. Change (Yes/No)	Gas Produced (Yes/No)	Chemical or Physical Change?
Burning sugar	Answers will vary.	yes	yes	yes	yes	chemical
Mixing salt and water	Answers will vary.	no	no	no	no	physical
Baking soda and vinegar	Answers will vary.	yes	no	yes	yes	chemical
Stretching a rubber band	Answers will vary.	no	no	yes	no	physical
Cabbage extract and ammonia	Answers will vary.	no	yes	no	no	chemical
Epsom salts and ammonia	Answers will vary.	yes	yes (May turn murky)	(possibly)	no	chemical
Cabbage extract and vinegar (opt.)	Answers will vary.	no	yes	no	no	chemical

Procedure F: The addition of ammonia should produce a whitish precipitate. This reaction may take several minutes to occur.

General Comments

1. Review the chemical hazards associated with the new substances in this lab. In particular, warn students about inhaling the ammonia fumes, which can cause severe irritation to breathing passages. Store the ammonia in capped bottles except when actually pouring.

2. If you want to emphasize MSDS familiarity, you may have the students fill in a copy of the blank MSDS form in the back of the lab manual for the household chemicals in this investigation.

3. A good lab technique to begin emphasizing to your students is tightly recapping reagent bottles immediately after use.

4. If you are using Bunsen or similar propane or butane burners for the first time with your class, you must demonstrate the operation of the burners and lighters. The flame of a burner may become unstable if the burner is tilted far from the vertical, so be alert for flare-ups. The students should tilt the burner as little as possible to ignite the sugar.

5. Emphasize to the students not to spill any grains of sugar into the barrel of the burner. Melted sugar in the barrel is difficult to clean up.

Discussion Questions

1. What is a physical change? Give four examples. _A physical change is a change that does not alter the identity of the material. Examples include boiling, freezing, crushing, bending, and tearing._

2. What is proof that a chemical change has occurred? _The only valid proof that a chemical change took place is to chemically identify a new substance as a result of the change._

3. What are the evidences that a chemical change has occurred? _A solid separates from a liquid, a gas is produced, the colors of the chemicals change permanently, the temperature of the substance changes, and light or sound is produced._

4. In general terms, what is the difference between evidence and proof? _Answers will vary. Evidence consists of observations that can be associated with more than one kind of phenomenon. Proof consists of observations that are associated with only one particular phenomenon._

5. Give an example from this investigation of a physical change producing evidence of a chemical change. _The stretching of the rubber band released heat, but no chemical change took place._

6. Identify each of the following as a physical or a chemical change:
    a. Making ice cubes _physical_
    b. Coals burning in a barbecue _chemical_
    c. Meat cooking _chemical_
    d. A pencil being sharpened _physical_
    e. Sugar dissolving in water _physical_
    f. Gunpowder exploding _chemical_
    g. Paper being folded _physical_
    h. Gasoline evaporating _physical_
    i. Gasoline burning _chemical_

6. If you do not have a Bunsen burner, the flame from a butane lighter will also work.

7. This is a good opportunity to emphasize observation techniques. As the students attempt to describe the various substances, suggest various terms that make their descriptions less ambiguous.

8. Encourage your students to check for temperature changes in all of the demonstrations, not just the ones specified.

4B INVESTIGATION
Finding Absolute Zero

Objectives

The purpose of this investigation is to:

1. Demonstrate Charles's law.

2. Experimentally determine absolute zero, using the temperature range available in the laboratory.

Materials

Graph paper
Ice
Salt

Equipment

Beakers (600 mL) (2)
Beaker tongs
Bunsen burner
Burner lighter
Metric ruler
Stirring rod
Syringe (50 cm^3 with cap)
Test tube clamp
Thermometer (2)
Tripod or support stand with ring
Wire gauze

Introduction

The method used in this investigation approximates the actual method used to originally determine absolute zero. The method of extrapolation is common in science, especially in environmental and astronomical sciences. This investigation demonstrates the limitations of this method. If the students follow the directions carefully and make careful measurements, their results can be fairly close to the actual value. Charles's law is introduced as a key formula in associating temperature with volume. Both gas laws (Charles's law and Boyle's law) will be explored further in Chapter 15.

Introduction

Temperature is a measure of the average molecular kinetic energy. **Absolute zero** is the lowest theoretical temperature. It is thermodynamically impossible to reach absolute zero, although scientists have come within billionths of a degree of that elusive point. Scientists are not sure what might occur at that temperature, but it is assumed that all molecular motion and subatomic particle movement within atoms would cease. Some matter very near absolute zero (-273.15 °C) can change into another state called the Bose-Einstein Condensate (BEC).

How can absolute zero be determined if you cannot reach it? The original method was performed by a French physicist named Jacques Charles. Through experimentation, he discovered that the ratio of the volume of a gas and its Kelvin temperature is constant if the amount of gas and pressure are held constant. This relationship, known as **Charles's law,** is expressed by the equation

$$\frac{V_1}{T_1} = \frac{V_2}{T_2}$$

(NOTE: In the equation, the subscript 1 refers to the original condition of volume and temperature, while the subscript 2 refers to the new or final volume and temperature.) In other words, as the motion of the molecules slows down, the volume of the gas gets smaller (at constant pressure). Theoretically, this continues until the motion of the molecule stops and the volume becomes zero. (This is actually impossible for several reasons that you will learn in more advanced physical science courses.) Charles plotted a number of points on a graph comparing volume (on the vertical axis) and temperature (on the horizontal axis) for a sample of gas at constant pressure. He then extended a straight line through these plotted points until it reached zero volume. The temperature at which this occurs is absolute zero. This process of extending a relation beyond the range of available data to make a prediction is called **extrapolation.**

Pre-Laboratory Questions

Read the entire investigation. Answer the following questions prior to class on a separate sheet of paper. Use complete sentences.

1. What is believed to happen to molecules at absolute zero?

2. Why is absolute zero only a theoretical number?

3. State Charles's law in words and in a formula.

4. Through what standard method can absolute zero be estimated?

5. State the research question.

6. State your hypothesis.

Procedures

A. Establishing the Initial Syringe Volume

1. Pull the cap off the syringe tip and pull out the plunger so that the syringe contains 20 cm^3 of air.

2. Replace the cap back on the syringe and **do not remove it** during the rest of the investigation.

3. Record the room temperature in the data table in Results. (If you are observing SDs, record to the appropriate precision.)

4. Pour about 400 mL of water into a 600 mL beaker.

5. Assemble the tripod and wire gauze and place the beaker on the wire gauze. Light the burner, obtain a proper flame, and begin heating the water to about 90°C. Monitor the temperature with a thermometer.

Do not exceed 95°C or cause the water to boil. Do not record the temperature until Part C.

B. Low Temperature Measurement

1. While heating the water, fill another 600 mL beaker about half full with ice.

2. In a second beaker, dissolve about 15 cm^3 (1 tbsp.) of salt in 500 mL of water. Pour the saltwater mixture over the ice until the beaker is about three-fourths full of water. The salt will keep the temperature of the ice water at or below 0°C.

3. Place another thermometer in the ice water and stir the water with a stirring rod (NOT the thermometer!) until the temperature is about 0°C.

5. Immerse the syringe in the ice water so that the entire syringe barrel is covered by water.

6. While the syringe is in the water, **slightly** push the plunger in every minute for three minutes to ensure that it is not sticking.

7. After you have pushed the plunger the third time, record the volume of the gas. Lift the syringe out of the water only enough to read the volume. You may be able to take the reading through the side of the beaker.

   This reading is the Low volume: _____cm³.

8. Immediately pull the plunger out **slightly** and read the volume.

   This reading is the High volume: _____cm³.

9. Calculate the average for the Low and High volumes: V_{avg} = _____cm³.

10. Record the average volume and the temperature from the cold water in the data table.

C. High Temperature Measurement

1. Using beaker tongs or a hot mitt, place the beaker with the hot water on the table and turn off the burner.

2. Submerge the syringe barrel in the hot water.

3. Use a test tube clamp to lift the plunger of the syringe out of the hot water. Keep the barrel submerged. Repeat steps 6 through 10 of Part B, except **pull** the plunger slightly three times. Record the High volume after three minutes.

   High volume: _____ cm³

4. Immediately push the plunger in **slightly** and read the volume.

   Low volume: _____ cm³

5. Calculate the average for the Low and High volumes: V_{avg} = _____cm³.

6. Record the average volume and the temperature from the hot water in the data table.

Results

A. Tabulated Data

Data Table: Charles's Law

Condition	$T(°C)$ x-axis	$V_{avg}(cm^3)$ y-axis
Cold		
Room		
Hot		

B. General Rules for Creating a Graph

1. Use a pencil.

2. Give the graph a title. Center it at the top of the graph on the paper.

3. Determine the independent variable (e.g., temperature) and the dependent variable (e.g., volume).

4. Name the x-axis with the independent variable and the y-axis with the dependent variable. Include the symbol and the units with the name, for example, "Temperature, T (°C)."

while writing it or explaining the procedure.

4. The terms independent variable *and* dependent variable *may be unfamiliar to your students, but understanding their function in producing a graph from data is important. An independent variable is a fundamental quantity such as time or one that can be controlled by the experimenter. It does not depend on the other variable. The dependent variable responds to or is a direct result of the value of the independent variable. In almost every case, the independent variable is plotted on the horizontal axis and the dependent variable is plotted on the vertical.*

5. The most difficult aspect of plotting the data will be selecting appropriate scales. Be sure that students do not pick awkward units such as 5°C every two divisions. It is helpful to have a sample graph for the students to see while they are constructing their graphs.

6. In the Discussion Questions, you can show that V/T = a constant (k). To find the volume change for a given temperature change, multiply the ΔT by k.

5. Select the appropriate size units so that you fill each axis as much as possible without creating gridline markings that are difficult to use. Make the graphing area as large as possible. Mark the axes indicating the intervals.

6. Use a ruler to draw the axes and other straight lines.

C. Finding Absolute Zero

1. Use one piece of 1/8- or 1/10-inch ruled graph paper or tape two pieces of 1/4-inch ruled graph paper together end to end.

2. Use the long dimension of the graph for the x-axis, which will represent temperature. Make the temperature in intervals of 5 or 10°C from −325°C to 100°C.

3. Mark the y-axis in intervals of 1 cm^3 from 0 to 25 cm^3.

4. Plot the three pairs of coordinates from the data table on the graph paper.

5. Lay a ruler on the graph paper so that it lies as close as possible to all of the points. The points probably will not lie on a single line; therefore, adjust the ruler so that the straight edge passes through one point and "splits the difference" between the other two. Draw a single straight line along the ruler.

6. Extend the line until it crosses the x-axis. Note that the y-coordinate (volume) at this point is 0 cm^3.

7. What is the temperature when the volume is zero? This is your estimate of absolute zero.

Discussion Questions

1. According to Charles's law, what happens to the volume of a gas as it is heated? *The volume increases.*

2. According to Charles's law, what happens to the volume of a gas as it is cooled? *The volume decreases.*

3. Explain why it is dangerous to store aerosol cans in extremely hot places.
   The gas will try to expand because it is being heated, but because the can's volume is constant, the additional energy of the gas molecules produces higher pressure that could cause the can to explode.

4. Convert your room temperature from °C to K (K = °C + 273).
   T_{room} = *(Assuming room temperature = 25°C, T_{room} = 298 K. Answers will vary.)*

5. Recall from Charles's law that the ratio for a constant amount of gas at a constant pressure is V/T. Substituting the room-temperature values for V and T, find the volume-temperature ratio for your air sample.

$$\frac{V_{room}}{T_{room}} = \frac{_____ cm^3}{_____ K} = \frac{cm^3}{K}$$

This means that the volume will change by _____ cm^3 for every _____ K.

6. If the original 20.0 cm³ volume of air at room temperature (T_1) is heated to _____ °C (enter T_2—the recorded temperature of the hot water), determine the expected or theoretical volume in the syringe.

   a. Determine the change in temperature (ΔT): $T_2 - T_1 =$ _____ °C. Recall that Celsius degrees and Kelvins are the same "size," so $\Delta T =$ _____ K.

   b. A one Kelvin increase will cause a _____ cm³ increase in volume (from question 5).

   c. A two Kelvin increase will cause a _____ cm³ increase in volume.

   d. A (ΔT, from 6a) _____ Kelvin increase will cause a _____ cm³ increase in volume (ΔV).

   e. The theoretical volume of gas at T_2 will be the sum of the original volume (20.0 cm³) and ΔV.

      Calculated volume at T_2 _____

      Measured volume at T_2 (V_{avg}) _____ (See data table.)

Experimental Evaluation

7. Ideally, the three data points should lie on a straight line. Explain why they did not. *Answers will vary, but students should mention equipment and human errors, sticking plunger, leaking seal in syringe, changes of temperature during reading of instruments, and so on.*

8. If a person could have used very accurate instruments, do you think that person could get the data points to fit exactly on a straight line? Explain *Answers will vary. Depending on how much emphasis you placed on Charles's law and the idealization of gas behavior, students may say that temperature and volume have a linear relationship (they do for small changes in temperature) or they may say that the relationship is not truly linear (which is correct for large temperature changes).*

9. Besides using more accurate instruments, give two ways this experiment could be improved. *Answers will vary. Suggested improvements include obtaining more data points over a greater temperature range, using a larger gas volume so that small errors are a smaller fraction of the measured change, and using a single gas rather than air.*

10. Did this experiment demonstrate the exact value of absolute zero? Explain. *No, besides the fact that the experimental design has many sources of error, the exact value of absolute zero cannot be measured because no measurement can be exact.*

11. (Optional) Some scientists think that absolute zero is not obtainable. Can you give a reason for this belief? *The thermodynamic reason is that the residual thermal energy that must be removed to arrive at absolute zero must flow to a point of lower temperature. Since there is no temperature lower than absolute zero, this is not possible.*

Objective

The purpose of this demonstration is to familiarize you with the appearance and use of selected elements.

Materials

Selected element samples

Equipment

Periodic table

MSDS file or data forms (Optional)

Introduction

As you learned from your textbook, elements are the building blocks of all substances. All pure substances are either elements or compounds. Compounds can be broken down into their elements, but elements cannot be broken down any further without changing them into other elements. We will be observing a number of elements and noting their similarities and differences.

Prior to participating in this demonstration, you should review the material from Investigation 1A: "Laboratory Safety." You may be asked to complete this exercise as homework.

Pre-Laboratory Questions

Read the entire investigation. Answer the following questions prior to class on a separate sheet of paper. Use complete sentences.

1. What is the key difference between elements and compounds?

2. What would happen if an element were broken down any further?

3. What is the range of possible numbers for a hazard index?

4. What standard protective equipment should be used in a laboratory when handling unfamiliar chemicals?

Procedure

As each element is presented (or at each station around the room), write the name of the element in the blank provided in each section below. As time permits, find the element's symbol and its atomic number on the periodic table on pages 144 and 145 in your textbook, but do not delay observing the characteristics of the elements to do this during the demonstration. If the sample can be handled, note its hardness, texture, how crystalline it is, relative density, color, state, smell, and so on. (DO NOT TASTE ANY SUBSTANCE IN A LABORATORY!) If the element is in a sealed container, describe those properties that can be observed without opening the container. **Do not shake**

Introduction

This demonstration introduces your students to some physical properties of elements. You will want to take every opportunity to point out the unique properties of each one. Be sure to save the elements used in this demonstration for comparison with compounds that contain them in Teacher Demonstration 5B.

Answers to Pre-Laboratory Questions

1. The main difference between elements and compounds is that compounds can be broken down into simpler substances and elements cannot.

2. An element broken down further would become a different element.

3. Hazard indexes range from 0 to 4.

4. One should wear an apron, gloves, and goggles to handle an unfamiliar chemical.

Preparation

1. This demonstration is best done using stations set up around the room, although you can show each element from the front. The latter will deprive your students of looking closely at each sample.

2. If possible, use at least ten elements from the following list. Laboratory-grade samples must be obtained well ahead of time from science supply companies. There are household sources for many of the listed elements. Many

of these elements are used
for other exercises in this
course and in other courses
using BJUP science
textbooks.

Aluminum   Lead
Antimony   Magnesium
Bismuth   Mercury
Calcium   Nickel
Carbon   Nitrogen (Air)
 (Graphite)   Oxygen*
Copper   Sodium
Hydrogen*   Sulfur
Iodine   Tin
Iron   Zinc

*Hydrogen and oxygen can
be prepared from
electrolysis of water.

3. If you want the students
to record safety information
in this demonstration, you
will need to verify that the
information is available in
your laboratory MSDS file. A
more efficient solution is to
make several copies of the
applicable MSDSs as
handout folders so that the
students can quickly obtain
the information in the class
period.

General Comments

1. Have the students start
with one at each station.
Unassigned students line up
at the first station and move
in as the line advances. For
large classes, you can
double up. Have the
students rotate after two or
three minutes at each
station.

2. It would add interest to
the exercise if you can
obtain native ores of several
of the elements such as
copper, silver, and carbon
ores. Placer gold can often
be obtained from sources in
the western United States.

liquids. If the element is transparent, observe what it does to light, if anything. If the element has been artificially processed or formed, do not describe its man-made properties (e.g., spherical shape of lead shot).

You may also be required to note the safety information for each element using MSDS or other sources provided by your teacher. Fill this information in on copies of the blank MSDS form found in the back of this lab manual. Staple all pages together when you are finished.

A. Element _____ Symbol _____ Atomic Number _____

a. State	
b. Hardness	
c. Color	
d. Relative density	
e. Smell	

f. Appearance—Circle all that are appropriate.

Transparent	Translucent
Opaque	Metallic
Crystalline/Faceted	Fibrous
Dusty/Sandy/Particles	Other: _____

B. Element _____ Symbol _____ Atomic Number _____

a. State	
b. Hardness	
c. Color	
d. Relative density	
e. Smell	

f. Appearance—Circle all that are appropriate.

Transparent	Translucent
Opaque	Metallic
Crystalline/Faceted	Fibrous
Dusty/Sandy/Particles	Other: _____

C. Element _____ Symbol _____ Atomic Number _____

| a. State |
| b. Hardness |
| c. Color |
| d. Relative density |
| e. Smell |

f. Appearance—Circle all that are appropriate.

Transparent	Translucent
Opaque	Metallic
Crystalline/Faceted	Fibrous
Dusty/Sandy/Particles	Other: _____

D. Element _____ Symbol _____ Atomic Number _____

| a. State |
| b. Hardness |
| c. Color |
| d. Relative density |
| e. Smell |

f. Appearance—Circle all that are appropriate.

Transparent	Translucent
Opaque	Metallic
Crystalline/Faceted	Fibrous
Dusty/Sandy/Particles	Other: _____

E. Element _____ Symbol _____ Atomic Number _____

| a. State |
| b. Hardness |
| c. Color |
| d. Relative density |
| e. Smell |

f. Appearance—Circle all that are appropriate.

Transparent	Translucent
Opaque	Metallic
Crystalline/Faceted	Fibrous
Dusty/Sandy/Particles	Other: _____

F. Element _____ Symbol _____ Atomic Number _____

a. State	
b. Hardness	
c. Color	
d. Relative density	
e. Smell	
f. Appearance—Circle all that are appropriate.	

      Transparent   Translucent

         Opaque   Metallic

      Crystalline/Faceted   Fibrous

      Dusty/Sandy/Particles   Other: _____

G. Element _____ Symbol _____ Atomic Number _____

a. State	
b. Hardness	
c. Color	
d. Relative density	
e. Smell	
f. Appearance—Circle all that are appropriate.	

      Transparent   Translucent

         Opaque   Metallic

      Crystalline/Faceted   Fibrous

      Dusty/Sandy/Particles   Other: _____

H. Element _____ Symbol _____ Atomic Number _____

a. State	
b. Hardness	
c. Color	
d. Relative density	
e. Smell	
f. Appearance—Circle all that are appropriate.	

      Transparent   Translucent

         Opaque   Metallic

      Crystalline/Faceted   Fibrous

      Dusty/Sandy/Particles   Other: _____

I. Element _____ Symbol _____ Atomic Number _____

a. State
b. Hardness
c. Color
d. Relative density
e. Smell
f. Appearance—Circle all that are appropriate.

    Transparent   Translucent

    Opaque   Metallic

    Crystalline/Faceted   Fibrous

    Dusty/Sandy/Particles   Other: _____

J. Element _____ Symbol _____ Atomic Number _____

a. State
b. Hardness
c. Color
d. Relative density
e. Smell
f. Appearance—Circle all that are appropriate.

    Transparent   Translucent

    Opaque   Metallic

    Crystalline/Faceted   Fibrous

    Dusty/Sandy/Particles   Other: _____

K. Element _____ Symbol _____ Atomic Number _____

a. State
b. Hardness
c. Color
d. Relative density
e. Smell
f. Appearance—Circle all that are appropriate.

    Transparent   Translucent

    Opaque   Metallic

    Crystalline/Faceted   Fibrous

    Dusty/Sandy/Particles   Other: _____

Objective

The purpose of this investigation is to demonstrate that the physical properties of a compound are different from the properties of the elements of which it is composed.

Materials

Baking soda—$NaHCO_3$
Calcium chloride—$CaCl_2$
Copper(II) sulfate—$CuSO_4$
Epsom salts—$MgSO_4$
Lead dioxide—PbO_2
Mercury(II) chloride—$HgCl_2$
Sodium chloride—NaCl
Vinegar—$C_2H_4O_2$

Equipment

Beakers, 100 mL (8)

Introduction

The **Law of Definite Composition** states that atoms of elements combine to form compounds in specific ratios. No matter where a compound is found, it always has the same composition with the same ratio of elements. The relationship between elements and compounds is similar to the relationship between letters and words. Words can be broken down into individual letters, but letters cannot be meaningfully broken down any further. It is only if letters are combined in specific ways that they form words with unique properties (meanings). Just as a word has properties different from the letters of which it is composed, a compound can have chemical and physical properties that are very different from the elements that make it up. For example, mercury(II) oxide (HgO) is composed of the two elements mercury and oxygen. Mercury is a liquid, silvery, toxic metal; and oxygen is a colorless, breathable gas that causes flammability in other substances. The compound mercury(II) oxide, however, is a bright orange solid powder. Its physical properties are totally different from the constituent elements.

You read in your book that sodium chloride is a harmless compound composed of two dangerous elements. However, combining toxic elements to form a compound does not always yield a harmless substance. This is particularly true of compounds containing heavy metals such as cadmium, mercury, and lead. Though their physical appearance may be quite different from their constituent elements, many compounds still require special handling and disposal procedures to protect people, animals, and the environment from harm.

General Comments

1. As in Teacher Demonstration 5A, the compounds can be presented in two ways: the teacher can display each in front of the class, describing its physical properties for the students to write down, or the samples can be placed in stations around the room. Lead dioxide and mercury(II) chloride are included in the demonstration. However, because of the toxicity of these compounds, the students should not touch them. They may be displayed in covered beakers or sealed bottles.

2. If you were not able in Teacher Demonstration 5A to display all of the elements featured in this demonstration, you may either provide the students the omitted elements' characteristics or you may omit the applicable compound from this demonstration (less preferred).

3. Other compounds graphically demonstrate the change in properties between elements and their compounds. Several include mercury(II) oxide (mentioned in the demonstration introduction) and carbon disulfide (CS_2)—a black solid and a yellow solid combine to form a toxic, highly refractive, liquid solvent for nonmetals.

4. If you desire to include hazard information in this demonstration, you may have students fill in a copy of the blank MSDS sheet in the back of the lab manual.

Pre-Laboratory Questions

Read the entire investigation. Answer the following questions prior to class on a separate sheet of paper. Use complete sentences.

1. What does the Law of Definite Composition state?

2. Does a compound usually have physical properties similar to the elements from which it is made? Give an example to support your answer.

3. Name three common household chemicals that we will be examining in this demonstration.

4. Do toxic elements become harmless when bonded in compounds? Give an example of a compound from this demonstration that you think may be harmful.

Procedures

As each compound is presented (or at each station around the room), describe its physical appearance, noting especially its color, state, and whether it is crystalline or powdery. Do not touch, taste, or shake the samples. On the subsequent lines, list the elements of which the compound is composed and summarize each element's physical properties from the information gathered in Teacher Demonstration 5A. The first one is done for you. You may also be required to note the safety information for each element using the MSDS or other sources provided by your teacher.

A. Table Salt ($NaCl$)   - White, crystalline solid, edible
Sodium   - Poisonous, soft reactive metal
Chlorine   - Greenish, poisonous gas

B. Baking soda ($NaHCO_3$)   - White, powdery solid, edible
Sodium   - Poisonous, reactive metal
Hydrogen   - Colorless gas, flammable
Carbon   - Dull black solid
Oxygen   - Colorless gas, promotes flammability, nontoxic

C. Epsom salts ($MgSO_4$)   - White, medium-to-coarse crystalline solid
Magnesium   - Bright, soft, silver metal
Sulfur   - Yellow crystalline solid
Oxygen   - Colorless gas, promotes flammability, nontoxic

D. Calcium chloride (CaCl₂) - *White, finely-divided crystalline solid*

Calcium - *Dark gray metal*

Chlorine - *Greenish, poisonous gas*

E. Copper (II) sulfate (CuSO₄) - *Blue crystals or powder*

Copper - *Shiny copper-colored metal*

Sulfur - *Yellow solid*

Oxygen - *Colorless gas, promotes flammability, nontoxic*

F. Lead dioxide (PbO₂) - *Black, powdery solid*

Lead - *Dull, dark gray or silvery metal*

Oxygen - *Colorless gas, promotes flammability, nontoxic*

G. Mercuric chloride (HgCl₂) - *White powdery or crystalline solid*

Mercury - *Shiny, silvery metallic liquid*

Chlorine - *Greenish, poisonous gas*

H. Vinegar (C₂H₄O₂) - *Colorless or amber-colored, sour-smelling liquid*

Carbon - *Dull black solid*

Hydrogen - *Colorless gas, flammable*

Oxygen - *Colorless gas, promotes flammability, nontoxic*

Discussion Questions

1. Explain what happens when the two hazardous elements sodium and chlorine are combined? *They form an edible crystalline solid—sodium chloride, table salt.*

2. Do you think that you should dispose of lead and mercury compounds in the sink? *No, they require special disposal procedures because compounds containing lead and mercury are toxic.*

3. Why are mercury thermometers rarely used in the laboratory? *You could be exposed to the poisonous mercury if the thermometer breaks.*

5. The formula for copper(II) sulfate is _____*CuSO₄*_____. One formula unit of this compound contains a total of ___*6*___ atoms: ___*1*___ atom(s) of copper, ___*1*___ atom(s) of sulfur, and ___*4*___ atom(s) of oxygen.

6. In the compound lead dioxide (PbO₂), the ratio of the number of Pb atoms to O atoms is ___*1*___ to ___*2*___.

5C INVESTIGATION

Mixtures

Objectives

The purpose of this investigation is to

1. Understand the differences between compounds and mixtures.

2. Demonstrate that the substances that make up a mixture retain their physical properties.

3. Separate a mixture based on the physical properties of its constituent substances.

Introduction

This is a good investigation to emphasize the difference between proof and evidence. A mixture is defined as a combination of two or more compounds. Demonstrating the presence of two or more substances proves the existence of a mixture.

Materials

Aluminum foil
Distilled water
Ice
Iron filings (15 cm^3 or 1 tbsp)
Orange juice, pulp free (75 mL)
Salt (15 cm^3 or 1 tbsp)
Sand (15 cm^3 or 1 tbsp)

Equipment

Beaker, 500 mL
Beakers, 100 mL (2)
Beaker, 50 mL
Bunsen burner
Burner lighter
Magnet
Microscope (low & 600+ power)
    (Optional)
Rubber band, wide
Rubber stoppers, small (3)
Stirring rod
Tripod
Wire gauze

Introduction

When two or more pure substances are combined without a subsequent chemical reaction, the result is called a **mixture.** These substances could be either elements or compounds. Mixtures differ from compounds in several ways. As you learned in Teacher Demonstration 5B, when elements react chemically to form a compound, the new substance often has physical properties that are different from those of the pure elements. In a mixture, each of the combined substances retains its original physical properties. Compounds and mixtures also differ in the method of separation of the original components. The elements in a compound have been combined chemically and have to be separated chemically. This requires energy in a form that will break the chemical bonds (usually heat or electricity). Mixtures, however, have undergone only a physical change. Often separating a mixture involves causing a phase change or using some physical process such as filtering. If heat is required to separate a mixture, the heat energy is not changing the composition of the substances; it is merely changing their state. The research question is "How can you separate the substances of a mixture?"

Many familiar materials are actually mixtures. Examples include air, salt water, paper, 14 kt. gold, steel, paint, chocolate, butter, ink, and concrete. Remember that mixtures can be combinations of either elements or compounds. A **homogeneous** mixture is one that is so well mixed that its appearance is the same throughout. Air, salt water, and 14 kt. gold are examples of homogeneous mixtures. No matter how small a sample you looked at, you could not visually tell the different substances apart. In a **heterogeneous** mixture, the parts can be visually identified or the particles are so different in size that they do not meet the definition of a homogeneous mixture. Concrete, composed of cement, sand, and gravel, is a good example of this kind of mixture. (Note that the composition of gravel is most likely a heterogeneous mixture as well.)

Pre-Laboratory Questions

Read the entire investigation. Answer the following questions prior to class on a separate sheet of paper. Use complete sentences.

1. What is a mixture composed of?

2. What kind of change is involved in separating a mixture?

3. What are two ways that mixtures differ from compounds?

4. What is the physical property of iron filings that allows it to be easily separated from its mixture in this investigation?

5. State the research question.

6. State a testable hypothesis concerning this investigation.

Procedures

A. Separating a mixture of iron filings, sand, and table salt

1. Mix the iron filings, sand, and table salt thoroughly together with the stirring rod in a 100 mL beaker. Note the appearance of the mixture.

2. Stir the mixture with the magnet. Periodically brush the iron filings off the magnet onto a piece of paper. Continue stirring the mixture with the magnet until no more iron filings adhere.

3. Add about 75 mL of distilled water to the beaker containing the sand and the salt and stir for two minutes to dissolve the salt.

4. Allow the sand to settle and carefully pour off as much of the salt water as possible into the second 100 mL beaker.

5. Light the Bunsen burner and place the *second* 100 mL beaker on the wire gauze on top of the tripod.

6. Heat the water to boiling and allow it to boil until almost all of the water has disappeared. Watch the beaker carefully. Remove the beaker from the flame just before the last of the water boils away. Allow the residual heat to evaporate the remaining water. Turn off the burner.

7. Discard the sand into the trash and wash both of the beakers. Place the iron filings in the designated receptacle.

B. Separating Water from Orange Juice

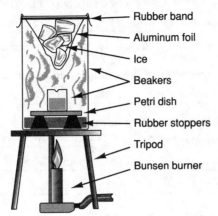

Rubber band
Aluminum foil
Ice
Beakers
Petri dish
Rubber stoppers
Tripod
Bunsen burner

1. Pour about 50 mL of the orange juice into the 500 mL beaker. The bottom should be covered with about 1 cm of fluid. Note the appearance of the orange juice.

2. Place the three rubber stoppers in the beaker, wide end down, in a triangular pattern.

3. Place a petri dish (or other flat support) on top of the rubber stoppers and place an empty 50 mL beaker on top of that positioned in the center of the large beaker.

4. Cover the mouth of the large beaker with aluminum foil making sure that there is a cone-shaped depression in the foil. Be sure that the tip of the depression is directly over the empty 50 mL beaker. Fasten the foil to the rim of the beaker with a rubber band.

5. Place three or four ice cubes in the depression in the foil.

6. Carefully place the large beaker on top of the wire gauze on the tripod.

7. Light the Bunsen burner underneath, placing the flame under the space between the stoppers, and gently heat the beaker.

8. Turn off the burner when 5-10 mL of liquid has dripped into the small beaker. Note the color of the liquid in the small beaker. It is not necessary to boil off all of the liquid in the large beaker.

9. Make sure that the beakers and other parts are thoroughly cleaned when you are finished.

C. Optional Observations

1. Following the instructions of your teacher, use a microscope to observe under low power a slide of the iron filing-salt-sand mixture. Note any differences among the particles you can see.

2. Observe under high power a microscope slide of a sample of orange juice. Note anything that might indicate the presence of more than one substance.

Discussion Questions

A. Separating Iron Filings, Sand, and Salt

1. Was this a homogeneous or a heterogeneous mixture? Explain. *This was a heterogeneous mixture. After it was mixed together, you could still see the different colors of the particles that were mixed together.*

2. What physical property of the salt allowed you to separate it from the sand? *The salt dissolved in the water, and the sand did not.*

3. How could you separate two substances such as sand and gravel that are not soluble in water? *They have different-sized particles, so you could separate them using a fine sieve that would allow the sand to pass through but not the gravel.*

B. Separating an Orange Juice Mixture

1. What was the appearance of the liquid in the small beaker? *The liquid was clear.*

2. What do you think it was? Where did it come from? *The clear liquid in the beaker appeared to be water. It boiled out of the orange juice.*

3. What was the function of the ice in the foil? *The ice cooled the foil, which provided a cold surface for the water vapor to condense onto.*

4. How does this demonstrate that orange juice is a mixture and not a compound? *If it were a compound, you would not be able to separate water from it by evaporating it.*

5. Was the orange juice a homogeneous or a heterogeneous mixture? Explain. *Orange juice appears to be a homogeneous mixture to the naked eye. (Optional) Microscopic analysis will show that it is really a heterogeneous mixture. Without the microscope, the orange juice appears the same throughout. With a microscope, you can see the tiny oil and juice plastids from the fruit cells floating around in the field of view.*

Flame Tests

Name _____

Date _____ Hour _____

Objectives

The purpose of this investigation is to

1. Illustrate the limitations of relying solely on your senses for scientific observations.

2. Attempt to identify two different elements by their flame test emissions.

Introduction

The connection between the electron's change in energy levels and the production of light should be emphasized. Understanding this connection will help the students understand light production in the later chapters. The condition of materials when heated so that they produce an emission is called incandescence.

Materials

Calcium chloride ($CaCl_2$)
Copper(II) chloride ($CuCl_2$)
Lithium chloride (LiCl)
Manganese chloride ($MnCl_2$)
Potassium chloride (KCl)
Sodium chloride (NaCl)
Strontium chloride ($SrCl_2$)
Wooden splints

Equipment

Bunsen burner
Safety glasses
Diffraction grating spectroscopes
  (optional)

Introduction

The electrons surrounding the nucleus of an atom exist in specific energy levels. When an element is heated, its electrons gain energy. If enough energy is added, an electron will jump to a higher energy level, called an excited state. This state is not stable, and the electron will immediately return to a lower energy level. When this happens, the excess energy is released as visible light or some other form of radiant energy. The wavelength of the light given off (its color) depends on the difference between the energy levels. Each element has a specific arrangement of electrons that can change energy levels in unique ways. As a result, each element gives off a distinctive set of wavelengths called an **emission spectrum.** This spectrum is unique to each element and can be used to identify it. If the emission spectrum contains several distinct wavelengths (bright line spectrum), they are often not apparent to the naked eye. For example, when an element is heated, it may appear to our eyes to glow orange; but if that orange light were dispersed by a prism, it could separate into several individual color bands. A **spectroscope** is a device that can disperse a beam of light into a spectrum.

A **spectrometer** is a laboratory instrument that displays the emission spectrum of a substance on a numerical scale and can give an accurate analysis of elemental composition. The composition of stars is determined by this very process.

Answers to Pre-Laboratory Questions

1. Electrons jump to higher energy levels.

2. The excess energy is released as some form of light.

3. An emission spectrum is the set of wavelengths of light given off when an element is heated.

4. Each element gives off a unique emission spectrum because its arrangement of electrons is different from that of any other element.

5. The color of the flame could interfere with observing the emission of the incandescent element.

6. Using contaminated wood splints would display emissions from other elements.

Demonstration Procedure

With appropriate care, students may perform this demonstration themselves.

1. Soak the wooden splints overnight in water so that they will not readily burn during the flame tests.

2. Obtain a small sample of each of the salts. Dip a moist splint into a sample of one of the salts until some of the salt adheres.

3. Tip the Bunsen burner slightly so that no grains of the salt will fall down the barrel. If this happens, the flame will be colored by the salt in subsequent tests.

4. Place the salt into the hottest part of the flame (the upper third). Do not leave it in the flame long enough for the splint to begin burning. Dip the splint into a container of water to extinguish and then discard it into the trash.

Pre-Laboratory Questions

Read the entire demonstration. Answer the following questions prior to class on a separate sheet of paper. Use complete sentences.

1. What happens to electrons when they gain energy?

2. What happens to the excess energy when the electrons return to lower energy levels?

3. What is an emission spectrum?

4. Explain why each element gives off a unique emission spectrum.

5. Why is the burner flame adjusted to eliminate the orange tip of the flame?

6. Why must a clean wood splint be used for each new sample?

Procedures

1. Observe as your teacher adjusts the burner flame to be nearly invisible or emitting only a blue glow.

2. Next, your teacher will dip a fresh, damp wood splint into a sample of each element, one at a time, and then place the element into the hottest part of the flame to produce the incandescent emission.

3. Record the color you observe in the table below. Be as descriptive as possible (e.g., write "red-orange" rather than just "orange"). This will establish your list of reference colors for the unknown samples.

4. Observe as your teacher tests two samples of unidentified elements in the flame. These unknowns are among those you have already observed. Record their colors in the table for Unknown I and II.

5. (Optional) Using a spectroscope, attempt to identify any bright lines in the spectra of selected elements as they are being tested. Record their colors and the number of lines of each, if applicable.

Results

Table: Emission Data

Element	Color	Bright Lines (Optional)
Calcium	Orange	Answers will vary.
Copper	Blue-green	Answers will vary.
Lithium	Red-orange	Answers will vary.
Manganese	Yellow-green	Answers will vary.
Potassium	Orange	Answers will vary.
Sodium	Orange	Answers will vary.
Strontium	Red	Answers will vary.
Unknown I—*Strontium*	Red	Answers will vary.
Unknown II—*Sodium*	Orange	Answers will vary.

Experimental Evaluation

1. Does the flame test as demonstrated provide evidence or proof of the identity of an element? Explain. *The flame test provides only evidence of an element's identity. Several of the colors were difficult to distinguish from each other.*

2. Why was it difficult to identify Unknown II? *The color it emitted is like that of other elements.*

3. Do you think that the elements that appeared to be the same color in the flame tests would show that same similarity if their emission spectra were analyzed? Explain. *Their spectra would not be the same because each element has its own unique arrangement of electrons and, therefore, its own unique spectrum.*

4. What would you need to do to positively identify Unknown II? *You would need to analyze it using a spectrometer.*

5. Repeat the above procedure, using a clean splint for each of the salts to be tested.

6. Test the unknowns, using strontium chloride for Unknown I and sodium chloride for Unknown II.

General Comments

1. While the students should be able to identify Unknown I (strontium) because of its distinctive color, Unknown II (sodium) should be difficult to identify because several of the elements produce a similar color. This illustrates the subjective nature of identifying colors. An objective analysis of the emission spectra for these elements would show a clear difference between them.

2. (Optional Spectroscopy) Classroom kits for building simple diffraction grating spectroscopes can be obtained for just a few dollars per instrument from most of the popular science equipment suppliers. You should have your students first observe the flame tests without the spectroscopes and then conduct the tests again using the spectroscopes. A little practice is required to obtain a spectrum using a diffraction grating spectroscope. One must orient the slot vertically parallel to the grating rules, point the instrument at the light source, then look into the barrel toward the left or right to observe the spectrum (do not look directly at the light source as with a telescope). Students should be able to note bright lines for sodium, lithium, copper, and strontium. You should try this yourself before lab time to understand the technique needed to be successful.

INVESTIGATION

6B

Radioactive Decay

Name _____

Date_____ Hour_____

Objective

The purpose of this investigation is to illustrate radioactive decay.

Materials

Pennies (or M&Ms™)

Introduction

From your textbook, you learned that some atoms undergo changes where their nuclei emit rays and/or particles in a process called radioactive decay. The rate at which this occurs varies among isotopes and is measured by the time it takes for one-half of a given isotope to decay to (be converted into) a different isotope. This interval is called the **half-life** and is unique to each isotope for a certain kind of decay. Suppose isotope A decays into isotope B with a half-life of one year. If you start with 100 g of isotope A, at the end of one year there will be about 50 g of isotope A and about 50 g of isotope B. In other words, each atom has a 50-50 (50%) chance of decaying during the first half-life. During the second half-life (the second year), each remaining atom of isotope A has a 50% chance of decaying again. At the end of two years, there will be about 25 g of isotope A left and about 75 g of isotope B. Why doesn't all of the remaining 50 g of isotope A decay during the second half-life? The principle of **independence** states that each event of radioactive decay is not affected by (is independent of) what has happened before. In other words, no matter how many half-lives have already passed, the chance that any of the remaining atoms will decay during the next half-life remains only 50%. In our example, at the end of three years, there will be about 12.5 g of isotope A remaining; at the end of four years, 6.25 g, and so on. You can see that even with a relatively short half-life of one year, it would take a long time for an isotope to be completely eliminated through radioactive decay. The concern that many people have about the safety of nuclear power facilities stems from the fact that much of the waste contains radioactive elements with very long half-lives emitting hazardous radiation.

Introduction

This investigation employs some basic concepts of probability. Students may have had some exposure to probability in pre-algebra or algebra courses. If so, you should relate what they have learned to the concepts in this exercise. If probability is unfamiliar to the students, then it is not necessary to elaborate unless you want this to be more specifically a probability exercise.

The concept of independence of events is fundamental to an understanding of many statistical phenomena as well as radioactive decay and should be stressed.

In nuclear chemistry the first isotope in a decay chain is called the parent isotope and the product of nuclear decay is called the daughter product. You may want to use these terms to keep the process clear as the exercise progresses.

Radioactive decay as presented in this investigation has been highly simplified. Naturally occurring radioactive materials are a mix of different isotopes, and many isotopes can decay in different ways with different half-lives. For simplicity's sake, we will assume that all of the atoms under consideration are of a single isotope, that the isotope decays in only one way, and that the parent and daughter isotopes have the same mass. Also, we look at a sample at specific points of time called half-lives to determine the amounts of

Radioactive Decay

parent and daughter substances at those times.

In reality, radioactive decay is a continuous process. From moment to moment, half of the isotopes of interest may decay to the daughter isotope over the next half-life. Plotting the remaining parent isotope over time (rather than in half-lives as we do in this exercise) produces a smooth curve based on an inverse exponential function. The function is of the form $A_t = A_0e^{-\lambda t}$, where A_t is the amount of the parent at time t; A_0 is the original amount; e is the natural logarithmic base; λ is the decay constant, which is based on the half-life of the parent isotope ($\lambda = 0.693 \div$ half-life) and t is the amount of time that has elapsed. (λ has units of $\frac{1}{time}$ so that the product "λt" is a pure number.) With this information, you may use a graphing calculator to produce a sample curve.

Answers to Pre-Laboratory Questions

1. The half-life of a radioactive isotope is the length of time that it takes for half of the material to decay into another isotope.

2. It means that the probability of an event occurring for a specific case or object is not affected by events that have already occurred with other cases or objects. In relation to radioactive decay, it means that the probability of any atom decaying in the next half-life of time always remains 50 percent.

Beta decay does not measurably change the mass of the daughter isotope.

Pre-Laboratory Questions

Read the entire investigation. Answer the following questions priot to class on a separate piece of paper. Use complete sentences.

1. Define the term *half-life*.

2. What does it mean to state that one event is independent of another?

3. Isotope A beta decays to isotope B and has a half-life of six months. If you begin with 500 g of isotope A, how much of each isotope will be present after six months, twelve months, and eighteen months?

Procedures

A. Using Penny Flips as a Model for Radioactive Decay

In this exercise, each penny will represent a radioactive atom. A flip represents the period of one half-life. Also, each flip of a penny, like each event of radioactive decay, is an independent event. This means that the chance of getting tails (50%) is not affected by the previous flip. If a person flips a penny five times and obtains five tails in a row, the chance of obtaining tails on the sixth flip is still only 50%.

1. Everyone in the class should obtain a penny. (For small classes, you may be asked to take two or more.) Record the total number of pennies in Table 1. This figure represents the initial number of "radioactive atoms."

2. At a signal from the teacher, everyone should flip his coin(s).

3. Record the number of heads and tails on the blackboard or on a sheet of paper.

4. The teacher will flip a penny, and the side showing will be noted. The students' pennies that had the same side showing as the teacher will represent the radioactive atoms that have decayed during the first half-life and should be removed. The affected pennies should not be flipped in any future trials.

5. Record the number of pennies remaining (undecayed) in Table 1 for half-life 1.

6. Repeat steps 2–5 with the remaining pennies until all the pennies have "decayed."

7. Plot your results on the blank graph provided. Carefully sketch a *smooth* curve through the data points. This curve is called a **decay curve.**

B. M&Ms (Alternative)

In this exercise, each M&M will represent a radioactive atom.

1. Place forty M&Ms in a box.

2. Cover the box and shake it briefly but vigorously.

3. Remove the cover and count the M&Ms that landed with the printed side up. These represent atoms that have decayed. Remove and eat them.

4. Record the number of M&Ms remaining in Table 2 for half-life 1.

5. Repeat steps 2–4 until all the M&Ms are gone. Each trial represents one half-life.

6. Plot your results on the blank graph provided. Carefully sketch a *smooth* curve through the data points. This curve is called a **decay curve.** (*Note:* If you are performing both experiments in this investigation, use a different color from the penny data.)

Results

Table 1: Radioactive Decay (Pennies)

Number of half-lives	Pennies Remaining
0	Initial _____
1	
2	
3	
4	
5	
6	
7	
8	
9	
10	

Table 2: Radioactive Decay (M&Ms)

Number of half-lives	M&Ms Remaining
0	40
1	
2	
3	
4	
5	
6	
7	
8	
9	
10	

3.	A	B
6 months	250 g	250 g
12 months	125 g	375 g
18 months	62.5 g	437.5 g

General Comments

1. If your class is small, you may have students flip more than one penny so that the total number of pennies at the start is between 30 and 40. This will provide more meaningful data for the graph.

2. Having the teacher flip a separate penny to determine the "decayed" pennies adds an extra level of randomness into the exercise.

3. We have provided space for 10 trials. In actual experience, you should not need more than 7 or 8 trials to eliminate the pennies/M&Ms. Using the natural decay function discussed above, the amount of the original isotope remaining after <u>five</u> half-lives is only 3 percent, after <u>six</u> half-lives, 1.5 percent, and so on.

4. Emphasize that when sketching the curves on their graphs, students should not go dot-to-dot due to the probabilistic nature of the data. The curves should smoothly pass through the data points.

5. An excellent, if somewhat technical, reference discussing radioactive dating techniques from a Creationist perspective is "The Mythology of Modern Dating Methods" by John Woodmorappe, published by the Institute for Creation Research.

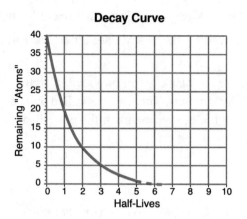

Decay Curve

Discussion Questions

1. The half-life of carbon-14 is about six thousand years, and carbon-14 decays to nitrogen-14. If an Egyptian mummy contained 10 g of carbon-14 when it was buried and now has 5 g, how old is the mummy? __*6,000 years*__ How many grams of nitrogen-14 were produced during that time? ____*5 g*____ In another six thousand years, how much carbon-14 will remain? ____*2.5 g*____ What would be the total amount of nitrogen-14 produced in twelve thousand years after the burial of the mummy? ____*7.5 g*____

2. What is the chance that a carbon-14 atom will decay in six thousand years? ____*50%*____ If that atom does not decay after six thousand years, what would be the chance of that atom decaying in the next six thousand years? Explain. *Its chance of decaying is still 50 percent. Only 50 percent of all of the atoms remaining after one half-life will decay during the next half-life. This is the principle of independence.*

Experimental Evaluation

3. What was the chance of any of the "radioactive atoms " decaying during each trial? ____*50%*____

4. If you performed a decay trial with fifty of your "atoms" (pennies or M&Ms), would you expect to obtain exactly twenty-five "decays"? Explain. *No, probability gives a number that would be accurate if averaged over a great many trials, but each individual trial will vary in the number of "decays."*

5. How many half-lives were needed to eliminate nearly all of the original "isotopes"? *Answers will vary, but the average for the class should be around five to six half-lives.*

6. Based on your answer to question 5, if the hazardous radioactive isotope cobalt-60 has a half-life of five years, how long will it be until essentially all of the cobalt-60 has decayed away? _____ *25-30 years* _____

7. Describe the shape of your graphs. Discuss steepness of slope and relative height of the curve with increasing half-lives. *The decay curve(s) started* *high on the vertical axis and initially dropped steeply to the right. The* *slope leveled out (became more horizontal) as the line approached the* *horizontal axis.*

8. (Optional) If you performed both of the experiments in this investigation, how do the shapes of the graphs compare? *Both curves were similar in* *shape.*

9. (Optional) What are some assumptions scientists must make when using radioactive decay to date ancient objects? *The following assumptions must* *be made:*

   a. The half-life of the isotope has not changed.

   b. The amount of the first isotope originally in the sample can be determined.

   c. There was no gain or loss of either the first or final isotope by natural *processes such as groundwater leaching or evaporation.*

   d. There was no other radioactive parent for the final isotope.

   e. Other plausible answers may be accepted.

7 INVESTIGATION
Metals and Nonmetals

Name _____

Date _____ Hour_____

Objective

The purpose of this investigation is to demonstrate the differing physical properties of metals, nonmetals, and metalloids.

Materials

Aluminum
Antimony
Bismuth
Carbon (coal)
Carbon (graphite, powdered, 15 cm^3)
Carbon (soft drawing pencil
  [4B or softer])
Copper (wire)
Iodine crystals
Iron (nail)
Silicon
Sulfur
Wood (drawing pencil)

Equipment

Beaker (250 mL)
Beaker tongs or hot mitt
Bunsen burner
Electrical conductivity apparatus
  (see Investigation 2B)
Multimeter (if available)
Tripod
Wire gauze

Introduction

The elements on the periodic table can be divided into three classes: the metals, the nonmetals, and the metalloids. The periodic table in your textbook contains a stair-step dividing line between the metals and the nonmetals. The elements in green that are adjacent to the dividing line are called the metalloids. Not surprisingly, the three classes of elements have different physical properties. The question is "Can certain physical properties of an element be predicted based on its location on the periodic table?"

In this investigation we will examine a few physical properties of several metals, nonmetals, and metalloids. Because the elements in a class have similar electron structures, you would expect them to have similar properties as well. Most metals are solids, will easily conduct electricity and heat, are malleable, and have a silvery luster. Nonmetals may exist as solids, liquids, or gases, though the gaseous state is the most common. They generally do not conduct electricity or heat well, and the solids are brittle. Rather than having a silvery luster, nonmetals exist in a variety of colors. The metalloids are a third class that fall around the dividing line and will have some of the properties of each of the other classes. For example, antimony (Sb) is an extremely brittle metalloid. It has a metallic luster with a flaky, crystalline texture. It is bluish white and conducts heat and electricity poorly.

Not all of the elements have all of the properties that would be expected of their class. Because they all have different electron structures, the elements also differ in the degree to which they exhibit these properties. For example, a

Introduction

One consequence of this investigation is that students will begin to understand that while generalities exist in science to simplify concepts, there are often many exceptions to the rules. This is a good opportunity to discuss with your students the fact that man's classification schemes are designed to help him make sense of God's creation, but God is not constrained to follow man's systems. Being infinite in every attribute, He has provided us with such a variety of creatures and objects that any man-made classification system will be incomplete and inadequate to catalog and generalize everything He has made. In this investigation students will discover that carbon in the form of compact graphite, being a nonmetal, nevertheless conducts electricity—a property possessed by metals.

The title of the investigation is Metals and Nonmetals, but metalloids are considered also. We include metalloids because they are transitional between metals and nonmetals and they display some of the properties of one or the other.

sterling silver spoon is malleable at room temperature and easily bent. Iron is also malleable, though it requires more vigorous pounding to deform it. Some metals are better conductors than others. Generally speaking, however, you can predict which physical properties an element will have based upon its location in the periodic table.

Pre-Laboratory Questions

Read the entire investigation. Answer the following questions prior to class on a separate sheet of paper. Use complete sentences.

1. Name the three classes into which the elements can be divided.

2. Name the four physical properties that we will be examining in this investigation.

3. What is distinctive about the metalloids?

4. State the research question.

5. For your hypothesis, first list each of the properties tested and then predict the results of your investigation on metals and nonmetals.

Procedures

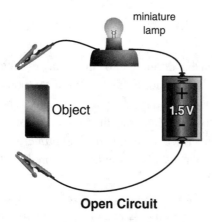

Open Circuit

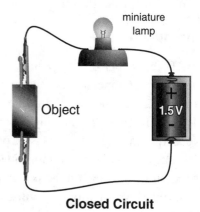

Closed Circuit

A. Electrical Conductivity

1. Obtain the electrical conductivity apparatus described in Investigation 2B (or a multimeter, if available) and make the connections to the battery and the test leads, as applicable.

2. Touch the ends of the two wires together and observe whether the conductivity apparatus lamp lights. If the bulb does not light, check the connections between the wires, the battery, and the lamp base. This type of control ensures that your apparatus is functioning properly. (If using a multimeter, turn it on, select "Ω" or the resistance scale, and touch the test leads together. The display should show zero ohms [Ω])

3. Test the electrical conductivity of copper by touching the ends of the wires to the copper wire. Record the results in Table 1. (If using a multimeter, record the numerical value of the resistance in ohms.)

4. Repeat step 3 with the aluminum, antimony, bismuth, carbon (coal), iron, lead, silicon, sulfur, and the *wooden* part of the drawing pencil. The pencil will be considered a nonmetal in the conduction tests because it is composed mostly of carbon, hydrogen, and oxygen.

5. Test the conductivity of both the *graphite* portion of the drawing pencil and the powdered graphite. Record your results in Table 1.

6. If you are using a multimeter, you may assume that a reading less than 10 ohms indicates the material is a conductor. A reading over 10 ohms indicates a nonconductor.

7. Clean the test leads with a damp paper towel. Store the parts of the apparatus for future use when finished. (Turn off the multimeter.)

B. Conduction of Heat

1. Pour about 150 mL of water into a 250 mL beaker.

2. Place the beaker on the wire gauze on the tripod, light the Bunsen burner, and heat the water to a near boil; then turn off the burner.

3. Using beaker tongs or another method of protection, carefully remove the beaker from the tripod.

4. Twist four 8 cm lengths of uninsulated copper wire together. Place the resulting wire bundle, the iron nail, and the pencil into the beaker so that their ends protrude out of the water.

5. After three minutes, carefully touch the upper ends of the wire bundle, the nail, and the pencil. Based on how warm they feel, record whether each is a good heat conductor in Table 2.

C. Malleability

Compare the flexibility of a copper wire, an iron nail, and a pencil. Record your results in Table 2.

D. Physical Appearance

Observe the color and luster of the elements listed in Table 3.

E. Cleanup

When finished, return all materials and equipment to their designated locations. If graphite was spilled, carefully clean it up with soap and water. Pour out the water and dry the beaker.

integer scale, such as 0-10 or 0-100 ohms.

3. Powdered graphite can be obtained from locksmiths or hardware stores in the security lock or lubricant departments.

4. The drawing pencils should be very soft, but avoid charcoal pencils. Hardness of pencils is determined by the quantity of a claylike binder included in the "lead." The softer the pencil (B-series with higher numbers), the less clay there is and the more graphite, which is what is being tested.

5. The iron nail should be a large lumber framing "spike" (10 penny nail or larger).

6. If you have time and assistance, try to polish the tarnish and corrosion off of the metal samples with steel wool or a scouring pad. The only metal that should NOT be polished is lead, since the residue can be ingested and it is toxic. Lead usually has a dull dark gray appearance unless it has been recently molten.

General Comments

1. You may set up this investigation in stations around the room. If you choose to give each group its own set of samples to test, you may still want to have only one station for the powdered graphite because it can get quite messy.

2. You may want to perform the heat conduction part of this investigation as a teacher demonstration.

3. Malleability is best demonstrated by pounding samples to see if they will deform without shattering. This cannot be done by the class as a whole, but if you have a large piece of dense rock (or even a portable

vise) as a base, you can attempt to flatten various samples with a hammer to demonstrate their malleability. Be sure to wear eye protection if you do this.

4. Other elements may be substituted in place of the ones listed in this investigation. Just be sure that representative elements from the metals and nonmetals are available.

Results

Table 1: Conduction of Electricity

Substance	Metal/Nonmetal/ Metalloid	Conductivity (Y/N)
Aluminum	Metal	Y
Antimony	Metalloid	N
Bismuth	Metalloid	N
Carbon (coal)	Nonmetal	N
Graphite (pencil)	Nonmetal	Y(N)
Graphite (powdered)	Nonmetal	N
Copper	Metal	Y
Iron	Metal	Y
Lead	Metal	Y
Silicon	Metalloid	N
Sulfur	Nonmetal	N
Wood	Nonmetal	N

Table 2: Heat Conduction and Malleability

Substance	Metal/ Nonmetal	Conduction of Heat (Good/Poor)	Malleable (Y/N)
Copper	Metal	Good	Y
Iron	Metal	Good	N
Wood	Nonmetal	Poor	N

Table 3: Appearance

Substance	Metal/Nonmetal/ Metalloid	Color	Metallic Luster (Y/N)
Aluminum	Metal	Silver	Y
Antimony	Metalloid	Blue-white	Y
Bismuth	Metalloid	Pink-white	Y
Carbon (graphite)	Nonmetal	Black	N
Copper	Metal	Coppery	Y
Iodine	Nonmetal	Purple	N
Iron	Metal	Light Gray	Y
Lead	Metal	Dark Gray	Y (N)
Silicon	Metalloid	Blue-gray	Y
Sulfur	Nonmetal	Yellow	N

Discussion Questions

Use complete sentences for your answers.

1. Did the results of your investigation match the predictions you made in your hypothesis? *Students' responses should indicate that their results matched the predictions fairly well, although some may note the exceptions.*

2. Would you expect the measurable physical properties of different metals (such as conductivity, hardness, malleability, etc.) to be exactly the same? Explain why or why not. *No, the properties of different metals are not going to be exactly alike because their electron structures are different.*

3. Give an example from this investigation of two metals that showed a difference in a physical property. *Copper was very flexible, and iron was not.*

4. You were told that nonmetals do not conduct electricity. You tested one nonmetal that in one form *was* a conductor. Name the element and which form conducted. *Carbon in the solid graphite form conducted electricity.*

5. If it were available, why would you not be able to test fluorine for the physical properties checked in this investigation? *Fluorine is a gas, and it either does not have the property or the required apparatus was not available to test the property (conductivity).*

6. Name the metalloids that you tested for electrical conductivity. Based on their appearance, what would you predict about their malleability? Why? *Antimony, bismuth, and silicon were tested. Students may say that they appear malleable because of their metallic luster, or they may say they look brittle (nonmalleable) because of their crystalline appearance.*

7. Which parts of computers are formed principally from silicon? *The computer microprocessor chips are formed from silicon.*

Name _____

Date _____ Hour _____

Objectives

The purpose of this exercise is to provide practice in

1. Determining the electron transfers and ionization state during the formation of selected ions.

2. Drawing electron dot diagrams for selected elements.

3. Drawing electron dot diagrams for selected ionic compounds.

Instructions

Review Section 8A in your textbook. Complete the following statements by supplying the appropriate word(s) or numerical answer(s). Note in your textbook that ionic charges are written with the number first followed by the sign.

1. What is an ion? *An ion is a charged atom (or group of atoms).* _____

For questions 2–7, the statements indicate how the atom will become ionized as it bonds ionically.

2. Potassium (Z = 19) has __*1*__ valence electron(s). Potassium will __*lose*__ (lose/gain) __*1*__ electron(s), resulting in an ion with a charge of __*1+*__.

3. Calcium (Z = 20) has __*2*__ valence electron(s). Calcium will __*lose*__ (lose/gain) __*2*__ electron(s), resulting in an ion with a charge of __*2+*__.

4. Oxygen (Z = 8) has __*6*__ valence electron(s). Oxygen will __*gain*__ (lose/gain) __*2*__ electron(s), resulting in a charge of __*2–*__.

5. Bromine (Z = 35) has __*7*__ valence electron(s). Bromine will __*gain*__ (lose/gain) __*1*__ electron(s), resulting in an ion with a charge of __*1–*__.

6. The oxygen (Z = 8) ion, O^{2-}, has __*8*__ protons and __*10*__ electrons.

7. The magnesium (Z = 12) ion, Mg^{2+}, has __*12*__ protons and __*10*__ electrons.

8. Give the following information about a neutral atom of Krypton-84 (Z = 36).

   The number of electrons in each energy level *Level 1–2, Level 2–8,* _____

   Level 3–18, Level 4–8 _____

   The atomic number __*36*__

   The number of protons __*36*__

   The number of electrons __*36*__

   The mass number __*84*__

   The number of neutrons __*48*__

For problems 9 and 10, practice arranging the dots in the order shown on page 167 of your textbook.

9. Draw the electron dot diagrams for the following elements using their symbols given below.

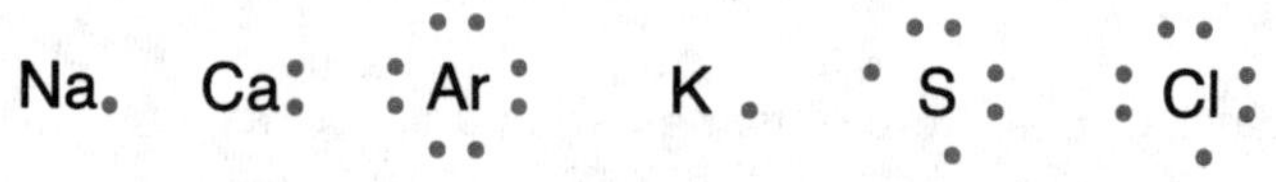

$$Na. \quad Ca: \quad :Ar: \quad K. \quad \cdot S: \quad :Cl:$$

10. Draw the electron dot diagrams to represent the steps in ionic bonding. Follow the example given for CaS.

Example:

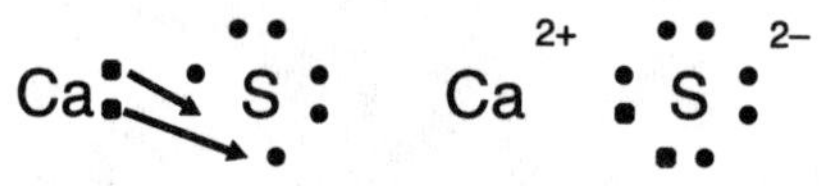

$$Ca: \searrow S: \quad Ca^{2+} \quad :S:^{2-}$$

a. KI

$$K. :I: \quad K^{1+} :I:^{1-}$$

b. NaBr

$$Na. :Br: \quad Na^{1+} :Br:^{1-}$$

c. $CaCl_2$

$$:Cl :Ca: :Cl: \quad :Cl:^{1-} Ca^{2+} :Cl:^{1-}$$

8B APPLICATIONS
Covalent Bonding

Name _____

Date_____ Hour_____

Objectives

The purpose of this exercise is to

1. Reinforce the concepts of covalent bonding you have learned.

2. Understand the restrictions that limit the number of covalent bonds in a compound.

Introduction

You have learned from your textbook and Applications 8A that elements with very different electronegativities form compounds by transferring electrons. Elements with nearly full (nonmetals) and nearly empty (metals) valence energy levels are able to bond to each other in this way. When nonmetals form a bond, however, there are two reasons electron transfer does not occur. Transferring all of a typical nonmetal's valence electrons would give the other nonmetal far more than the required eight electrons to meet the octet rule. In addition, the electronegativity of the nonmetal would not be strong enough to retain the extra electrons even if it could take them. Therefore, when nonmetal atoms (having similar electronegativities) form bonds, they must share just enough electrons with other atoms to complete their valence level. This is called **covalent** bonding. In this exercise we will use "jigsaw puzzle" models to illustrate the way that atoms form single covalent bonds with other atoms. (*Note:* Due to the limitations of the models, you will not be able to make double or triple bonds.) Recall that a covalent bond consists of a pair of electrons shared by two atoms. In this exercise, you will "build" a number of covalent molecules and you will learn why some covalent molecules (and their compounds) cannot exist.

Procedures

1. Cut out the puzzle pieces found on page 100. The dots on the models represent valence electrons. Using these pieces, construct the molecules listed in Table 1. Arrange the pieces so that there are two electrons around hydrogen and eight around each of the other elements. The diatomic element hydrogen (H_2) is shown as an example below.

2. Once you have constructed each molecule from the puzzle pieces, draw its electron dot structure in the right-hand column of Table 1.

Table 1: Electron Dot Models

Compound	Electron Dot Structure
Cl_2	:Cl:Cl:
CH_4	H H:C:H H
CCl_4	:Cl: :Cl:C:Cl: :Cl:
NH_3	H H:N: H
C_2H_6	H H H:C:C:H H H
CH_2Cl_2	H :Cl:C:Cl: H
(Give an alternate arrangement.)	:Cl: H:C:Cl: H

3. Attempt to construct the molecules of the compounds listed in Table 2. Not all of the compounds are valid because their molecules cannot be formed. Write *Y* in the blank if a valid molecule can be formed and *N* if it cannot.

Table 2: Molecular Validity

Formula	Valid? (Y/N)	Formula	Valid? (Y/N)
H_3	N	$HCNOH_4$	N
HCl	Y	$NHCl_2$	Y
CH_3	N	NH_4	N
NCl_4	N	C_2H_5OH	Y
$CHCl_3$	Y	CH_3Cl_2	N

Discussion Questions

1. What are valence electrons? *They are the electrons in the outermost energy level of an atom.*

2. What is the octet rule? *The octet rule states that an atom is most stable when its outer energy level contains eight electrons.*

3. Name an element that is an exception to the octet rule. *Hydrogen and helium are exceptions to the octet rule.*

4. Why is the element in question #3 an exception? *It is an exception because its outer shell can hold only two electrons.*

5. What is a covalent bond and why does it form? *A covalent bond is formed when nonmetal atoms share electrons to complete the octet in their valence energy levels.*

6. How is a covalent bond different from an ionic bond? *In an ionic bond, electrons are permanently transferred from one atom to another.*

7. Does the electron dot diagram of a molecule show all of its electrons? Explain your answer. *No, it shows only the valence electrons.*

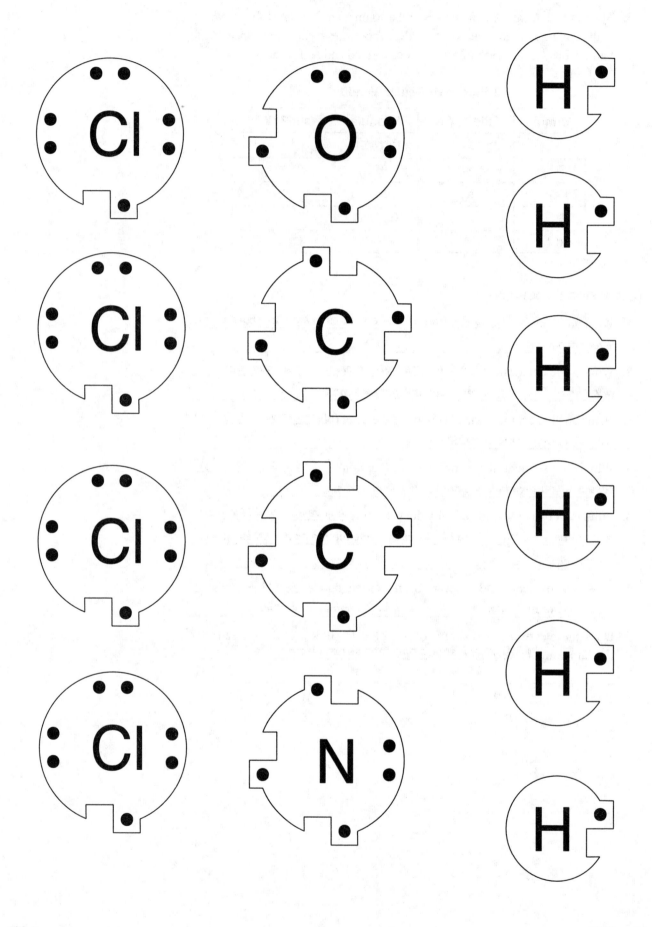

Name _____

Date _____ Hour _____

Objective

The purpose of this exercise is to provide additional review of covalent and ionic bonding concepts.

Questions

1. A bond that results from the transfer of electrons between two or more atoms is called a(n) _____ionic_____ bond.

2. A bond that results from the sharing of electrons between two or more atoms is called a(n) _____covalent_____ bond.

3. The type of bond that usually forms between two nonmetal atoms is called a(n) _____covalent_____ bond.

4. The type of bond that usually forms between metal and nonmetal atoms is called a(n) _____ionic_____ bond.

5. Sulfur (Z = 16) has _____6_____ valence electron(s). Sulfur can gain or share _____2_____ electrons.

6. Hydrogen (Z = 1) has _____1_____ valence electron(s). Hydrogen can gain or share _____1_____ electron(s).

7. When sulfur and hydrogen react together, one sulfur atom will combine with _____2_____ hydrogen atom(s).

8. Give the following information for arsenic-75.

    Atomic number: _____33_____

    Number of protons: _____33_____

    Number of electrons: _____33_____

    Number of electrons in each energy level: 1st Level—_____2_____, 2nd Level—_____8_____, 3rd Level—_____18_____, 4th Level—_____5_____

    Mass number: _____75_____

    Number of neutrons: _____42_____

Diagrams

1. Draw the electron dot diagrams for the following neutral elements. Follow the dot sequence given on page 167 of your textbook.

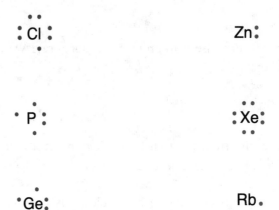

2. Draw the electron dot diagrams to illustrate covalent bonding in the following compounds.

   a. N_2

   b. H_2O

   c. C_2H_5OH (carbons go together)

   d. O_2

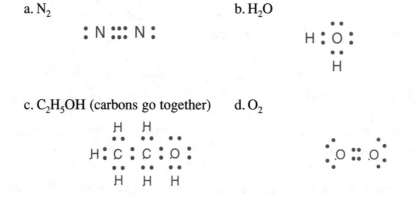

3. Draw electron dot diagrams to illustrate the steps in ionic bonding for the following compounds.

   a. KF

   b. MgS

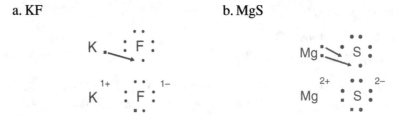

8D INVESTIGATION
Identifying Bond Types

Objective

The purpose of this investigation is to determine which types of bonds are present in some common materials by examining their electrical conductivities.

Materials

Baking soda
Brass (or some other metal)
Cola soft drink
Copper metal (wire or sheet)
Orange drink mix (e.g., Tang™)
Sugar
Table salt (NaCl)
Vegetable oil
Water (distilled)

Equipment

Beaker (250 mL)
Electrical conductivity apparatus
    assembled in Investigation 2B
Tablespoon

Introduction

You have learned from your study of chemical bonds that the type of bond often determines the physical properties of a material as well as its chemical properties. This fact was demonstrated in Investigation 7, "Metals and Nonmetals," where you compared appearance, electrical and thermal conductivity, and malleability of several different substances. You found that metals often have a similar appearance and good conductive characteristics, but the appearance of solid ionic and covalent compounds can vary greatly, and they generally conduct electricity poorly. The conductivity of the various types of bonds can be explained as follows:

Metals. Electricity is conducted through a substance by electrons or charged particles (ions) that are free to move around. The valence electrons of metals, whether in the solid or liquid (melted) state, are very mobile since they are not strongly attracted to any particular atom. This is a key principle of metallic bonding. Metals, therefore, conduct electricity in any state.

Ionic compounds. Ionic solids contain charged particles, but the crystal structure holds the ions in a fixed position. Since the charged particles cannot move, dry solid ionic compounds will not conduct electricity. However, if the ionic solid can dissolve in water or if the solid is melted, the charged particles separate from each other (dissociate) and become free to move. Consequently, an ionic compound dissolved in water or in the molten state will conduct electricity. Though polyatomic ions (HCO_3^-, for example) are held together with covalent bonds, the ions still carry charges and their solutions will conduct electricity.

Introduction

Much of this information should be review for your students. There are several factors that you need to point out to your students. Not all ionic compounds are soluble in water, so these will not conduct in solution. Some ionic substances are hydroscopic—that is, they extract water from the atmosphere, so these may conduct under certain circumstances. (The ionic substances chosen for this lab are not hydroscopic.) In addition, many common covalent substances can ionize in a water solution, so they will conduct. In this lab, the cola and orange drink mix may conduct because of the formation of carbonic or other acids in solution. Finally, depending on the hardness of the tap water in the area, you may or may not receive a positive result due to dissolved ionic compounds in the water.

Identifying Bond Types

Covalent compounds.   Covalent compounds in an un-ionized state have neither free electrons nor charged particles and will not conduct electricity. Most covalent compounds will not form a solution with water while some are only poorly soluble. Other covalent compounds such as sugar are readily soluble in water. A few covalent compounds ionize in water, and these will conduct electricity as in the case of ionic compounds.

If you were given an unknown solid, how could you determine with fair confidence if it contained metallic, ionic, or covalent bonds? In this investigation, you will use the property of electrical conductivity to help evaluate the kinds of bonds in several substances.

The following table summarizes the electrical properties of compounds containing the different types of bonds.

Bonding Type	State	Conduction
Metallic	Solid metal	Yes
	Molten metal	Yes
Ionic	Crystalline solid	No
	Solution (water)	Yes
	Molten	Yes
Covalent	Solid	No
	Liquid	No
	Solution (water)	No (possibly yes)

Pre-Laboratory Questions

Read the entire investigation. Answer the following questions prior to class on a separate sheet of paper. Use complete sentences.

1. What test will we be using in this investigation to determine the type of bond?

2. Why do metals conduct electricity?

3. Under what conditions do ionic compounds conduct electricity? Explain why.

4. Why do covalent compounds not conduct electricity easily?

5. Is it possible to determine the type of bond in a substance by using conductivity alone?

6. State the research question.

7. State your hypothesis and predict the conductivity of the following materials, given their composition.

Substance	Composition
Baking soda	$NaHCO_3$
Brass	Cu, Zn alloy
Copper	Cu
Cola	primarily C, O, and H compounds
Orange drink mix	primarily C, O, and H compounds
Sugar	C, O, and H compound
Table salt	NaCl
Vegetable oil	primarily C, O, and H compounds
Water (distilled)	H_2O

Answers to Pre-Laboratory Questions

1. We will be testing for electrical conductivity of various solids and solutions.

2. Metals conduct electricity because their valence electrons are free to move around.

3. Ionic compounds conduct electricity only when they form a solution or are in a molten state. In the crystalline solid state, the charged particles cannot move around, but in solution or when molten they can move.

4. Covalent compounds do not have free electrons or moveable charged particles.

5. No, all types of compounds can show conductivity depending on their composition and state.

6. Research question—How could you determine with fair confidence if a material contains metallic, ionic, or covalent bonds?

7. Hypothesis—You can determine the type of bond by examining the electrical conductivity of the substance when it is a dry solid and when it is dissolved in water.

Substance	Conductive?
Baking soda	No
Brass	Yes
Copper	Yes
Cola	No
Orange drink mix	No
Sugar	No
Table salt (NaCl)	No
Vegetable oil	No
Water (distilled)	No

Preparation

1. For materials and instructions needed to prepare the electrical conductivity apparatus, see Investigation 2B.

2. If your school emphasizes environmental sciences, you may have a conductivity tester available. As a demonstration, you should measure the conductivity of distilled water and show that even pure water has some conductivity due to the dissolved CO_2 in it.

3. The investigation can move more quickly if more beakers are available for each lab team.

General Comments

1. Ensure that the students understand the table in the Introduction before proceeding to the investigation.

2. To reduce the time necessary to complete this investigation, or simply to reduce the amount of cleanup, you may set this investigation up in stations around the room. For each of the substances that will be tested both dry and in solution, have the solutions already mixed in the beakers, using a separate testing apparatus for each.

3. For team or individual investigations (rather than at stations), be sure the students clean and dry the probes and beakers between each test. The probes have to be dry to accurately test the dry crystals, and the beaker must be clean to prevent contamination.

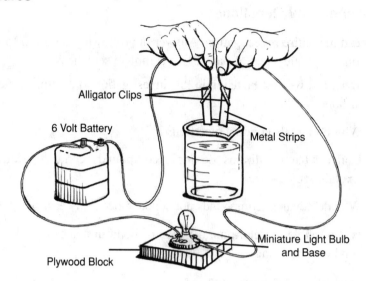

1. Obtain the parts for and assemble the electrical conductivity apparatus used in Investigation 2B. Since you will be testing solutions, the alligator clips and metal strips (probes) should be attached. Touch the two probes together to make sure that the light bulb works. If it doesn't light up, check all of the electrical connections.

2. Test the copper and the brass for conductivity by touching both probes to the surface of the solid. Record your results in the data table.

Note: Be sure to thoroughly clean and dry the probes and the beaker after each of the following liquid tests.

3. Test the four liquids (vegetable oil, cola, distilled water, and tap water) for conductivity, one at a time. Pour approximately 150 mL of the liquid into the 250 mL beaker. Test for conductivity by placing the probes in the liquid (do not let the probes touch each other). Record your results in the data table.

4. Put 30 cm³ (2 tablespoons) of baking soda in the dry beaker. Test the powder for conductivity by placing the probes in the material. Do not let the probes touch each other or the bottom of the beaker. Add 150 mL of distilled water to the dry material in the beaker and stir. After the baking soda is dissolved, test again for conductivity by placing the probes in the solution. Record your results for both the dry and the dissolved baking soda in the data table.

5. Repeat step 4 using table salt, sugar, and the orange drink mix. Record your results for both dry and dissolved materials in the data table.

6. In the third column write *M* if you believe metallic bonds are present, *I* if ionic, and *C* if covalent. If the test is inconclusive, write a question mark.

Results

Data Table: Properties of Compounds

These solutions may conduct due to the reasons discussed in the Introduction in the Teacher's Notes.

Compound	Conducts? (Y/N)	Bond Type
Brass	Y	M
Copper	Y	M
Cola	N (Y)*	C or ?
Vegetable oil	N	C
Distilled water	N	C
Tap water	N (Y)*	C or ?
Baking soda powder	N	I
Dissolved powder	Y	
Table salt crystals	N	I
Salt water solution	Y	
Sugar crystals	N	C
Sugar water solution	N	
Orange drink mix (dry)	N	C or ?
Orange drink (liquid)	N (Y)*	

Discussion Questions

1. Why do ionic compounds not conduct electricity when they are in the crystalline solid state? The charged particles are not able to move around when they are in the crystalline solid state.

2. Fill in the following blanks with *metals* or *nonmetals*.

   a. Metallic bonds form between two elements that are ___metals___.

   b. Ionic bonds form between ___metals___ and ___nonmetals___.

   c. Covalent bonds form between two ___nonmetals___.

3. Predict the type of bond in each of the following compounds.

   a. CO_2 ___Covalent___

   b. $MgCl_2$ ___Ionic___

   c. LiCl ___Ionic___

   d. SO_2 ___Covalent___

   e. Ni-Cu alloy ___Metallic___

Experimental Evaluation

4. Your results for baking soda ($NaHCO_3$, sodium bicarbonate) should have showed that it contained ionic bonds.

   a. Name the cation (positive ion). sodium ion, Na^+

   b. Name the anion (negative ion). bicarbonate ion, HCO_3^-

5. What type of bonds exist between the atoms of the anion in question 4? Covalent

6. If the conductivity test demonstrates that a substance has ionic bonds, does this demonstrate that the substance does not have **any** covalent bonds? Explain. *No, one of the ions may contain covalent bonds.*

7. If some of your covalently-bonded materials conducted electricity, how can you explain those observations? *If an answer is appropriate, students should say that the covalent substances ionized in water.*

8. Suppose that during one of the tests the light bulb did not light up and you concluded that the material had covalent bonds. If you had not performed the bulb check at the beginning, how sure could you be of your results? *You could not be sure; the bulb may not have lighted because the material was nonconductive or because the apparatus was defective in some way.*

9. What does this tell you about the necessity of controls in a scientific experiment? *Controls are necessary to ensure that there are not other factors affecting your observations.*

9A APPLICATIONS
Chemical Formulas

Objectives

The purpose of this exercise is to

1. Provide practice in determining oxidation numbers for various elements.

2. Write correct compound formulas using the information gained from oxidation numbers.

Introduction

A chemical formula is an abbreviated way to represent the composition of a pure substance. It tells you which elements are part of the compound, as well as the actual number of atoms of each element that are present in a molecule of the compound. If the compound is ionic, then the formula gives the relative numbers of atoms of each element in the *formula unit*. For example, the chemical formula for the molecular compound water is H_2O. The subscript *2* reveals that there are two hydrogen atoms. The oxygen lacks a subscript, which indicates there is only one in the molecule. If a subscript follows parentheses containing part of the formula, then the number applies to each atom inside the parentheses. For example, the formula unit for the ionic compound calcium hydroxide, $Ca(OH)_2$, contains one calcium atom, two oxygen atoms, and two hydrogen atoms. The formula unit for aluminum sulfate, $Al_2(SO_4)_3$, contains two aluminum atoms, three sulfur atoms, and twelve oxygen atoms.

The **oxidation number** of an element indicates how many electrons an element is likely to gain, lose, or share in order to achieve an octet in its outer electron level when it bonds with other atoms. Therefore, the oxidation number of an element is directly related to the number of valence electrons it has.

Elements that have low electronegativities tend to have few valence electrons, and they lose electrons when they bond. These are assigned positive oxidation numbers. The alkali metals (Group IA) have only one valence electron. When they form ionic bonds, they lose their one electron, so they are assigned an oxidation number of $+1$. The alkaline-earth metals (Group IIA) lose two electrons and so are assigned an oxidation number of $+2$.

Elements that have high electronegativities tend to have many valence electrons, and they gain electrons when they bond to form a stable octet. These are assigned negative oxidation numbers. The members of the halogen family (Group VIIA), with seven valence electrons, gain one electron when they bond and are assigned oxidation numbers of -1. The members of the oxygen family (Group VIA) gain two electrons and are assigned the oxidation number of -2.

Most of the transition metals and some nonmetals can have more than one oxidation state, depending on the compound. It is possible to form two or more different compounds from the same elements.

When elements combine to form ionic compounds, the number of electrons lost must equal the number gained within a formula unit. The sum of the oxidation numbers in a correctly written formula for both ionic and covalent compounds will always equal zero. We use oxidation numbers to help us determine the correct chemical formula.

In this course, when writing the oxidation number, the sign precedes the number. However, when indicating the charge on an ion, the sign follows the number. For example, calcium is assigned an oxidation number of +2, but the charge on a calcium ion would be written as 2+.

Exercises

Carefully read the example. Write the chemical formulas for the problems below.

Example

Problem: Write the chemical formula for a compound of calcium and bromine.

Step 1: Determine the oxidation numbers of the elements involved.

One Ca atom (Group IIA) has ___2___ valence electrons. When it bonds, Ca will __*lose*__ (gain/lose) ___2___ electron(s), resulting in a charge of ___2+___. The oxidation number of Ca is ___+2___.

One Br atom (Group VIIA) has ___7___ valence electrons. When it bonds, Br will __*gain*__ (gain/lose) ___1___ electron(s), resulting in a charge of ___1−___. The oxidation number of Br is ___−1___.

Step 2: Write the symbols of the two elements next to each other with the oxidation numbers of the elements above their symbols.

$$+2 \qquad -1$$
$$\textbf{Ca} \qquad \textbf{Br}$$

Is the sum of the oxidation numbers zero? If not, you know that CaBr is not the correct formula.

Step 3: Determine which charge needs to increase in order to balance the formula. In this case, the negative charges need to increase. Add another bromine atom.

$$+2 \qquad 2(-1)$$
$$\textbf{Ca} \qquad \textbf{Br}_2$$

$(+2) + 2(-1) = 0$. The sum of the oxidation numbers is now zero; therefore, the formula $CaBr_2$ is correct.

Step 4:   Write the correct formula: **CaBr$_2$**. Notice that the oxidation numbers are *not* part of the final formula.

When writing formulas involving elements with oxidation numbers that are not integer multiples of each other (for example, 2 and 3), use the *least common multiple* method as explained in your textbook.

A. **Write the correct chemical formula for a compound that contains the following elements or ions. The applicable oxidation numbers are given in parentheses.**

1. Li (+1)   and   Cl (−1)   _LiCl_

2. Na (+1)   and   Cl (−1)   _NaCl_

3. H (+1)   and   O (−2)   _H$_2$O_

4. Na (+1)   and   OH$^-$ (−1)   _NaOH_

5. Ca (+2)   and   O (−2)   _CaO_

6. C (+4)   and   O (−2)   _CO$_2$_

7. S (+6)   and   O (−2)   _SO$_3$_

B. **Whenever a chemical formula requires more than one polyatomic ion, parentheses must be included around the formula for the entire ion and the subscript should follow the parentheses.**

Example   Mg (+2) and OH$^-$ (−1) : **Mg(OH)$_2$**

1. Ba (+2)   and   OH$^-$ (−1)   : _Ba(OH)$_2$_

2. Al (+3)   and   OH$^-$ (−1)   : _Al(OH)$_3$_

3. NH$_4^+$ (+1)   and   S (−2)   : _(NH$_4$)$_2$S_

4. Al (+3)   and   SO$_4^{2-}$ (−2)   : _Al$_2$(SO$_4$)$_3$_

C. Apply What You Have Learned

1. The oxidation number of Mg is ___+2___ and the oxidation number for Cl is ___−1___. This means that each atom of Mg ___loses___ (gains/loses) ___2___ electron(s) and each atom of Cl ___gains___ (gains/loses) ___1___ electron(s). In the compound magnesium chloride, one atom of Mg will combine with ___2___ Cl atom(s) and the chemical formula is ___MgCl$_2$___.

2. Ca(OH)$_2$ contains ___1___ atom(s) of calcium, ___2___ atom(s) of oxygen, and ___2___ atom(s) of hydrogen.

3. Ca$_3$(PO$_4$)$_2$ contains ___3___ atom(s) of calcium, ___2___ atom(s) of phosphorus, and ___8___ atom(s) of oxygen.

4. Oxygen almost always has an oxidation number of -2. Therefore, in the formula for magnetite, FeO, the oxidation number for iron must be ___+2___. In the formula for rust, Fe_2O_3, the oxidation number for iron must be ___+3___.

5. Based on the common oxidation number for chlorine, which is usually -1, the oxidation number for lead in $PbCl_2$ must be ___+2___. In the compound lead oxide, PbO_2, the oxidation number for lead must be ___+4___.

6. (Optional) As you can see, some metals can have more than one oxidation number. Write a brief rule that will allow you to determine the correct oxidation number of a metal in any given compound. *First determine the total negative oxidation number opposite the metal. Divide this number by the metal's subscript to determine the positive oxidation number per metal atom.*

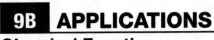

9B **APPLICATIONS**

Chemical Equations

Name _____

Date_____ Hour_____

Objectives

The purpose of this assignment is to

1. Review writing correct compound formulas and names.
2. Practice writing and balancing chemical equations.

Review Exercises

A. Writing Formulas

1. Write the compound formulas for the following combinations of elements and ions.

   a. C (+4) and Cl (−1) → _CCl₄_

   b. Ca (+2) and OH⁻ (−1) → _Ca(OH)₂_

   c. Al (+3) and O (−2) → _Al₂O₃_

2. $Ba(HCO_3)_2$ contains ___1___ atom(s) of barium, ___2___ atom(s) of hydrogen, ___2___ atom(s) of carbon, and ___6___ atom(s) of oxygen.

3. Use numbers to complete each of the following statements. Elements combine in specific ratios for each compound. Barium and chlorine will always react so that ___1___ atom(s) of Ba combine(s) with ___2___ atom(s) of Cl to form barium chloride. Therefore, the ratio of barium to chlorine is ___1___ : ___2___. If a sample of barium chloride contains 10 atoms of barium, it will have ___20___ atoms of chlorine. If a sample of barium chloride contains 1,000 atoms of chlorine, it will have ___500___ atoms of Ba.

B. Naming Compounds

Name the following compounds.

1. Na_2S _Sodium sulfide_

2. CO   _Carbon monoxide_

3. NH_4Cl _Ammonium chloride_

4. Na_2CO_3 _Sodium carbonate_

5. CS_2 _Carbon disulfide_

6. $Mg(OH)_2$ _Magnesium hydroxide_

7. P_2O_5 _Diphosphorus pentoxide_

8. $Al_2(SO_4)_3$ _Aluminum sulfate_

The same two elements can often form more than one ionic compound when the metal has more than one common oxidation number. Compounds of iron and oxygen are good examples of this. These elements can form both FeO and Fe_2O_3. If you called them both iron oxide, you could not tell them apart. Chemists use a notation called the *Stock system* to differentiate between them. The Stock system inserts a Roman numeral in parentheses after the metal in the compound name. The Roman numeral is equal to the oxidation number of the metal. The iron and oxygen compounds mentioned are then named iron(II) oxide and iron(III) oxide, respectively. **Note that the Stock system is not used for metals that have only one common oxidation number and never for naming covalent compounds.**

Practice naming the following compounds using the Stock system:

9. FeS   *Iron(II) sulfide*

10. $Pb(NO_3)_2$ *Lead(II) nitrate*

11. Cu_2SO_4 *Copper(I) sulfate*

Balancing Equations

Write and balance the formula equations for the following word equations. Refer to your textbook, p. 199, to review the steps to follow. If either a reactant or a product occurs as a diatomic molecule, be sure to write its formula correctly. The first problem is done as an example.

1. Silver nitrate plus copper metal produces copper(II) nitrate plus silver metal.

   Write: $AgNO_3 + Cu \rightarrow Cu(NO_3)_2 + Ag$

   a. It is often best to begin with the most complicated formula first—in this case, $Cu(NO_3)_2$. Notice that there are two nitrate groups on the right, so a 2 must be written in front of the $AgNO_3$.

   $$2\,AgNO_3 + Cu \rightarrow Cu(NO_3)_2 + Ag$$

   b. Now there are two Ag on the left, so you must write a 2 in front of Ag on the right. (Pure metals are never given subscripts when balancing equations.)

   c. There is one Cu on the left and there is one on the right, so they are balanced.

   d. The balanced equation is $2AgNO_3 + Cu \rightarrow Cu(NO_3)_2 + 2Ag$.

2. Barium plus water produces barium hydroxide and hydrogen gas.

   $$Ba \quad + \quad HOH \quad \rightarrow \quad Ba(OH)_2 \quad + \quad H_2$$
   $$Ba + 2H_2O \rightarrow Ba(OH)_2 + H_2 \text{ (Balanced)}$$

3. Aluminum plus fluorine produces aluminum fluoride.

   $$Al \quad + \quad F_2 \quad \rightarrow \quad AlF_3$$
   $$2Al + 3F_2 \rightarrow 2AlF_3 \text{ (Balanced)}$$

4. Mercury (II) oxide is decomposed with heat to form metallic mercury and gaseous oxygen.

$$HgO \overset{\Delta}{\to} Hg\ O_2$$

$$2HgO \overset{\Delta}{\to} 2Hg + O_2\ (Balanced)$$

5. Supply the missing coefficients and symbols to balance each equation.

a. __2__ H_2 + __O_2__ → __H_2O__

b. _____ Zn + __2__ $AgNO_3$ → _____ $Zn(NO_3)_2$ + __2 Ag__

Objectives

The purpose of this demonstration is to

1. Observe four types of chemical reactions.
2. Determine the type of reaction when given the chemical equation.

Materials

Copper sulfate solution
Powdered zinc

Equipment

Apron
Beakers (50 mL), 3
Bunsen burner
Bunsen burner lighter
Chemical scoop
Crucible tongs
Graduated cylinder, 25 mL
Stirring rod
Tripod
Wire gauze square

Introduction

Scientists are able to classify most chemical reactions into four general types. **Combination reactions** (also called synthesis reactions) combine two or more substances to form one product. They take the form

$$X + Y \rightarrow XY$$

The reactants can be elements or compounds, solid, liquid, or gas, but the key feature of this type of reaction is that there is more than one reactant but only one product.

Examples: $2Na + Cl_2 \rightarrow 2NaCl$

$$H_2O + SO_3 \rightarrow H_2SO_4$$

In **decomposition reactions,** one reactant breaks apart to form two or more products. The form of this reaction is

$$XY \rightarrow X + Y$$

Heat or electrical energy is usually required to decompose substances. The key feature of this type of reaction is that there is only one reactant, but there are several products. Many decomposition reactions give off a gas as a product.

Introduction and Precautions

These reactions should be presented as a teacher demonstration due to the hazards involved or because of the limited availability of equipment. The single-replacement zinc and copper (II) sulfate reaction is simple and safe enough to be performed by the students, so detailed instructions have been provided for them if you want them to perform that procedure.

You should be dressed with a rubber apron and with safety glasses for these demonstrations. The safety equipment is necessary, as well as being a good example of lab safety to your students. Be sure to have the students keep their distance during the combustion demonstrations.

Lead nitrate and potassium chromate are both toxic substances and require special handling. You should check with your local hazardous waste coordinator as to disposal requirements BEFORE preparing the solutions for this demonstration. The potassium chromate and lead chromate are both carcinogens because of the presence of chromium(VI) in the chromate. Be sure to wear rubber gloves while preparing the chemicals, and wash your hands thoroughly after cleaning up.

Materials

*Copper(II) sulfate ($CuSO_4$)
Lead nitrate [$Pb(NO_3)_2$]
Magnesium (Mg), strip
Potassium chromate ($KCrO_4$)*

Equipment

Electrolysis equipment
Eyedropper (2)
Mortar and sestle
Test tube
Test tube rack

See Equipment List in the back of this manual for optional equipment and materials.

Preparations

The following solutions will need to be prepared:

1. 0.1 M potassium hydroxide (KOH)—Dissolve 2.8 g per 500 mL hot distilled water as needed.

2. 0.5 M lead nitrate (Pb(NO$_3$)$_2$)—Add 1.66 g to 10 mL distilled water.

3. 0.5 M potassium chromate (K$_2$CrO$_4$)—Add 0.97 g to 10 mL distilled water.

4. 1 M copper(II) sulfate (CuSO$_4$·5H$_2$O)—Add 49.9 g to 200 mL warm distilled water. (If using anhydrous CuSO$_4$, add 31.8 g to 200 mL warm distilled water.) This will yield more than enough for five groups.

Answers to Pre-Laboratory Questions

1. The electrolysis of water results in the formation of oxygen and hydrogen.

2. An ionic solute such as KOH can be added to the water.

3. When combined, lead nitrate and potassium chromate will likely form a precipitate.

4. A double-replacement reaction almost always involves two ionic solutions.

5. The reactant that is in short supply is called the limiting reactant.

Example: $CaCO_3 \rightarrow CaO + CO_2$

In a **single-replacement reaction,** one more active element takes the place of a less active element in a compound. The form of this reaction is

$$X + YZ \rightarrow XZ + Y$$

X and *Y* are (usually) metal elements and *Z* may be either an element or a polyatomic anion. The activity of an element is generally related to its electronegativity. The more electronegative metal will usually be replaced by the less electronegative one. It is this difference in bond energy that causes the reaction to take place. In order to predict whether one element will replace another in a compound, you need to know the relative electronegativities of the different elements. This information is found in many chemistry textbooks.

Examples: $Mg + 2HCl \rightarrow MgCl_2 + H_2$

$Zn + H_2SO_4 \rightarrow ZnSO_4 + H_2$

A **double-replacement reaction** almost always involves a combination of two ionic solutions. The form of this reaction is

$$WX + YZ \rightarrow WZ + YX$$

There are always two reactants and two products. It is called a double-replacement because both cations and both anions take the opposite partners. Because the ions are dissociated, or separated from each other in solution, the ions are free to combine in new ways. This type of reaction often results in a solid precipitating out of the solution, the formation of a gas, or the production of water, which becomes part of the water in the solution.

Example: $NaCl + AgNO_3 \rightarrow NaNO_3 + AgCl(ppt)$

Pre-Laboratory Questions

Read the entire investigation. Answer the following questions prior to class on a separate sheet of paper. Use complete sentences.

1. What products do you expect to result from the electrolysis of water?

2. What can be done to make the electrolysis of pure water more efficient?

3. Name the reactants in this investigation that, when combined, will most likely form a precipitate.

4. Which type of reaction almost always involves two ionic compounds?

5. If there is not enough of a reactant to completely combine with another reactant, what do we call the first reactant?

6. Which type of reaction always yields only a single product?

7. How is the reaction between zinc and sulfur started?

8. What color does the copper(II) ion (Cu^{2+}) impart to a solution?

9. Why is the copper(II) sulfate solution heated before it is added to the zinc?

Procedures

A. Electrolysis of Water

Water is composed of the two elements oxygen and hydrogen. When an electric current is passed through water, the electrical energy breaks the chemical bonds holding the oxygen and hydrogen together. Oxygen (O_2) is formed at the positive electrode, and hydrogen (H_2) is formed at the negative one. This process is called electrolysis. Often an ionic solute such as potassium hydroxide (KOH) is added to the pure water to improve the process.

Write a balanced chemical equation for the electrolysis of water. $\underline{2H_2O \rightarrow 2H_2 + O_2}$

_____

Examine the form of this equation and state what type of reaction it is. _This_
is a decomposition reaction.

1. Observe as your teacher operates the electrolysis apparatus. What do you notice accumulating in the inverted test tubes? _Gas is accumulating._

_____

2. Why would you want to include an ionic solute in the electrolysis solution?
   Pure water does not conduct electricity well. The ions make it a much better
   conductor, which makes the process more efficient.

6. A combination reaction always yields only a single product.

7. The reaction between zinc and sulfur is started with a burning magnesium strip.

8. The copper(II) ion will make the solution blue.

9. The solution is heated to make the reaction occur better (faster, more efficiently).

Procedures

The demonstrations should be performed in the order listed in order to use the time most efficiently.

Electrolysis of Water

1. An inexpensive electrolysis apparatus can be purchased from many scientific supply companies. You will need to provide your own DC (not AC!) electrical source. An inexpensive electric train transformer works well, but a 6 V battery can also be used. Assemble the apparatus according to the instructions included with it. Teachers who will be using this apparatus for several years or in more advanced chemistry courses will find it worth the money to invest in a kit that has corrosion-resistant electrodes built into a small tank and test tubes calibrated to indicate the gas volumes.

2. Electrolysis of pure distilled water will occur, but the reaction rate is very low. Fill the electrolysis apparatus with 0.1 M potassium hydroxide solution to make the reaction proceed rapidly.

3. Start the reaction and move on to the next demonstration. Monitor the tube levels periodically.

4. If you desire to demonstrate that the gases are different, allow the

3. Look at the product side of the electrolysis reaction. How should the volume of hydrogen produced compare to the volume of oxygen? Why?

There should be twice as much hydrogen gas produced. There are two molecules of hydrogen produced for every molecule of oxygen.

B. Lead nitrate ($Pb(NO_3)_2$) and potassium chromate (K_2CrO_4)

What happens when a solution of potassium chromate is added to a solution of lead nitrate? Before these two ionic solutions are mixed together, all of the ions are dissociated. When they are mixed, however, the lead ions (Pb^{2+}) form bonds with the chromate ions (CrO_4^{2-}), forming a solid that separates out of the solution (a precipitate) and leaving the potassium (K^+) and nitrate (NO_3^-) ions still dissociated in the solution. If you do not add enough chromate ions to pair up with all of the lead ions, there will still be lead ions in the solution when the reaction is finished. When there is not enough of one reactant to completely combine with the other reactant, the first is called the *limiting reactant*. If you had an abundance of chromate ions and fewer lead ions, the lead would be the limiting reactant.

Write a balanced chemical equation for the reaction. _____

$Pb(NO_3)_2 + K_2CrO_4 \rightarrow PbCrO_4 + 2KNO_3$

Examine the form of the equation and state what type of reaction this is. _____

This is a double replacement reaction.

1. Your teacher will first put an eyedropper full of lead nitrate in a test tube.

2. Observe as your teacher adds drop by drop an eyedropper full of potassium chromate solution to the test tube that contains the lead nitrate solution.

3. What evidence do you observe that a chemical reaction has taken place?
   A yellow precipitate formed in the test tube.

4. What is the chemical formula of the precipitate? *$PbCrO_4$*

5. What is the chemical formula of the compound that remained in solution in the test tube? *KNO_3*

6. Lead chromate was an ingredient in exterior and interior house paint for many years. Why do you think that commercially available house paint no longer contains lead-based compounds? *Lead is poisonous. Children and animals chewing on paint flakes can be poisoned. Workers removing lead-based paints must wear extra protective clothing.*

7. (Optional) How did your teacher separate the lead chromate from the dissolved compound? *The teacher poured the solution through a filter paper funnel. The liquid passed through, and the solid was retained.*

C. Zinc and Sulfur

Zinc (Zn) is assigned an oxidation number of $+2$ because it has two valence electrons. Sulfur (S), being a member of the oxygen family, is assigned an oxidation number of -2. When ignited, these two elements will react to form a new compound, zinc sulfide.

Write a balanced chemical equation for this reaction. $\underline{Zn + S \rightarrow ZnS}$

Examine the form of the equation and state what type of reaction this is. _____
This is a combination or synthesis reaction.

1. Enter the chemical formula of the product of the reaction in the data table below.

2. Note the appearance of the zinc and the sulfur as demonstrated to you by your teacher. Record your observations in the table.

3. Watch as your teacher mixes the zinc and the sulfur and ignites it. Do not look directly at the magnesium strip as it is burning.

4. What evidence did you observe that a chemical reaction has taken place?
   Flame, heat, and light production; formation of a new substance

5. Record the appearance of the product of the reaction in the data table.

6. If this reaction forms only one product, what substance is in the smoke?
   The heat of the reaction produces air currents that carry particles of ZnS
   into the air.

Data Table: Zinc and Sulfur

	Appearance
Sulfur (S)	*Yellow powder*
Zinc (Zn)	*Dark gray powder*
Product _____	*Fluffy, yellowish particles*

D. Zinc and Copper Sulfate

Your teacher may have you perform this demonstration yourself. If so, carefully follow the instructions below. What happens when you add metallic zinc (Zn) to a solution of copper sulfate ($CuSO_4$)? Because the zinc is a more "active" metal, it will take the place of the copper, leaving the copper as a metal solid in the resulting zinc sulfate solution. The blue color of copper sulfate solutions is due to the presence of the copper(II) ion (Cu^{2+}). If you added enough zinc, the solution would appear colorless because the zinc would completely replace the copper ions in solution.

Write a balanced chemical equation for the reaction (assume an oxidation state of $+2$ for the Zn). $\underline{Zn(S) + CuSO_4 \rightarrow Cu(S) + ZnSO_4}$

Examine the form of the equation and state what type of reaction this is. _____
This is a single-replacement reaction.

tube to resuspend the solid. Quickly pour the contents into a folded paper towel. Rinse the test tube as necessary into the paper towel. If permitted by hazardous waste regulations, you may be able to dispose of the filtered solid as solid waste. The potassium nitrate may be rinsed down the sink.

Zinc and Sulfur

1. Clear the countertop of flammable materials and lay a sheet of thick cardboard or plywood to protect the demonstration area. Set up a tripod and a clay-centered gauze square on top of the tripod. Because this demonstration generates a lot of smoke, perform it in a fume hood if you have one. The smoke is not dangerous, but it can be irritating. You will need to be able to ventilate the room afterward.

2. Walk around the class and show the students the pure sulfur and zinc powders before mixing. Mix 5 g of powdered sulfur and 10 g of powdered zinc in a mortar or other small dish. When thoroughly mixed, show them the mixture, and pour the powder onto the clay disc of the wire gauze in a small compact mound.

3. Darken the room if you can to add to the dramatic demonstration. Caution the students to not look directly at the burning magnesium. Hold a 4 cm long piece of magnesium with crucible tongs or a pair of pliers and light the end of the strip with a Bunsen burner.

4. Standing at arm's length, place the lighted magnesium into the pile of powder until the powder ignites. Allow the magnesium to burn out before setting it down. The zinc-sulfur reaction will take place rapidly, flaring up and sometimes spewing burning particles to the side.

5. Show the students the product, ZnS, after the reaction stops and after allowing the residue to cool for a minute.

6. Ventilate the room as necessary by opening doors and windows and by using fans.

Zinc and Copper Sulfate

1. If time is short, perform this section as a teacher demonstration; otherwise, allow the students to perform it in lab teams. The people actually handling the chemicals should have lab aprons on.

2. The reaction is very rapid as the copper replaces the zinc in the bottom of the beaker.

3. You could substitute iron nails for the powdered zinc. This would have to be done a day ahead. Increase the volume of the copper sulfate solution in the experimental and control beakers to 200 mL. Polish five or six large iron nails with steel wool to remove any corrosion and leave them in the experimental beaker over night. You will see elemental copper in the experimental beaker. Have some polished nails that were not placed in the solution for the students to compare with those that were.

4. At the conclusion of the demonstration, have the students pour and rinse the solid copper and the solutions into a large beaker. Decant the solution into the sink and scrape the solid copper onto paper towels. Dispose as solid waste.

1. Label three 50 mL beakers **1, 2,** and **3.** Add 18 mL of $CuSO_4$ solution to both beakers **1** and **2.**

2. Measure about 0.9 g of powdered zinc with a balance. Add the zinc to beaker **3.**

3. Place beaker **1** on the wire gauze on the tripod. Light the Bunsen burner and warm the solution gently. Do not cause the solution to boil.

4. Turn off the Bunsen burner. Using crucible tongs, remove beaker **1** from the tripod and slowly pour the warm $CuSO_4$ onto the powdered zinc in beaker **3.** Stir the reactants with a stirring rod during the addition. If the reactants begin to froth, pour more slowly.

5. When the reaction has ceased, place beakers **2** and **3** side by side.

6. What color is the solution in beaker **2**? *The solution is blue.*

7. What is the appearance and color of the solid in beaker **3**? *The solid is a light brown or coppery colored sludge.*

8. List the observations that indicate to you that a chemical reaction has taken place in the experimental beaker. *A new substance was formed (Cu). The solution experienced a permanent color change (a weaker blue or colorless solution).*

9. In this reaction, what happened to the copper and the zinc? *The zinc became ionized and entered the solution, while the copper ions precipitated as a solid metal.*

10. Which beaker was the experimental control? *Beaker 2 was the experimental control. It contained only $CuSO_4$ solution.*

Objective

The purpose of this investigation is to demonstrate the effect of a solute on the freezing and boiling points of water.

Materials

Distilled water
Ice
Table salt

Equipment

Beakers (250 mL), 2
Beakers (500 mL), 3
Beaker tongs
Bunsen burner
Burner lighter
Stirring rods, 2
Tablespoon
Thermometers, 2
Tripod
Wire gauze

Introduction

We know from observing the various substances that make up our physical environment that different substances have different freezing and boiling points. Pure water freezes at 0.0°C and boils at 100.0°C. Pure acetic acid, however, which is also a liquid at room temperature, freezes at 16.6°C and boils at 117.9°C. The melting and boiling points for each substance are different because the strengths of the forces between particles varies with the substance. For example, the particles (ions) of ionic solids are held together by extremely strong electrostatic forces. As a result, ionic compounds generally have much higher melting points than do covalent compounds, whose molecules are held together by relatively weak intermolecular forces.

Boiling points of liquids are affected by atmospheric pressure as well as bond strength. The values given above for the boiling points of water and acetic acid are the values determined at one atmosphere of air pressure (measured at sea level). If you were to climb a mountain to an altitude of one mile and compare boiling point temperatures, you would find them somewhat lower than normal because of the decrease in the air pressure. Since water boils at a lower temperature at higher altitudes, food must be cooked for a longer time. This is why you may see alternate cooking directions for higher elevations included on the containers of many prepackaged foods.

A **solution,** you will recall from your textbook, is a type of homogeneous mixture in which a **solute** is dissolved in a **solvent.** The question for this investigation is "Will the presence of a solute affect the phase changes of a solution?" It has been found that solutions do not freeze or boil at the same temperature as the pure solvent. Why is this? Let's start with pure water as an

Introduction

The reference to "intermolecular forces" in the first paragraph may be unfamiliar to your students. These are the forces between molecules, not the forces bonding the atoms in a molecule together (covalent bonds). Intermolecular forces include hydrogen bonds and what used to be called van der Waals forces.

Colligative properties of solvents are any property that is affected by the concentration of solutes in solution. These properties include conductivity, resistivity, and osmotic pressure, in addition to the ones mentioned here.

Preparations

1. Each lab team will require at least 900 mL of distilled water for this exercise.

2. Consider using distilled water to make the ice cubes prior to the lab. Doing so will eliminate a variable that could affect the results of the freezing point depression determination.

3. You will not be actually observing freezing, but observing the temperature of an ice water slurry that is at equilibrium during a phase change. In order to establish this state, the ice needs initially to be colder than 0°C so that it will quickly cool the water without completely melting. Crushed ice increases the surface contact of the ice and water, thus increasing the efficiency of chilling the water. Crush the ice at least one hour before the class period and place it back in the freezer to chill. Placing the crushed ice in an ice chest with dry ice will ensure very cold temperatures. Remember that it is not the salt that determines the temperature of the slurry but the temperature of the ice.

Answers to Pre-Laboratory Questions

1. Salt is the solute and water is the solvent.

2. A solute normally will raise the boiling point and lower the freezing point.

3. The control is the beaker containing only distilled water. You have to include the control to demonstrate that the boiling point changes when you add salt.

4. Stirring the ice slurry with a thermometer may break it.

5. Will the presence of a solute affect the phase changes of a solution?

6. Adding a solute will change the boiling and freezing points of a solvent.

General Comments

1. Prior to starting the investigation, divide the class into teams of at least three students each and assign them team letters. During the data taking, it is necessary that two people stir the ice slurries while a third is reading and recording temperatures. The team letters assist with bookkeeping in the data table.

2. Review how to make measurements with thermometers. Depending on the length and type of the thermometer, you should stipulate whether you want the measurements reported to the nearest tenth degree for long thermom-

example. Water molecules have a certain attraction for each other. At temperatures just above the freezing point, the attractive forces and the disruptive effects of molecular motion are balanced. The molecules are still vibrating too fast to be held in the solid crystal form (ice). As the water molecules lose kinetic energy (cool down), the attractive forces of the molecules for each other become strong enough to pull them into the ice crystal structure and the water freezes. Adding a solute, however, interferes with the freezing process by physically getting in the way of the water molecules lining up with each other to form the crystal structure. The water molecules thus need to lose even more kinetic energy (get even cooler than usual) in order to freeze. For this reason, pure seawater that is 3.5 percent salt by mass freezes at around $-1.2°C$. With few exceptions, adding any solute to any solvent causes a lowering of the freezing point, or **freezing point depression.**

Solutes also tend to interfere with the boiling process. At the normal boiling point, water molecules only have to break away from the attraction of other water molecules. But the presence of solute particles increases the attractive forces on individual water molecules, so they need greater kinetic energy to break free. This translates into a higher boiling temperature. Pure seawater boils at about $100.3°C$. This increase in boiling point is called **boiling point elevation.** The magnitude of these two effects (called *colligative effects*) depends on the solvent (*not* the solute) and the concentration of the solute.

Pre-Laboratory Questions

Read the entire investigation. Answer the following questions prior to class on a separate sheet of paper. Use complete sentences.

1. For salt water, state which is the solute and which is the solvent.

2. What effect does a solute have on the boiling and freezing points of a solvent?

3. In the section of the investigation measuring boiling point elevation, which beaker is the control? Why is it important to include this?

4. Why should you *not* stir the ice slurry with a thermometer?

5. State the research question.

6. State your hypothesis regarding the relationship between presence of a solute and solvent phase changes.

Procedures

A. Boiling Point Elevation

1. Using masking tape, label one thermometer "beaker 1" and the other "beaker 2." Use these thermometers only in their respective beakers for the entire investigation.

2. Label two 250 mL beakers "1" and "2" with a water-soluble marker. Pour about 150 mL of distilled water into each beaker.

3. Add about 15 cm³ (one tablespoon) of NaCl to the water in beaker 2 and stir until the salt is completely dissolved.

4. Place beaker 1 on top of the wire gauze on the tripod.

5. Light the Bunsen burner and heat the water to a rolling boil.

6. Measure the temperature of the beaker **while the water is boiling.** Make sure the thermometer is submerged in the water without touching either the sides or the bottom of the beaker. Keep the thermometer in the water until the temperature no longer changes.

7. Record the boiling temperature for distilled water in the data table. Report temperature to the nearest 0.1°C.

8. Using the beaker tongs, carefully remove the beaker from the tripod and pour the hot water in the sink.

9. Repeat Steps 3–7 with beaker 2 containing the salt water.

10. Turn off the Bunsen burner.

11. Wash and dry both beakers.

12. Obtain distilled and salt water boiling point data from three other groups and record them in the data table.

13. Average the observed boiling points for the distilled and saltwater samples and record these temperatures in Table 1 (to the nearest 0.1°C).

B. Freezing Point Depression

1. Label two 500 mL beakers "1" and "2." Fill each of them to the rim with cold, crushed ice.

2. In a third 500 mL beaker or other clean container, mix 300 mL of distilled water and 30 cm³ (2 tablespoons) of salt until the salt is completely dissolved.

3. Pour 300 mL of distilled water over the ice in beaker 1 and the salt solution over the ice in beaker 2.

4. Stir both beakers with a separate stirring rod continuously. Observe the temperature of the ice slurry in each beaker every 60 seconds and note the temperature on a piece of scratch paper. **Do not stir with the thermometers!**

5. When the temperature of the slurry has not changed for two measurements, or if you note the temperature beginning to rise, record the lowest temperature observed in Table 2. Report temperature to the nearest 0.1°C.

6. Pour the ice water slurries into the sink. Wash and dry both beakers, utensils, and the thermometers.

7. Obtain distilled and salt water temperature data from the same three groups as in part A above and record them in the data table.

8. Average the lowest recorded temperature for the distilled and salt water and record this value in the data table (to the nearest 0.1°C.)

---

eters or the nearest half degree (0.5°C) for short ones. Digital thermometers should be read to the precision of the readout.

3. It is important to measure the boiling water while it is still boiling. Also, taking the temperature when the thermometer is touching the beaker can cause significant errors. Caution your students when taking the temperature of boiling water. The steam can cause a burn.

4. Mixing the saltwater solution before adding it to the ice ensures that the salt is completely dissolved. This may not happen if you add the salt directly to the ice slurry.

5. The following information is provided to allow you to evaluate the results of this investigation:

The change of boiling point for pure water is +0.51°C for each mole of dissolved solute particles per kilogram of water. Assuming 15 cm³ of NaCl with a density of about 2 g/cm³, the mass of NaCl used is ~30 g, which is equal to about 0.51 mole NaCl. When dissolved in 0.150 L (0.150 kg) of water, this produces about 6.8 moles of particles per kilogram ($\frac{2 \times 0.55}{0.150}$). The boiling point elevation could be as high as 6.8 × +0.51 = +3.5°C (B.P. ≈ 104°C).

The change in freezing point for pure water is −1.86°C per mole of dissolved particles per kilogram of water. Using 30 cm³ of NaCl yields ~1.0 moles NaCl. Assuming that the ice dilutes the saltwater solution to 400 mL (0.4 kg), the concentration of the liquid portion of the slurry is about 5.0 moles of particles per kilogram. The freezing point depression could be as great as −1.86°C × 5.0 = −9.3°C (F.P. ≈ −9°C).

Results

Table 1: Boiling Points of Water Solutions

	Distilled	Salt
(Your group)		
Group _____		
Group _____		
Group _____		
Averages—		

Table 2: Freezing Points of Water Solutions

	Distilled	Salt
(Your group)		
Group _____		
Group _____		
Group _____		
Averages—		

Discussion

1. Summarize the observations made in this investigation. *The boiling point of pure water was increased (elevated) by NaCl, and the freezing point of pure water was lowered (depressed) by NaCl.*

2. From a molecular point of view, make a general inference from these observations. In other words, why did the boiling and freezing points change? *The dissolved solute particles interfered with the solvent molecules in the various phases.*

3. Would your interpretation of the facts be different if you had not included the controls in this experiment? *Yes, without an experimental standard (control), you could not tell if the observed temperatures were due to a solute effect or due to the instruments.*

4. Based on this investigation, why do you think salt is added to the ice surrounding the freezer when making homemade ice cream? *Salt is added to melt the crushed ice at a lower temperature so that the ice water slurry will be more effective in removing heat from the ice cream container.*

5. Why is salt sometimes spread on icy roads? *The salt lowers the freezing point of water. If the temperature of the ice is higher than the new freezing point, the ice will melt.*

6. What do you think would have happened to the boiling point of the water if you had added more salt? *The boiling point would have been raised even more.*

Experimental Evaluation

7. What was the highest recorded temperature for distilled water *boiling point?* What was the lowest? What is the difference in these two temperatures? Show your calculations. *Answers will vary. Check to ensure*

   that the student considered the correct values. You can expect between 0

   and 3°C difference.

8. What is the difference between the average distilled water boiling point and 100.0°C? Show your calculations. *Answers will vary. The average B.P.*

   could be greater or less than 100.0°C depending on thermometer accuracy,

   student proficiency, and atmospheric pressure. Check that correct values

   were used.

9. What is the difference between the salt water average boiling point and the distilled water average boiling point? Show your calculations. *Answers*

   will vary. Theoretical differences could be as great as 4°C. The saltwater

   B.P. should be greater than that of the distilled water.

10. How do instrumental errors affect the measuring of physical quantities? How are the effects of these errors minimized when collecting data?

    Students may see thermometer errors equal to or greater than the

    difference in temperature between distilled and saltwater boiling points.

    Instrument errors are minimized by using several instruments and

    averaging multiple readings together.

11. What other factor could have influenced boiling point measurements? (Review the Introduction.) *The atmospheric pressure can have a*

    measurable effect on boiling point. In addition to altitude effects, high

    pressure weather systems can raise B.P., while low pressure systems will

    lower it.

11 INVESTIGATION
pH of Common Solutions

Objectives

The purpose of this exercise is to

1. Observe the use of various pH indicators and methods.

2. Determine the pH of several common substances.

Materials

Ammonia, household
Clear soda
Cola
Dishwashing detergent
HCl solution
Lemon juice
Litmus paper
Milk
NaOH solution
pHydrion™ paper or equivalent
Vinegar
Other household items (optional)
Bromothymol blue indicator (optional)
Phenolphthalein indicator (optional)

Equipment

Beakers, 50 mL
Eyedroppers
Test tubes
Test tube racks

Introduction

Review the introductory material after assigning and discussing Section 11B in the textbook.

Introduction

The pH of solutions can be determined subjectively by acid-base indicators. Recall from your textbook that these are organic substances that change color in the presence of an acid or a base. Litmus is an indicator extracted from a certain kind of lichen, a mossy substance that grows on rocks and trees. In its indicator form, litmus is red from a pH of 0.0 to 4.5 (acid) and blue from 8.3 to 14.0 (base). Between a pH of 4.5 and 8.3, the color of the chemical is intermediate between red and blue and is not a good indicator of the pH. Litmus is used to determine if a substance is an acid or a base, but it cannot provide numerical pH values. Other pH indicators, such as phenolphthalein or bromothymol blue, change color at different, specific pH values. They can tell you whether the pH is above or below their specific turning points, but, like litmus, they cannot give you a specific pH determination. Some substances turn many colors over a wide range of pH values. These indicators are the most useful because they can determine not only whether a solution is an acid or a base, but they can also indicate the numerical pH of the solution. This kind of substance is called a **universal indicator**. pHydrion paper is one such indicator. The numerical pH value of the tested solution is determined by comparing the color of the universal indicator in the solution with a standardized color chart that is provided by the manufacturer.

Pre-Laboratory Questions

Read the entire investigation. Answer the following questions prior to class on a separate sheet of paper. Use complete sentences.

1. From what is the chemical litmus obtained? For what is it used?

2. Between what pH values is litmus not a reliable indicator?

3. What information can the indicator phenolphthalein give you?.

4. What specific information do universal indicators provide that many other indicators are not able to provide?

5. Why shouldn't you use the same eyedropper for several chemicals when transferring chemicals from one container to another?

Procedures

Testing stations are placed around the room with various pH indicators and substances. Carefully read and follow the instructions below. The results from the stations testing the specific indicators will be entered in Table 2. When testing pH using any kind of testing paper, dispose of the paper in the container provided. When using eyedroppers, use only the eyedropper labeled for its solution. When finished with the eyedropper, return any unused chemical to the proper container and lay it down on the paper towel provided. Promptly wipe up any spills.

A. Stations A - ____, Testing Common Solutions for pH

Your teacher will have several stations set up to test the pH of some common solutions. You will be using the universal indicator paper at each station to obtain a numerical value for the pH. Follow the steps below.

1. Dip a piece of the universal indicator paper into the solution.

2. Match the resulting color to the color scale on the indicator-paper package.

3. Record the numerical pH and whether the solution is an acid or a base in Table 1 below.

4. Dispose of the paper in the container provided.

B. Litmus Paper Station

Correct Use of Litmus Paper

1. Dip one piece each of blue and red (pink) litmus paper in distilled water. What happens? _The paper becomes wet, but no color change occurs._

2. Dip a piece of blue litmus paper into the NaOH solution. What happens? _The paper becomes wet, but no color change occurs._

3. Dip a piece of red (pink) litmus paper into the NaOH solution. What happens? ____The paper turns blue.____ The color change indicates that NaOH in water is a(n) ___base___.

4. Enter the color the litmus turned in NaOH in Row 1 of Table 2 under the column for base color.

5. Which step, 1 or 2, served as the control? Why? *Step 1 is the control because no chemical was present in the solution being tested.*

Incorrect Use

6. Dip a fresh piece of red litmus paper in the NaOH solution. What happens? *The red litmus turns blue.*

7. After blotting the blue end of the same litmus paper on a paper towel, dip it into the HCl solution. What happens? *The blue end turns red again.*

8. After blotting the wet end of the same litmus paper on a paper towel, again dip it into the NaOH solution. What happens? *The litmus turns blue again.*

9. What would happen if you did not blot the excess chemical before testing the other solution? *The excess chemical would contaminate the other chemical.*

10. How do you prevent this kind of problem from occurring when testing several solutions in a row? *You must use a fresh piece of litmus for each test.*

C. Red Cabbage Extract Station

1. Add one dropper full of ammonia to one test tube. Add one dropper full of HCl to another test tube.

2. Test each of the solutions with the universal indicator paper. Match the resulting color to the color scale on the indicator-paper package. Record the pH values in Table 2 for red cabbage extract.

3. Add one dropper full of the cabbage extract to the two test tubes.

4. Note the color in each solution and record your results in Table 2.

5. Based on your observations, for what kind of scientific purpose could you use red cabbage extract? *The cabbage extract could be used as an acid-base indicator.*

6. Rinse the test tubes with water and place them upside down in the test tube rack.

D. Bromothymol Blue Station (Optional)

1. Add one dropper full of NaOH solution to one test tube and a dropper full of HCl solution to a second test tube.

2. Add two drops of bromothymol blue indicator to each of the test tubes.

3. Record the resulting colors in Table 2.

4. Rinse the tubes with water and place them upside down in the test tube rack.

as this practice can cause spills.

5. For part C (and optional parts D and E), if you do not have a sink for rinsing test tubes, provide a large beaker or jar and a wash bottle at each station. Have students pour the test tube contents into the container and rinse them with the wash bottle.

6. Solution preparations:

Amounts can be proportionately larger or smaller depending on your class size.

a. HCl—Add 1 mL conc. (12 M) HCl to 99 mL distilled water to create a 0.1 M solution. The pH will be about 0.9.

b. NaOH—Mix 2 g NaOH in 500 mL warm water to create a 0.1 M solution. The pH will be about 13.1.

c. Red cabbage extract— See Investigation 4A for instructions on preparing red cabbage extract.

d. Bromothymol blue (Optional)—Follow the instructions on container. Requires distilled water.

e. Phenolphthalein (Optional)—Purchase prepared 1% solution or follow instructions on container. Requires isopropyl alcohol.

7. If you have sufficient test tubes or small bottles, you may want to prepare a set of solutions that will calibrate pH values with colors for the red cabbage extract. Starting with 10 mL of the 0.1 M HCl solution, take 1 mL and dilute it to 10 mL in a clean test tube. The new solution should have a pH of around 2. Take 1 mL of this and dilute it to 10 mL in a clean test tube, which should produce a pH of 3. Repeat this process three

more times. Be sure to label
the test tubes with the pH
value from 1 through 6. Take
the 0.1 M NaOH solution (pH
13) and perform the same
kind of dilutions until you
have pH 13 through pH 8.
Line the test tubes up in
order from pH 1 to pH 13.
Add 10 mL of distilled water
to a test tube and label it pH
7. Place it in the middle of
the line of test tubes. At this
point, you should check the
pH of each test tube with
pHydrion paper to determine
the actual pH and mark
them accordingly. Add an
eyedropper full of cabbage
extract to each test tube and
agitate. Display the tubes in
a prominent place for
students to observe.

General Comments

*1. Caution students about
handling the HCl and NaOH
solutions. Brief contact with
skin should not cause
injury, but prolonged
exposure will cause some
irritation and redness.
Solutions spilled on clothing
may cause spotting.*

*2. Remind students to use
the correct eyedroppers in
their respective solutions
during part C (and optional
parts D and E).*

*3. This lab can be
performed individually or
using teams. Have the
students begin at a station,
rotating to the next station
every few minutes.
Encourage a quiet,
businesslike environment.*

*4. If your school has a pH
meter, consider showing
how it works by testing the
HCl and NaOH solutions.
Demonstrate the increase of
precision available from the
use of instruments.*

*5. The students will need to
look up the pH range
information for Table 2 from
the indicator bottle labels or*

E. Phenolphthalein Station (Optional)

1. Add one dropper full of NaOH solution to one test tube and a dropper full of HCl solution to a second test tube.

2. Place two drops of phenolphthalein indicator into each of the test tubes.

3. Record the resulting colors in Table 2.

4. Rinse the tubes with water and place them upside down in the test tube rack.

Results

Table 1: pH of Common Solutions

Station	Solution	pH	Acid or Base?	Station	Solution	pH	Acid or Base?
A				I			
B				J			
C				K			
D				L			
E				M			
F				N			
G				O			
H				P			

Table 2: Indicator Color Ranges

Indicator	Acid		Base	
	Color	pH (Range)	Color	pH (Range)
Litmus	Red	0.0–4.5	Blue	8.3–14.0
Red Cabbage Extract	Red	1–3	Yellow	12–14
Bromothymol Blue	Yellow	0.0–6.0	Blue	7.6–14.0
Phenolphthalein	Clear	0.0–8.0	Pink	8.0–14.0

Note: You can obtain pH range information from science supply catalogs, *The Merck Manual,* or on the Internet.

Discussion Questions

1. What was the most basic solution tested? Most acidic? _____
   Answers will vary. _____

   _____

2. Bases produce an excess of __hydroxide (OH⁻)__ ions.

3. Acids produce an excess of __hydronium (H_3O^+)__ ions.

4. At a pH of 7, the concentrations of H_3O^+ and OH^- ions are [different] (equal) (circle one).

5. The numbers on the pH scale go from __*0.0*__ to __*14.0*__ .

from a science supplies catalog.

6. The numbers for the pH scale indicate the concentration of what ions?
   hydronium (H_3O^+ or H^+)

7. Substances that are acidic taste [sour] [bitter]. Farmers in times past have tasted the soil to determine its quality. If the soil tasted slightly sour, they would say that the soil needed to be sweetened. This was usually done by adding ashes or, today, by adding lime. This simple taste test indicated that the soil needed to be made more [acidic] [basic].

8. It can be observed that many preferred food items tend to be [acidic] [basic] and cleaning items tend to be [acidic] [basic].

Experimental Evaluation

9. The acid-base indicators used in this investigation gave pH values to the nearest [ones] [tenths] [hundredths] place.

10. Work with DNA often requires pH values to the nearest tenths place. Would any of the tests in this investigation be suitable? Explain. *No, none of the indicators have a high enough precision.*

11. In what pH range would litmus paper give an uncertain result? _____
    pH 4.5 to 8.3

12. Can litmus paper be used to test the pH of water (pure or tap)? Explain.
    No, pure water and most tap water have pHs very close to 7.0, which is in the uncertain range for litmus.

13. What serves as the control (basis of comparison) for the universal pH paper? *The color scale on the container provides the necessary control.*

12 APPLICATIONS
Stopping Distances

Objective

The purpose of this exercise is to show the relationships among the speed of a car, its kinetic energy, and the distance it takes to stop.

Introduction

Mathematical formulas are equations that relate two or more measurable physical quantities to each other. Because they are equations, it is never appropriate to give only one side or the other of the formula. For example, if you were asked for the formula for kinetic energy, you should provide $K.E. = \frac{1}{2} mv^2$, not just $\frac{1}{2} mv^2$. Formulas are essential for understanding how the physical world works. They represent the orderliness of physical processes. When studying mechanical motion, it is often easier to assume that motion is in geometrically simple patterns such as straight lines, and we ignore effects such as friction, which are not important at this time. This allows the formulas we use to be as simple as possible so that we can better understand the underlying principles. Of course, the result often does not exactly match what is seen in the real world.

In Chapter 12, you learned about the conservation of energy and the transformation of one form of energy into another. In particular, you learned about mechanical energy and momentum. In this exercise, you are going to gain an appreciation for the mechanical energy contained in a moving car—something that will be very valuable to know as you begin to learn about driving. As mentioned in the paragraph above, we will be making some simplifying assumptions to help us understand the problems and the principles involved.

Assumptions:

1. The car is traveling in a straight line.

2. All conditions are normal and optimal—alert, skilled driver; dry, clean road pavement; brakes work continuously at maximum efficiency until the car stops.

3. The car slows at a constant -5.0 m/s^2 when the brakes are applied under the above conditions.

Recall that a negative acceleration means that the car is reducing its speed with time. The assumptions are reasonable and realistic except for idealized brake operation and constant deceleration. These are allowed so that you can make some calculations using math you are familiar with.

Problems

Solve the following problems according to the directions for each. Show your work in the space provided below each question. Write your final answers in the specified table. Include the correct units. If you are observing significant digits (SDs), round your final answer to the correct number of SDs; otherwise, round your answers to one decimal place.

Definitions

d is the distance traveled in an interval of time. Units are kilometers, meters, centimeters, and so on. Its formula is $d = r \cdot t$. The rate, r, is the same as average velocity, v_{avg}.

t is the length of the time interval. Units are hours, minutes, or seconds.

v is the speed of an object. Units are in km/h, m/s, and so on.

v_{avg} is the average speed during an interval of time. Its formula is
$$v_{avg} = \frac{v_1 + v_2}{2}.$$

m is the mass of an object. Units are kilograms, grams, and so on.

a is the acceleration of an object, the change in speed in a given time interval. Its formula is $a = \dfrac{v_2 - v_1}{t}$.

Subscript 1 refers to the first measurement taken during a time interval.

Subscript 2 refers to the second or last measurement taken during a time interval.

Stopping Distance

Suppose a car is moving 5.0 m/s (11 mph). How far will it take the car to stop if it can decelerate at -5.0 m/s²?

1. The given information is the initial speed ($v_1 = 5.0$ m/s) and the acceleration ($a = -5.0$ m/s²). We are looking for the distance (d) traveled until the car stops ($v_2 = 0.0$ m/s).

2. To find distance, we see that the applicable formula is $d = v_{avg} \cdot t$.

3. The car slows from 5.0 m/s to 0.0 m/s; therefore, the average velocity will be

$$v_{avg} = \frac{5.0\,\frac{m}{s} + 0.0\,\frac{m}{s}}{2} = 2.5\,\frac{m}{s}$$

4. In order to find the distance, you must still find elapsed time. The only formula provided that has all of the required information is that for acceleration: $a = \dfrac{v_2 - v_1}{t}$.

$$a = \underline{\quad -5.0\ m/s^2 \quad}$$

$$v_1 = \underline{\quad 5.0\ m/s^2 \quad}$$

$$v_2 = \underline{\quad 0.0\ m/s^2 \quad}$$

Rearrange the acceleration formula and solve for t before substituting values.

$$t = \dfrac{\dfrac{v_2 - v_1}{a}}{} \quad \text{(Rearrange)}$$

$$t = \dfrac{\dfrac{0.0\,\frac{m}{s} - 5.0\,\frac{m}{s}}{-5.0\,\frac{m}{s^2}}}{} \quad \text{(Substitute)}$$

$$t = \underline{1.0\ s} \quad \text{(Solve) Write this answer in Table 1 for "Time"}$$
at 5.0 m/s.

5. Now the original distance equation (see 2, above) can be solved.

$$d = \underline{2.5\ m/s \cdot 1.0\ s} \quad \text{(Substitute)}$$

$$d = \underline{2.5\ m} \quad \text{(Solve) Write this answer in Table 1 for "Distance"}$$
at 5.0 m/s.

6. Using the same process, fill in Table 1 for 10. m/s and 20. m/s. Show your work in the spaces below (remember that a decimal point after a trailing zero indicates that the zero is significant).

$v_1 = 10.\ \text{m/s},\ a = -5.0\ \text{m/s}^2 \qquad v_1 = 20.\ \text{m/s},\ a = -5.0\ \text{m/s}^2$

$$v_{avg} = \frac{10.\,\frac{m}{s} + 0.0\,\frac{m}{s}}{2} = 5\,\frac{m}{s} \qquad v_{avg} = \frac{20.\,\frac{m}{s} + 0.0\,\frac{m}{s}}{2} = 10.\,\frac{m}{s}$$

$$t = \frac{0.0\,\frac{m}{s} - 10.\,\frac{m}{s}}{-5.0\,\frac{m}{s^2}} = 2.0\ s \qquad t = \frac{0.0\,\frac{m}{s} - 20.\,\frac{m}{s}}{-5.0\,\frac{m}{s^2}} = 4.0\ s$$

$$d = 5\ m/s \cdot 2.0\ s = 10\ m \qquad d = 10.\ m/s \cdot 4.0\ s = 40.\ m$$

Table 1: Stopping Distances

Velocity	Time	Distance in m and ft.
5.0 m/s (11 mph)	1.0 s (2 SDs)	2.5 m (2 SDs)/8.3 ft.
10. m/s (22 mph)	2.0 s (2 SDs)	10 m (1 SD)/33 ft.
20. m/s (45 mph)	4.0 s (2 SDs)	40. m (2 SDs)/130 ft.

Kinetic Energy of the Car (Collision Energy)

Suppose the car has a mass of 1000. kg (2200 lb.). How much kinetic energy will the car have at a speed of 5.0 m/s?

1. The kinetic energy formula is K.E. $= \frac{1}{2} mv^2$.

   m = _1000. kg_ v = _5.0 m/s_

   $K.E. = $ _$\frac{1}{2} \cdot$ 1000. kg $\cdot$ (5.0 m/s)²_   (Substitute)

   $K.E. = $ _12,500 $\frac{kg \cdot m}{s^2} \approx 1.3 \cdot 10^4$ J (2 SDs)_   (Solve) Record this answer for a velocity of 5.0 m/s in Table 2, below.

2. Calculate the kinetic energies for the same car at 10. m/s and 20. m/s and enter them in Table 2.

   m = _1000. kg_ v = _10. m/s_ m = _1000. kg_ v = _20. m/s_

   $K.E. = $ _$\frac{1}{2} \cdot$ 1000. kg $\cdot$ (10. m/s)²_ $K.E. = $ _$\frac{1}{2} \times$ 1000. kg $\cdot$ (20. m/s)²_

   $K.E. = $ _50,000 $\frac{kg \cdot m}{s^2} \approx 5.0 \cdot 10^4$ J (2 SDs)_ $K.E. = $ _200,000 $\frac{kg \cdot m}{s^2} \approx 2.0 \cdot 10^5$ J (2 SDs)_

Table 2: Kinetic Energies

Velocity	Kinetic Energy
5.0 m/s	1.3×10^4 J
10. m/s	5.0×10^4 J
20. m/s	2.0×10^5 J

Discussion Questions

1. If the initial speed of the car is doubled, its new stopping distance will be about ___4___ times its original stopping distance.

2. If the initial speed of the car is doubled, its new kinetic energy will be about ___4___ times its original kinetic energy.

3. If a safe distance behind another car driving 30 mph is 40 feet (12 m), you should stay _160 feet (48 m)_ behind a car on the highway when driving 60 mph.

4. A collision at 60 mph will be ___4___ times more energetic than a collision at 30 mph.

5. In your own words give two important driving principles illustrated by this study. _Answers will vary. Students should recognize that following_ _distances need to increase with speed and that collision energies quadruple_ _with a doubling of speed._

Experimental Evaluation

6. In order to solve these problems, certain assumptions were made. List these assumptions. *a. The car is traveling in a straight line.*

   b. All conditions are normal and optimal—alert, skilled driver; dry, clean

   road pavement; brakes work continuously at maximum efficiency until

   the car stops.

   c. The car slows at a constant −5.0 m/s² when the brakes are applied under

   the above conditions.

7. List some of the factors discussed in the Facet on page 276 of your textbook that make one or more of these assumptions invalid in the real world. *The tires may skid; the reaction time of the driver must be factored*

   into total stopping distance; car brakes work less efficiently at higher

   speeds; the road may not be level; the road surface may not be dry, or it

   may be covered with gravel or leaves.

8. (Optional) Discuss why a safe following distance may be less than the braking distance for a given speed (see page 276 in your textbook).
   The braking distance is the distance the car covers from the time the brakes

   are applied until it stops. If the car you are following could stop in an

   instant, then braking distance would also be the minimum safe following

   distance. But since the car you are following must take some time to slow

   to a stop, you also have that additional distance to stop.

9. (Optional) In question 4 above, what were some assumptions that you made to answer the question? *Answers will vary. Students may assume*

   that the collision occurred at the stated speed of the car (no slowing down

   prior to collision) and that their car was the only one moving. Others may

   be accepted if reasonable.

10. (Optional) In a collision of your car with another, what are some other factors besides the speed of your car that would determine the severity of the accident?
    Answers will vary. Accept any of the following: speed of the other car, angle

    of impact, car masses, car design (rigidity), time duration of impact, and

    severity of injuries sustained by occupants.

13A APPLICATIONS
Yellow Light: Stop or Go?

Objectives

The purpose of this problem-solving exercise is to

1. Use basic equations of motion to investigate what can happen when a speeding car approaches a yellow light.

2. Determine some dynamic effects on the vehicle in this situation.

Introduction

You are driving a brand new SUV, approaching an intersection controlled by traffic lights. In your lane the light is green. Just seconds from the intersection, though, the light turns yellow. What are you going to do? In a split second you must decide whether there is enough time to go through the light while it is still yellow and, at the same time, estimate if you have enough room to stop safely if you want to stop. This is a real-world situation that drivers face all of the time.

We are going to apply some of the principles you have learned in Chapter 13 to this question. Scientific investigations often require simplified mathematical models in order to understand the complicated underlying principles. Scientists develop mathematical models to study problems that are too small, too large, or too complex to observe directly. Often the problem is simplified by making certain assumptions as we did in Applications 12 when studying stopping distances. This exercise will take this approach and then draw some inferences to real driving conditions.

In our problem, should you increase speed, coast, or try to stop? Your decision should be based on the following considerations: the approaching speed of the vehicle, the distance to the stoplight, the time duration until the traffic light turns red, the working condition of the brakes, your experience, and the road conditions. Traffic engineers take all of these factors into consideration and have coordinated safe speed limits with the duration of the yellow traffic light for normal driving conditions. This exercise will investigate some of the effects on a vehicle only when it coasts or tries to stop as it approaches a yellow traffic light. The option of increasing the car's speed to make it through the light will not be considered since this is unwise as well as illegal in most states.

Problems

Assumptions

1. No part of your vehicle is allowed to be in the intersection when the light turns red.

2. "In the intersection" means within the street area between the near curb and the far curb.

3. The street is 10. m (33 ft.) wide.

4. The SUV is 5.0 m (16.5 ft.) long.

5. You, the driver, are alert and skilled.

6. The road conditions are ideal.

7. The SUV's brakes are working properly.

8. You begin braking the same instant that the light turns yellow.

Initial Conditions

We will first consider the situation where you are approaching an intersection in a 30 mph zone. You are exceeding the speed limit, moving at 25 m/s (55 mph). The light turns yellow and it is timed to be on for 2.0 seconds before changing to red. Keeping in mind the assumptions, do you coast through the light at constant speed or do you brake to a stop (decelerate at −5.0 m/s² or −11 mph/s)?

Fill in the table with the initial conditions provided. These values can be considered realistic.

Initial Conditions

Condition	Value
Speed (m/s)	*25 m/s*
Yellow Light Time (s)	*2.0 s*
Deceleration (m/s²)	*−5.0 m/s²*

Coasting Through the Yellow Light

Assume you choose to coast through the yellow light—in other words, you will maintain constant speed. You believe that the combination of your speed and the remaining distance to the far side of the intersection will permit you to clear the intersection in 2.0 seconds or less. How far can you be from the intersection and coast through? This is the same as asking how far can the vehicle travel in 2.0 seconds. To answer this question, complete the following steps.

1. Picture the problem. Examine the diagram and write in the values of the initial conditions.

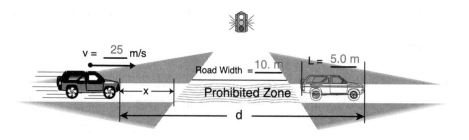

2. Write the applicable equation. $\underline{d = vt}$ _____

3. $d =$ _25 m/s · 2.0 s_   (substitute)

4. $d =$ _50. m_   (solve)

5. What must you do to find the maximum distance to the intersection to safely coast through (x)? _You must subtract the road width and the length_

   of the SUV from the distance traveled in 2.0 seconds (50. m).

6. Calculate x: _x = 50. m − 10. m − 5.0 m = 35 m_

7. At 55 mph, if you are **less than** _35 m_ from the intersection, you can safely coast through the yellow light.

8. How many car lengths is this distance? _7 car lengths_

   Recall that you were speeding in this situation!

9. Calculate in the space below the maximum distance that you could safely coast through the light if you were driving at the speed limit (13 m/s).

   _d = 13 m/s · 2.0 s = 26 m_

   _x = 26 m − 10. m − 5.0 m = 11 m_

10. At 30 mph, if you are less than _11 m_ from the intersection, you can safely coast through the yellow light. In car lengths, this distance is _a little more than two_ car lengths.

Braking for the Yellow Light

Assume now that you decide to stop. You believe that there is sufficient distance for you to safely slow to a stop from the speed you are driving, considering the assumptions given. How far can you be from the intersection while driving 55 mph (25 m/s) and slowing to a stop by braking hard ($-5.0 \, \text{m/s}^2$)? We will use the same distance equation as in the first case, but you are missing some information that will have to be found by additional calculations. Complete the following steps to find the answer.

1. Picture the problem. Examine the diagram and write in the values of the initial conditions.

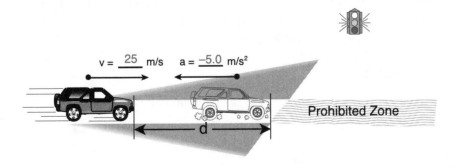

2. Write the applicable equation. _d = vt_

3. Since the speed is changing while the SUV is stopping, you will have to find its average speed, v_{avg}, to solve for d. To find v_{avg}, we must average the initial and final speeds. The initial speed (v_1) is ___25 m/s___, and the final speed (v_2) is ___0.0 m/s___.

$$v_{avg} = \frac{v_1 + v_2}{2} = \frac{25\frac{m}{s} + 0.0\frac{m}{s}}{2} = 12.5\frac{m}{s} \approx 13\frac{m}{s} \text{ (2 SDs)}$$

4. Stopping time must be found using the acceleration formula $a = \frac{v_2 - v_1}{t}$.

   Rearranging: $t = \frac{v_2 - v_1}{a}$

   Solve for t: $t = \frac{v_2 - v_1}{a} = \frac{0.0\frac{m}{s} - 25\frac{m}{s}}{-5.0\frac{m}{s^2}} = 5.0 \text{ s (2 SDs)}$

5. We now have average speed and time. Calculate in the space below the minimum distance required to stop safely without entering the intersection.

   $d = 13 \text{ m/s} \cdot 5.0 \text{ s} = 65 \text{ m (2 SDs)}$

6. At 55 mph, if you are **more than** ___65 m___ from the intersection, you can safely stop for a yellow light.

7. How many car lengths is this distance? ___13 car lengths___

8. Calculate in the space below the minimum distance required to safely stop for the light if you were driving at the speed limit (13 m/s).

   $$v_{avg} = \frac{v_1 + v_2}{2} = \frac{13\frac{m}{s} + 0.0\frac{m}{s}}{2} = 6.5\frac{m}{s} \approx 7\frac{m}{s} \text{ (1 SD)}$$

   $$t = \frac{v_2 - v_1}{a} = \frac{0.0\frac{m}{s} - 13\frac{m}{s}}{-5.0\frac{m}{s^2}} = 2.6 \text{ s (2 SDs)}$$

   $$d = 6.5 \text{ m/s} \cdot 2.6 \text{ s} = 16.9 \text{ m} \approx 17 \text{ m}$$

9. At 30 mph, if you are **more than** ___17 m___ from the intersection, you can safely stop for the yellow light. In car lengths, this distance is ___three and a half (3.4)___ car lengths.

Evaluating the Results

1. Write the applicable distances in the diagram below:

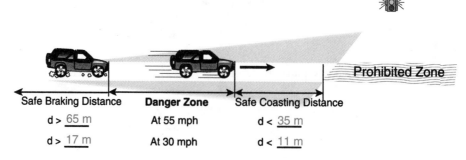

Safe Braking Distance	Danger Zone	Safe Coasting Distance
d > 65 m	At 55 mph	d < 35 m
d > 17 m	At 30 mph	d < 11 m

2. Why is the space between the safe coasting distance and the safe braking distance called the "danger zone"? *It is called the danger zone because* *you can neither coast nor stop safely and still remain out of the intersection* *when the light turns red.*

3. If you believe you are in the danger zone as you approach a traffic light, what is your safest option? *You should apply your brakes as hard as* *possible to keep from entering the intersection.*

4. How would a traffic engineer eliminate the danger zone at this traffic light, assuming the speed limit must remain 30 mph? *The engineer could* *increase the time of the yellow light so that the safe coasting distance is at* *least as long as the minimum braking distance at the design speed limit.*

5. Which assumption stated at the beginning of the exercise was the least realistic? *The assumption that the brakes were applied at the same instant* *as the light turned yellow.*

6. What real-world effect would this have on the problem? *It would have* *no effect on the maximum coasting distance since that is determined by* *the duration of the yellow light. However, it would increase the minimum* *braking distance to stop. Therefore, when considering driver reaction time,* *the size of the danger zone is increased.*

7. Based on what you have learned, give a reason that speeding is dangerous. *Speeding is dangerous because it increases the size of the danger zone.* *This can cause accidents because you are more likely to be in the* *intersection when the light turns red.*

Yellow Light: Stop or Go?

Dynamics of Stopping a Vehicle

1. Assume that your SUV has a mass of 1500. kg. What force must be applied to the vehicle to stop it at the assumed deceleration of -5.0 m/s^2? Recall that deceleration is negative acceleration.

   a. Write the formula that relates mass, acceleration, and force: <u>*F = ma*</u>

   b. Solve for force: $F = $ <u>*1500 kg · (-5.0 m/s^2) = $-7500 \frac{kg · m}{s^2}$ = -7500 N*</u>

   c. Why is this force negative? <u>*It is acting in the direction opposite to the motion of the vehicle.*</u>

   d. Where does this force come from to stop the vehicle? <u>*The force is generated by the brakes.*</u>

   e. The force exerted by the brakes through the wheels contacts the ground. Which law of motion says that the ground will push back at the wheels with the same force but in the opposite direction? <u>*Newton's third law of motion*</u>

   f. What physically happens to a vehicle when the ground cannot push back with the same reaction force as the vehicle exerts when it is slowing? <u>*The vehicle will skid.*</u>

2. If you have a mass of 70. kg and your SUV decelerates at -5.0 m/s^2, what will your deceleration be? Explain your answer. <u>*If you have your seat belt on, you will slow down with the vehicle, so your deceleration will be the same as the SUV's, or -5.0 m/s^2.*</u>

3. Based on your answer to question 2, what force will your body feel as you stop for the yellow light? _____

   F = ma, so F = 70. kg · (-5.0 m/s^2) = $-35 \frac{kg · m}{s^2}$ = -35 N.

13B **INVESTIGATION**
Center of Gravity

Objectives

The purpose of this investigation is to

1. Locate the center of gravity of an object.

2. Determine the stability of an object based on the location of its center of gravity.

Introduction

The centers of mass and gravity are not distinguished in this investigation. In most cases, these two centers are close enough to be considered the same. The distinction is important when considering gravitational effects of the moon on the earth. The center of gravity of the earth is not its geometric center but is on the side closer to the moon. This is because the part of the earth closest to the moon is more strongly attracted to the moon. This is what causes the ocean tides.

Materials	Equipment
Paper	Forks (2)
String	Hanger
Styrofoam™	Laboratory mass
Tape	Mounting block
Thread	Thumbtack
Thumbtack	Wooden block

Introduction

As you learned in your textbook, two objects exert a gravitational force on each other that is proportional to their masses. The gravitational force exerted by an object draws the matter surrounding it toward a point located in the exact center of mass of the object. We call this point the **center of gravity (c.g.).** The location of the c.g. is important for determining the *stability* and the *balance point* of an object, concepts that will be discussed later. For simple geometric objects, even three-dimensional ones, locating the c.g. is relatively easy. If you assume that mass is uniformly distributed throughout the object, then the c.g. is located at its geometric center. For example, the center of gravity of a sphere is located at the intersection of two or more diameters of the sphere (see A, below). The c.g. of a rectangular block is located at the point of intersection of the diagonal lines extending from one corner through the block to the opposite corner (see B, below). The c.g. of a cylinder is at the midpoint of a line passing through the centers of the circles at the ends of the cylinder (see C, below).

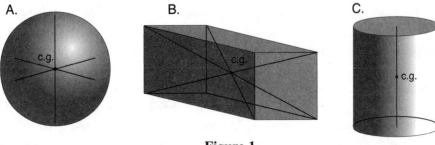

Figure 1

The c.g. of irregular objects can be found experimentally by using a device called a *plumb line or bob*. This is a builder's aid that determines the line of the force of gravity at a given location. It is used to ensure that the walls of buildings are vertical (plumb) during construction. When an object is suspended, the point of suspension and its c.g. lie in the line of gravity. If you attach a plumb bob to the point of suspension, the plumb line will pass through the location of the object's c.g. While this will work theoretically for all objects using an imaginary plumb line, in practice it is useful only for two-dimensional (flat) objects because a string will not pass through the center of a three-dimensional solid. If you suspend a flat object at two or more points and trace the lines of gravity, they will intersect at the c.g. (see Figure 2).

Figure 2

The location of the center of gravity of an object is directly related to its stability. A **stable** object will return to its original position if tilted. An **unstable** object will tumble until it arrives at a new stable position different from the original. Your own experience will demonstrate this. You are in a stable position walking along the sidewalk. If you trip, however, you become unstable and fall. After you have stopped tumbling, you are again stable, but you are now in quite a different position. Stability is determined by the relative positions of an object's c.g. and its **support base.** The support base of an object is the two-dimensional surface that supports a three-dimensional object. One example would be the base of a pyramid. The support base can also be a one-dimensional edge or side that supports a two-dimensional object such as a triangle. As long as the c.g. of the object lies on a vertical line that passes through the object's base, the object will retain some stability. If the c.g. is moved to a point that lies outside of the object's base of support, the object will fall over. When it comes to rest, it will have a new base and the c.g. will again lie above the base.

Stability is related to two factors: the vertical distance of the c.g. from the base and the length of the base. Changing either of these factors affects the stability of an object. For example, lowering the c.g. and increasing the length of the base both increase stability for the same reason; you must tip the object farther before the c.g. falls outside of the base.

Pre-Laboratory Questions

Read the entire investigation. Answer the following questions prior to class on a separate sheet of paper. Use complete sentences.

1. What is the point in an object called toward which the masses of all other objects are attracted?

2. Where is this point located?

3. What assumption must be made to find the c.g. geometrically?

4. What determines the stability of an object?

5. What common carpentry tool will you use to find the center of gravity of a hanger?

6. If the center of gravity were lowered below the base of support or the fulcrum of an object, how stable would it be?

7. Which vehicle would be more stable, a Formula 1 racing car or a large SUV? Explain your answer.

Procedures

A. Locating the Center of Gravity

As discussed earlier, the center of gravity of a two-dimensional object can be found by using a plumb line that is simply a weight attached to a string.

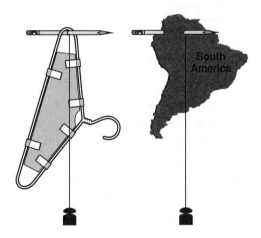

Figure 3

1. Cut a piece of paper to the size of the open space of a clothes hanger. Tape the paper so that the open space is covered. Leave a gap at the two corners large enough to insert a pencil.

2. Tie some thread to the weight and secure the other end of the thread to a pencil. Make sure that the pencil-to-weight distance is longer than the coat hanger.

Answers to Pre-Laboratory Questions

1. The point toward which all other objects are attracted is called the center of gravity.

2. This point is located in the exact center of mass of the object.

3. You must assume that the mass of the object is uniformly distributed throughout.

4. The stability of an object is determined by the location of the center of gravity with respect to the object's base of support.

5. We will use a plumb bob (or plumb line) to find the c.g. of a hanger.

6. The object would be more stable.

7. The Formula 1 racer would be more stable because its center of gravity is much lower compared to the size of its base than the SUV.

Preparation

Prepare the mounting blocks by cutting a thick sheet of dense Styrofoam to approximately 3 × 3 × 6 cm blocks. The dimensions are not critical, but they should be large enough to hold the forks in several positions. The blocks can also be carved from potatoes or other large root vegetables. You will need to prepare the potato blocks ahead of time and keep them in cold water to keep them rigid and to prevent browning. Insert the toothpick as close to the center of one of the faces of the block as possible. In this part of the investigation, the weight of the metal forks must be greater than the weight of the mounting block.

1. Laboratory mass weights or even a large nail or bolt could be used to construct the plumb line. To save time, have the plumb lines made up before class.

2. The relationship between the center of gravity, the base, and stability is not intuitive to most students. They often have trouble predicting at what point the block will become unstable. Make sure students understand the introductory section before proceeding with the rest of the investigation.

3. As an additional exercise, have available two blocks that have the same base but very different heights. As the students perform the same exercise on both blocks, the effect on stability of raising the center of gravity will be well illustrated.

3. Insert the pencil at one of the corners of the hanger and allow it to hang so that the thread lies against the paper. Without disturbing the position of the hanger or thread, mark several points along the thread on the paper, then lay the hanger on a table and connect the dots using a ruler to reconstruct the position of the thread.

4. Repeat step 3 twice, suspending the hanger first from the other corner and then from the hook at the top.

5. The three pencil lines should intersect at the center of gravity.

6. Try to balance the hanger on the eraser of a pencil placed at the center of gravity. Does it balance? _Answers will vary, but students should see that that the hanger is close to balancing._

Sometimes a town claims to be the geographic center of that country or state. This claim can be verified by cutting out the shape of the country and locating the center of gravity using this same method. Be sure to make the holes large enough that the pattern can hang freely from the pencil (see Figure 3).

B. Stability

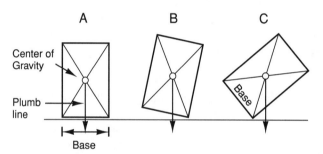

Figure 4

1. Draw two diagonal lines connecting opposite corners on the end of a wooden block with a pencil and a ruler. Be as accurate as possible. Assuming the block is uniform through its length, the point of intersection lies on an imaginary line through the middle of the block. The c.g. is at the midpoint of this line in the geometric center of the block. Therefore, we can use the intersection of diagonals at the end of the block to represent the position of the center of gravity.

2. Set the block at the edge of a table or desk. Insert a thumbtack into the intersection of the two diagonals you drew. Tie the plumb line to the thumbtack so that it can hang freely.

3. Rock the block slightly onto a corner so that the plumb line falls within the base as in B above. Release the block.

   a. Did the block return to its original position? _Yes_

   b. Was the block stable? _Yes_

4. Tip the block again, this time making sure that the plumb line is beyond the base as in C above.

   a. Did the block return to the original position? _No_

   b. Was the block stable? _No_

   c. How would you describe the relative height of the c.g. when the block is completely stable and when it becomes unstable? _The c.g. is_ _lowest when the block is most stable, and it is the highest when the_ _block becomes unstable._

C. Optional Demonstration of Stability

Humans have a smaller base of support than four-footed animals because humans have only two feet. Humans and animals alike, however, must keep their centers of gravity above their bases of support to remain stable.

1. With your feet together, place a pencil on the floor just in front of your toes. Without moving your feet and keeping your legs straight, bend over to pick up the pencil off of the floor. Notice how your shoulders move in front of your feet and your hips move backward to compensate.

   a. Were you able to pick up the pencil? _Yes_

   b. Did your center of gravity remain above your base of support? How do you know? _Yes, the student did not fall over._

   c. Were you stable? _Yes_

2. Stand with the back of your shoes against a wall and try to repeat the same procedure.

   a. Were you able to pick up the pencil? _No_

   b. Did your center of gravity remain above your base of support? Explain. _No, the student lost his balance and fell forward._

   c. Were you stable as you leaned forward? _No_

D. Increasing Stability

Let us consider a teeter-totter (which is basically a plane supported at its center along a line) or a spinning top (which is supported by a single point). Either will be stable only when supported at its *balance point* (or fulcrum). Additionally, in order for it to be completely stable, the mass of the object must be distributed in such a way that its c.g. lies in a vertical line directly *below* its balance point. If the c.g. is in any other location, the object will be unstable and will tend to rotate around the balance point until it falls. If the c.g. is in a vertical line directly above the fulcrum, the object is completely unstable and its motion will be unpredictable. In the two examples mentioned, the legs of the riders of the teeter-totter lower the c.g. of the entire system below the fulcrum. The top maintains temporary stability through gyroscopic forces, but when it slows too much, it falls to its side, which provides a larger base. Increasing the distance of the c.g. below the fulcrum increases stability because it increases the force that tends to return the object to its original position.

In the investigation below, you will observe the effects of changing the location of the center of gravity of an object relative to its balance point.

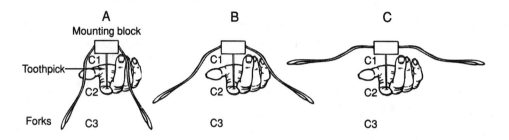

Figure 5

1. Obtain a mounting block of styrofoam or other material, two forks, and a toothpick.

2. Insert the two forks and the toothpick into the mounting block as shown in A of Figure 5, above. To start with, the middle of the fork handles should be below the free end of the toothpick. Attempt to balance the assemblage by placing the end of the toothpick on your fingertip.

   a. Did the assemblage balance? _Yes_

   b. Is the assemblage stable? _Yes_

   c. Referring to A in Figure 5, is the c.g. of the assemblage at C1, C2, or C3? _C3_

   d. Is this above or below the point of support? _It is below the point of support._

   e. Slightly tip the assemblage. Describe what happens when you release it.
      The assemblage rotates back to its original position.

   f. Describe the relative heights of the c.g. of the assemblage before you tipped it and the c.g. at its maximum angle before you released it.
      The c.g. was lowest before tipping, and it was highest when the assemblage was released.

   g. What inference can you make about the relationship between height of c.g. and stability? _An object is most stable when its c.g. is lowest._

3. Insert the two forks into the mounting block at increasingly wider angles, as shown in B and C. Attempt to balance the assemblage in each case.

   a. Could you balance the assemblage in every case? _No_

   b. When you *could* get the assemblage to balance, was it more or less stable than in question 2 of this part? _It was less stable._

   c. When the assemblage falls, what seems to be the relative height of the c.g. of the assemblage compared to the balance point? _The c.g. seems to be at or above the balance point._

4. Referring to Figure 5, which center of gravity position (C1, C2, or C3) was the most stable? *C3*

5. Which was the least stable? *C1*

6. What was the point of support? *The point of support was the end of the toothpick that was resting on the finger.*

7. How did raising the center of gravity compared to the base of support affect the stability of the assemblage? *The stability was lowered.*

8. Does this support the inference you made in question 2 of this part?
   Yes

Discussion Questions

1. Where would you expect to find the center of gravity of a wheel? *It would be at the center of the wheel.*

2. How does the size of the support base of a cow compare with the base of a human? *It is much larger.*

3. Explain why it is easier for a four-footed animal to learn to walk than a human. *Because the animal's base is so much larger, it is easier to keep its center of gravity over it.*

4. What happens to your center of gravity when you carry a loaded backpack?
   It shifts backward.

   How do you compensate for this change? *You have to lean forward.*

5. How does the *height* of the c.g of a fully loaded log truck compare to that of an empty log truck? *Its c.g. would be higher when it is full.*

   How would this affect the truck's stability? *It would make it less stable.*

6. Which shape in Figure 6, below, would be the most stable: A, B, or C? Why? *A is the most stable because it has the largest base.*

7. Which vehicle in Figure 6 would be more stable, D or E? Why? (Assume that the width of the trucks and of their tires is the same.) *D would be the more stable because it has the lower center of gravity.*

Figure 6

8. What features of a military Humvee (Hummer) make it more stable than a regular car? *It is wider compared to the height of its c.g. than a regular* *car, making it harder to tip over.*

9. A tightrope walker often carries a heavy, flexible pole whose ends droop below the level of the tightrope. Why does this make his job easier? *He is lowering his center of gravity, making him more stable on the rope.*

10. Sir Isaac Newton demonstrated that two objects do not have to be physically connected to have a common center of gravity. If you consider the earth and moon as a system, would the system's center of gravity be located at point A, B, C, or D in Figure 7? _____*B*_____ The earth and moon together revolve around their common center of gravity.

Earth   Moon

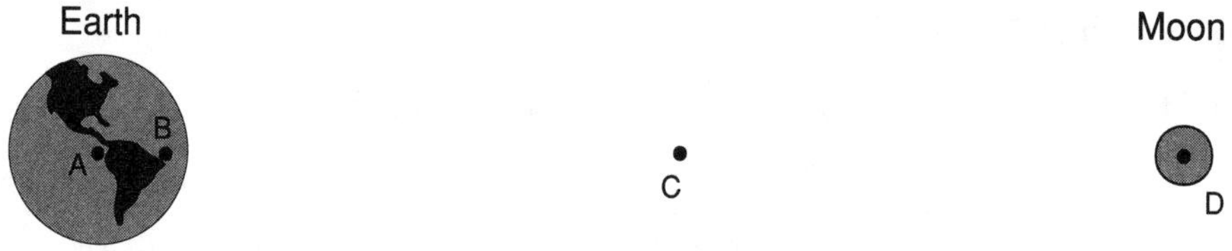

Figure 7

11. Based on your conclusion from question 10, if you threw a hammer, would it rotate around point A, B, C, or D in Figure 8? *It would rotate around* *point C.*

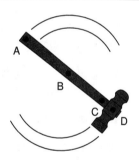

Figure 8

14A INVESTIGATION
First-Class Levers

Objectives

The purpose of this exercise is to

1. Review some basic concepts of levers.

2. Verify that the law of moments ($w_1 d_1 = w_2 d_2$) holds true for any first-class lever.

Equipment

Knife-edge clamp
Mass hanger clamps (2)
Mass set
Meter stick
Support stand
Unknown mass

Introduction

If you had to open a can of paint, which of the following would you prefer to use: A quarter, a brass key fob, or a screwdriver? Why?

The answer is, of course, that you have "more leverage" with the screwdriver. What does this actually mean? You have learned about the law of moments and the structure of a first-class lever. Let's apply that knowledge to opening the can of paint. There are three physical parts of a lever system. They are the resistance arm (the distance of the resistance force from the fulcrum), the effort arm (the distance of the moving force from the fulcrum), and the fulcrum (the pivot point around which the lever arms rotate). The two non-physical components of a lever system are the resistance and effort forces. In our paint can problem, the resistance arm is the distance from the can rim to the underside edge of the lid, the fulcrum is the can rim, and the effort arm is the distance from the rim to the end of the tool you choose to use. The resistance is constant for each case, amounting to several hundred pounds of frictional force between the lid and the can. The effort force depends to some extent on how good a grip you can get on the tool. The coin can be gripped only with fingertips, while the key fob and the screwdriver can be gripped with the whole hand.

Introduction

Cover the material in the introduction prior to the lab period. This can be done as part of the chapter discussion or as a separate pre-lab discussion. The textbook briefly mentions torques, but this investigation goes into more depth. Recognize that students will grasp only the concept of magnitude of torques, not the vector mathematics. The other key principle to emphasize is equilibrium. Students should be reminded that many significant phenomena in the physical world depend on equilibria, where two opposing processes maintain a constant condition. The concentration of oxygen in the atmosphere, the heat balance of the earth, and the students' body weights all depend on equilibria. The specific kind of equilibrium we are dealing with is called static equilibrium since we are dealing with stationary phenomena.

Before we attempt to "open the can," we need to discuss the concept of **torque.** A torque is the product of the force acting perpendicularly to a lever arm rotating around a fulcrum and the distance between the fulcrum and the point of application of the force. (See Figure 1, right.) The word *torque* itself comes from the Latin word meaning "to twist." Every time you unscrew a cap from a jar or bottle, you are exerting a torque. A torque is also called a **moment.** A first-class lever and, for that matter,

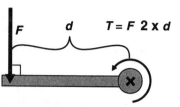

Figure 1: Torque (*T*)

any lever, consists of two torques working against each other. You have learned that for a change in motion to occur, an unbalanced force must be applied to an object. Motion around a fulcrum occurs only with unbalanced torques. In order to open the paint can, the effort torque (the force that you exert times the distance between the can rim and the end of your tool) must exceed the resistance torque (the frictional force of the can lid times the small distance from the can rim to the underside of the lid).

If there is no motion of a lever around a fulcrum, then how do the torques compare? The *torques* must be equal. This does not necessarily imply that the forces or the lever arms involved are equal. When this situation occurs, we say the lever system is in **equilibrium.** We will use this principle in our study of the first-class lever.

Pre-Laboratory Questions

Read the entire investigation. Answer the following questions prior to class on a separate sheet of paper. Use complete sentences.

1. Define in your own words the following terms:

   a. law of moments

   b. torque

   c. equilibrium

2. How many torques are applied in every simple lever system?

3. How do you calculate the weight of an object if you know its mass in kilograms?

4. How do you know that a lever system is in equilibrium?

5. If a lever system is in equilibrium, what do you know must be true about the torques acting on the lever?

6. Why must you balance the meter stick first before adding any masses to it?

7. How do you find the mechanical advantage (M.A.) of a first-class lever system?

Procedures

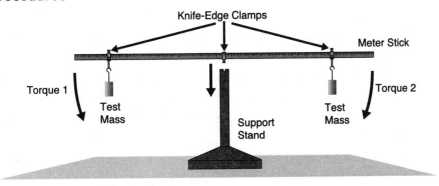

Figure 2: Lever Arm Assembly

Assemble the Apparatus

1. Slide the knife-edge clamp onto the meter stick to the 50 cm mark and gently tighten the screw.

2. Set the meter stick lever assembly onto the support stand and check the balance.

3. If the meter stick does not come to rest horizontally, loosen the set screw and move the stick toward the high end. Repeat until the stick balances horizontally.

4. Slide the mass hangers onto the lever assembly so that the wire hangers are below the meter stick, but do not tighten.

Identify Masses

1. Obtain the hooked or slotted masses to be used in this investigation.

2. Label the two 50. g masses **A** and **B.** Label the 100. g mass **C** and the 200. g mass **D.**

3. Write each mass in grams in the left column of Table 1 adjacent to the corresponding letter. If the masses you are using are different from those listed, then substitute as required. Assume their masses are precise to the nearest gram.

4. Convert each mass to kilograms in the middle column.

5. Calculate their weights by multiplying by 9.81 N/kg and write this value in the right-hand column.

6. Write the masses' weights in the corresponding blocks in Table 2.

Table 1: Test Masses

Mass Letter	Grams	Kilograms	Newtons
A	*50.* g	*0.050* kg	*0.49* N
B	*50.* g	*0.050* kg	*0.49* N
C	*100.* g	*0.100* kg	*0.981* N
D	*200.* g	*0.200* kg	*1.96* N

Preparation

The knife-edge clamps and the stand can be obtained at a reasonable cost from nearly all science supply companies. You will need three clamps per assembly. They come with wire hangers that are detachable. Note that the fulcrum for the lever system is a knife-edge clamp without a hanger attached. The standard masses can be obtained the same way, but they are fairly expensive. However, these sets can be used by many different subjects in all grade levels, so they are an essential item to have. They come with hooks or with slots. The hooks are better for this investigation because the mass of the hook is included in the stamped mass on the metal. The slotted masses require an additional hanger that must be factored into the mass calculations.

The entire assembly can be constructed of materials from around the house. The meter stick can be substituted with a plain piece of wood of similar dimensions. The knife-edge and support stand can be made from a 2 × 4 cut in a triangular shape. The hangers can be paper clips and the masses can be bundles of large washers, nut fasteners, or fishing weights.

Avoid using the really heavy masses (500 g or 1 kg) in the sets. If you must use them, you may have to modify the distances given in the trials.

The unknown mass can be any object that can be hooked to the apparatus and is less than about 900 g so that the apparatus will balance.

1. Caution your students
not to tighten the screws
too much on the knife-edge
clamps. This can damage
the meter sticks.

2. Observing SDs will make
this exercise more
meaningful. Not requiring
the use of SDs makes some
of the results trivial. The
Teacher's Edition answer
key shows the correct
number of SDs for the
recommended masses.

3. Be sure that students
report all measurements in
MKS units, that is, newtons,
meters, and kilograms.
Inform them that it is not
appropriate to mix newtons
and centimeters, for
instance.

4. We use the value of
g = 9.81 m/s² in order to
preserve an additional
significant digit in the
conversion of mass to
newtons.

5. The distances to the
fulcrum (d₁ and d₂) can be
quickly found as follows: If
using a meter stick and
assuming that it balanced at
50.0 cm, subtract 50.0 cm
from the higher-numbered
position measurement and
subtract the lower-
numbered position
measurement from 50.0 cm.
Review the precaution in
step 1 under Trial 1. If the
center of balance of the
meter stick alone is at 49.8
cm, for example, then that
value must be used instead
of 50.0 cm in these
determinations.

6. In the Experimental
Evaluation, we make some
simplifying statements to
help the students
understand the essentials of
torque. The calculation of
torque discussed in this
exercise gives only the
magnitude and not the

Trial 1—Using Two Equal Masses

1. Hang mass **A** 40.0 cm (0.400 m) to the left of the fulcrum. (Refer to Figure 2.) All masses that will produce Torque 1 (the resistance) in this and the following trials should be hung on the left side of the fulcrum.

2. In Table 2, multiply the weight of mass **A** by 0.400 m (d_1) to obtain the torque for mass **A**. Enter this value in the table under w_1d_1. Be sure to observe proper significant digits for all calculations if your teacher requires you to do so.

3. On the other side of the apparatus, hook mass **B** to the hanger and slide the hanger until the lever balances horizontally.

4. Measure the distance of mass **B** from the fulcrum to the nearest 0.1 cm. Convert the measurement to meters and record it in the column labeled d_2 for Trial 1. (**Note:** Record all distances in Table 2 in meters.)

5. Multiply the weight of mass **B** by d_2 to find the torque for mass **B** (the effort). Write this value in the column under w_2d_2 for Trial 1.

6. Carefully remove the masses from the lever arm.

Trial 2—Using Two Unequal Masses

1. Hang mass **C** at 20.0 cm (0.200 m) from the fulcrum. Assume that this is the *effort*. Calculate w_2d_2 for mass **C** and enter this value in Table 2 for Trial 2.

2. On the other side, hook mass **A** to the hanger and slide it until the lever balances horizontally.

3. Determine the distance d_1 for mass **A**. Complete Table 2 for Trial 2.

4. Remove the masses from the lever arm.

Trial 3—Using Specified Arms with Various Masses

1. Hang mass **D** at 30.0 cm (0.300 m) from the fulcrum. Calculate w_1d_1 for mass **D**.

2. On the other side of the lever, tighten the empty hanger 40.0 cm (0.400 m) from the fulcrum.

3. Experiment with various combinations of masses **A** through **C** until one is found that brings the lever into balance, or nearly so.

4. Record the mass letters under w_2 for Trial 3 and add the corresponding weights from Table 1. Write the total weight in the w_2 block.

5. Complete Table 2 for Trial 3.

6. Remove the masses from the lever arm.

Trial 4—Determining the Weight of the Unknown Mass

1. Hang mass **D** at 20.0 cm (0.200 m) from the fulcrum. Calculate $w_1 d_1$ for mass **D**.

2. On the opposite side, hook the unknown mass on the hanger and adjust its position until the lever system balances horizontally.

3. Record the distance of the unknown mass from the fulcrum under the d_2 column for Trial 4.

4. Since the lever system is in equilibrium, to what value must the torque $w_2 d_2$ be equal? _0.392 N·m (or the value of w₁d₁)_

5. Estimate the weight of the unknown mass using the law of moments as follows:

   law of moments: $w_1 d_1 = w_2 d_2$ weight of unknown $= w_2$

   solve for w_2: $w_2 = \dfrac{w_1 d_1}{d_2}$

   $w_2 = $ _Answers will vary depending on mass of unknown._

6. Complete Table 2 for the unknown mass.

orientation. Torques are actually computed from the cross product of the radius and force vectors. The direction of the torque vector is perpendicular to both of the other vectors, parallel to the axis of rotation. This is counter-intuitive and should not be stressed at this point.

7. Some textbooks give the units of torque as m·N to differentiate it from work (N·m or J).

8. Refer to the discussion of torque on page 315 in the margin notes of the Teacher's Edition of The Physical World that deals with a lever system where the fulcrum is not at the balance point of the lever alone.

9. Better results can be obtained by adding the mass of the recommended hanger to the metric masses listed in Table 1.

Results

Table 2: First-Class Levers

	Resistance Arm			Effort Arm		
Trial	w_1	d_1	$w_1 d_1$ Torque 1	w_2	d_2	$w_2 d_2$ Torque 2
1	0.49 N	0.400 m	0.20 N·m	0.49 N	~0.400 m	~0.20 N·m
2	0.49 N	~0.400 m	~0.196 N·m	0.981 N	0.200 m	0.196 N·m
3	1.96 N	0.300 m	0.588 N·m	A, C 1.47 N	0.400 m	~0.588 N·m
4	1.96 N	0.200 m	0.392 N·m	????	????	~0.392 N·m

Discussion Questions

1. What is the torque of the resistance arm in Trial 1? _0.20 N·m_

2. What is the torque of the effort arm in Trial 1? _0.20 N·m_

3. Compare the torque of the resistance and effort arms in the other trials. What does this comparison tell you about the law of moments? _When the lever is balanced (or in equilibrium), the torques of the effort and resistance arms are equal (in magnitude) (see question 13)._

4. What will happen if the torques are not equal? _The lever arm will rotate._

5. The mechanical advantage (M.A.) of a machine indicates how easy or hard it is to move the resistance. It is a measure of how much the simple machine multiplies the effort force. One way it can be determined is by finding the ratio of the resistance force to the effort force $\left(\text{M.A.} = \dfrac{R}{E}\right)$.

Find the M.A. for the levers in Table 2 of this investigation $\left(\text{M.A.} = \dfrac{w_1}{w_2}\right)$.

a. Trial 1 $\underline{M.A. = 1}$

b. Trial 2 $\underline{M.A. = 0.5}$

c. Trial 3 $\underline{M.A. \doteq 1.3}$

Notice that with first-class levers, the M.A. may be less than, greater than, or equal to 1, depending upon the position of the fulcrum. However, a first-class lever is not useful if its M.A. is less than 1.

6. Trial 1 corresponds to lever B in Figure 3, below, since the resistance arm and lever arm are the same length. The M.A. is _____1_____ (from question 5), which means that the lever does not make the resistance any easier or harder to move.

7. Trial 2 corresponds to lever C. The M.A. is [greater] ([less]) than 1, which means that the lever makes the resistance [easier] ([more difficult]) to move. (Circle the correct answers.)

8. Trial 3 corresponds to lever A, below. The M.A. is ([greater]) [less] than 1, which means that the lever makes the resistance ([easier]) [more difficult] to move.

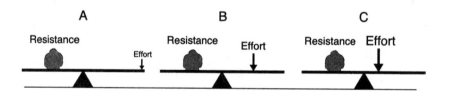

Figure 3: Various Combinations of Forces

9. The M.A. can also be found by comparing the effort arm (d_2) with the resistance arm (d_1). Give the M.A. for the trials using the ratio M.A. $= \dfrac{d_2}{d_1}$.

a. Trial 1 $\underline{M.A. = 1}$

b. Trial 2 $\underline{M.A. = 0.5}$

c. Trial 3 $\underline{M.A. \doteq 1.3}$

10. Compare these values to the values in question 5.

   a. What can be said about these two ratios (w_1/w_2 and d_2/d_1)?

   They are the same.

   b. Set up a proportion with these two ratios.
   $$\frac{w_1}{w_2} = \frac{d_2}{d_1}$$

   c. Cross-multiply the proportion.
   $$w_1 d_1 = w_2 d_2$$

   d. What do you call the resulting equation?

   The equation is called the law of moments.

Experimental Evaluation

11. Use Figure 2 for reference.

   a. In Trial 1, which direction would Torque 1 rotate the lever arm? *The lever arm would rotate counterclockwise.*

   b. In the same trial, which direction would Torque 2 rotate the arm? *The lever would rotate clockwise.*

   c. How do the magnitudes of the two torques in Trial 1 compare? *The magnitudes of the two torques are equal.*

   d. What do we call a quantity that has both magnitude and direction? *This kind of quantity is called a vector.*

   e. What kind of quantity is a torque? *Torque is a vector quantity.*

12. Your observations are recorded in Table 2. From these observations and the conclusion from question 11, what inferences can you make about the torques for a balanced lever? The torques on a balanced lever are _____*equal*_____ in magnitude but ___*opposite*___ in direction.

13. Theoretically, the torque of the resistance and effort arms should have been the same. Realistically, should you expect the two values to be identical? Explain. *Not necessarily. There are many factors that can vary the two torques, such as deviations in actual mass from the label, the additional mass of the hangers, non-uniform density of the meter stick along its length, and friction.*

14. This generalization can be applied to all levers, but can this be proved? Explain. *No, you would have to test every lever.*

   a. Can we achieve the second objective of this investigation? *No*

15. (Optional) What are the units of torque? *The units are N·m.*

   a. What other quantity have you learned about that has units of N·m?

   Work has units of N·m.

   b. Is this the same thing as torque? Explain your answer. *No, work is equal to the product of the force acting in the same direction as the object it is moving, while torque is the product of a force acting perpendicularly to a distance from a pivot.*

14B INVESTIGATION

Second- and Third-Class Levers

Objectives

The purpose of this exercise is to

1. Demonstrate the applicability of the law of moments to second- and third-class levers.

2. Determine the mechanical advantage of various lever systems.

Equipment

Knife-edge clamps, 4
Lever apparatus support
Meter stick
Metric mass set or equivalent
Spring balance, 10 N
Unknown masses

Introduction

Investigation 14A demonstrated the applicability of the law of moments to the first-class lever. The law of moments shows that the torque on one side of the fulcrum (w_1d_1) must be equal to, but in the opposite direction from, another torque (w_2d_2) if the lever arm is to be in equilibrium (motionless and balanced). Recall that torques are vector quantities, but the law of moments we use shows only the scalar values for these torques. This is an acceptable simplification for this level of instruction. The law of moments may be written in a more general form of $F_1d_1 = F_2d_2$. In this version, *any* force, not just a weight, acting perpendicular to a distance from a pivot or axis can create a torque. This is the principle by which an engine can apply rotational force to a drive shaft.

In the first-class lever, the torques are arranged on opposite sides of the fulcrum. In second- and third-class levers, however, the torques are both on the same side of the fulcrum. Does the law of moments still hold true in these cases? We will answer this question during this investigation.

Introduction

This investigation reinforces the principles introduced in Investigation 14A. Once the students have completed the exercise with first-class levers, they should be able to complete this one quickly. Remind students that one of the purposes of the laboratory exercises in this course is to give the students practice reading and following practical instructions. Students should be firmly corrected for improperly performing the investigation if their mistake followed an explicit explanation in the procedure. Many of the comments and recommendations from Investigation 14A are applicable to this lab. Demonstrate how a torque can be produced not only by a weight but by any kind of force.

To review the arrangements of the various classes of levers, examine Figure 1, below, and answer the following questions. Diagram A represents a first-class lever because the fulcrum is between the resistance and the effort. Diagram B represents a ____third____-class lever because the ____effort____ is between the ____fulcrum____ and the ____resistance____. Diagram C represents a ____second____-class lever because the ____resistance____ is between the ____fulcrum____ and the ____effort____.

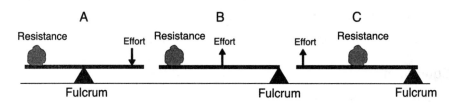

Figure 1

Pre-Laboratory Questions

Read the entire investigation. Answer the following questions prior to class on a separate sheet of paper. Use complete sentences.

1. In general, what is a torque?

2. Give an example of a torque you might use in your home.

3. How do you prepare the spring balance to measure force for this investigation?

4. What must you do in this investigation to compensate for the weight of the two hangers on the left side of the fulcrum?

5. Due to the construction of the third-class lever apparatus, what must be done differently from the other levers when taking data?

6. State a research question for this investigation.

Procedures

A. Assemble the Second-Class Lever Apparatus

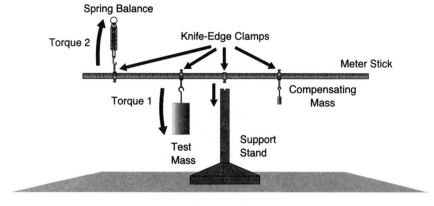

Figure 2

1. Obtain the equipment listed for this investigation and assemble the fulcrum clamp, the meter stick, and the stand according to Figure 2. Note that the fulcrum clamp does not have a mass hanger.

2. Balance the apparatus as you did in Investigation 14A. Gently tighten the clamp.

3. This investigation requires that both the resistance (Torque 1) and the effort (Torque 2) be on the same side of the fulcrum. Install the two knife-edge clamps on the left side of the fulcrum as shown in Figure 2. Do not tighten these clamps until required to do so in the following sections.

   a. What happened to the lever arm after you installed the clamps in step 3?
      The left end of the lever dropped.

   b. Is the lever arm in equilibrium at this point? Explain. *No, a lever in*
      equilibrium should be approximately horizontal.

4. Slide an additional clamp and hanger onto the right arm. This will be used to hang a compensating weight on the right arm to offset the additional weight of the two clamps/hangers on the left arm during the trials in the following sections.

5. Hold the spring balance vertically by the upper ring. Do not hook the balance to any weights for this check. Examine the location of the pointer compared to the zero point of the scale. If the pointer is not at zero, slide the scale up or down until the pointer is exactly on zero. This step is called *zeroing* the balance. Zeroing before taking a measurement is done for many kinds of scientific instruments.

B. Identify the Masses

1. Obtain the 500. g and the 200. g masses to be used in this investigation.

2. Write each mass in grams in the left column of Table 1. If the masses you are using are different from those listed, then substitute as required. Assume their masses are precise to the nearest gram.

3. Convert each mass to kilograms in the middle column.

4. Calculate their weights by multiplying by 9.81 N/kg and write this value in the right-hand column.

5. Write the weight for the 500. g mass in the F_1 column in Table 2 for Trials 1-3. Write the weight for the 200. g mass in the F_1 column in Table 3 for Trials 1-3.

Table 1: Test Masses

Grams	Kilograms	Newtons
500. g	*0.500* kg	*4.91* N
200. g	*0.200* kg	*1.96* N

Preparation

If your class is using metric mass sets, you should set aside the smallest masses for compensation masses. Spring balances should be the 10 N variety subdivided into 0.1 N. Larger capacity scales will work, but measuring precision will be lower. As with the previous investigation, you may use masses and equipment other than those specified in the procedure. Obtain unknown masses that can be hooked to the hangers. Their masses should be selected so that they do not overrange the spring balances. You should use different unknowns for Sections C and E.

General Comments

1. Spot check to ensure that the students are using the compensating masses to balance the lever arms correctly.

2. Encourage the students to use proper SDs when calculating their answers. Make a few practice calculations on the board to review.

3. The last two questions review the nature of science. The purpose of science is not necessarily to determine the truth of a law or theory but how well it works. All that is required of a law is that it consistently predicts behavior with an agreed amount of accuracy. Einstein's theory of relativity revised many of the laws in physics, but these revisions are frequently not used because the older laws are simpler to understand and are more than adequate for common everyday situations.

C. Second-Class Lever Trials

Trial 1

1. Slide the mass hanger closest to the fulcrum on the **left** arm to a point 10.0 cm (0.100 m) from the fulcrum. Gently tighten the clamp. If the meter stick did not balance with the fulcrum exactly at the 50.0 cm mark, do not simply clamp the hanger at the 40.0 cm (or 60.0 cm) mark but measure 10.0 cm from the actual balance point.

2. Slide the outermost clamp (with the hanger on top) on the **left** arm to a position 40.0 cm (0.400 m) from the fulcrum and tighten the clamp.

3. Note that the lever arm is not in equilibrium. Hook a 10 g mass on the **right-hand hanger** and slide it to a position where the lever is balanced. If a 10 g mass cannot balance the lever with the clamp at the extreme right end of the lever, balance the lever with the next larger mass.

4. With the clamps in position and the lever balanced, hook a 500. g mass to the inner hanger and the spring balance to the outer hanger on the left arm as in Figure 2.

5. Lift the spring balance until it is supporting the left arm of the lever. The 500. g mass must be off of the table, and the lever should be approximately horizontal.

6. Read the spring scale force in newtons to one-tenth of the smallest (decimal) graduation. Record this value as F_2 in Table 2 for Trial 1.

7. Unhook all masses and the spring scale from the lever.

8. Calculate Torque 1 and Torque 2 by multiplying the corresponding weights and lever arms. Record the results in Table 2 for Trial 1.

Trial 2

1. Loosen the left-most clamp and slide it to a point 30.0 cm (0.300 m) from the fulcrum and tighten.

2. Hook the compensating mass on the right-hand hanger and adjust its position until the lever arm balances. Tighten the clamp.

3. Hook the 500. g mass and the spring balance to the hangers as in Figure 2 and record the force needed to lift the left end of the lever arm to the equilibrium position as in Trial 1.

4. Record this value as F_2 in Table 2 for Trial 2.

5. Unhook all masses and the spring scale from the lever.

6. Complete Table 2 for Trial 2.

Trial 3

1. Loosen the left-most clamp and slide it to a point 20.0 cm (0.200 m) from the fulcrum and tighten.

2. Repeat the remaining steps as before for Trial 1.

3. Unhook all masses and the spring scale from the lever.

4. Complete Table 2 for Trial 3.

Trial 4 (Unknown Weight)

1. Loosen the left-most clamp and slide it to a point 40.0 cm (0.400 m) from the fulcrum and tighten.

2. Balance the lever arm as before.

3. Hook the unknown mass to the innermost hanger on the left arm.

4. Hook the spring balance to the outermost hanger as before and measure the force necessary to lift the lever arm to equilibrium. Record this as F_2 for Trial 4 in Table 2.

5. Determine the weight of the unknown.

   a. Calculate the magnitude of Torque 2 (F_2d_2). *Answers will vary.*

   b. If the lever was in equilibrium, what must be true about the *magnitudes* of Torque 1 and Torque 2? *The two torques must be equal in magnitude.*

   c. Write an equation that will allow you to solve for the weight of the unknown. $F_1d_1 = F_2d_2$; *accept an equation with the actual values substituted in this formula.*

   d. Solve for F_1 in Trial 4. *Answers will vary depending on the weight of the unknown.*

D. Results—Second-Class Levers

Table 2: Second-Class Levers

	Resistance Arm			Effort Arm		
Trial	F_1	d_1	F_1d_1 Torque 1	F_2	d_2	F_2d_2 Torque 2
1	4.91 N	0.100 m	0.491 N·m	~1.2(3) N	0.400 m	~0.491 N·m
2	4.91 N	0.100 m	0.491 N·m	~1.6(4) N	0.300 m	~0.491 N·m
3	4.91 N	0.100 m	0.491 N·m	~2.4(6) N	0.200 m	~0.491 N·m
4	???? N	0.100 m	???? N·m	???? N	0.400 m	???? N·m

E. Third-Class Levers

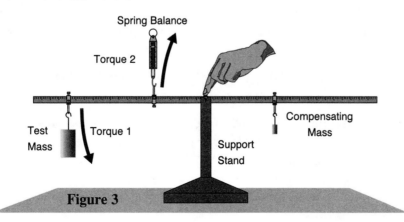

Spring Balance

Torque 2

Test Mass

Torque 1

Support Stand

Compensating Mass

Figure 3

Assemble the Apparatus

1. Rearrange the lever apparatus by swapping the positions of the hanger clips on the left-hand clamps. The hanger of the innermost clamp should be on top of the meter stick, and the left-most hanger should be below the meter stick.

2. The 200. g mass will be used for the known mass trials in this section.

Trial 1

1. Position the left-most hanger at 40.0 cm (0.400 m) from the fulcrum. Position the inner hanger at 10.0 cm (0.100 m) from the fulcrum.

2. Balance the lever with the compensating mass as before in Section C.

3. Hook the 200. g mass to the outermost hanger on the left. Hook the spring scale to the innermost hanger. See Figure 3.

4. Place a fingertip on the fulcrum clamp directly above the support stand. As you raise the spring scale to lift the lever arm, you will need to press down on the fulcrum just enough to prevent it from pulling out of the support. Do not exert so much force that you twist the lever arm with your finger.

5. Note the force on the spring scale required to lift the lever arm. Record as F_2 in Table 3 for Trial 1.

6. Unhook all masses and the spring scale from the lever.

7. Complete Table 3 for Trial 1.

Trial 2

1. Position the innermost hanger on the left to a point 20.0 cm (0.200 m) from the fulcrum.

2. Repeat the remaining steps as before in Trial 1 of this section.

3. Complete Table 3 for Trial 2.

Trial 3

1. Position the innermost hanger on the left to a point 30.0 cm (0.300 m) from the fulcrum.

2. Repeat the remaining steps as before in Trial 1 of this section.

3. Complete Table 3 for Trial 3.

Trial 4 (Unknown weight)

1. Position the innermost clamp on the left to a point 20.0 cm (0.200 m) from the fulcrum.

2. Balance the lever arm as before with the compensating mass.

3. Hook the unknown mass to the left-most hanger.

4. Hook the spring balance to the innermost hanger as before and measure the force necessary to lift the lever arm to equilibrium. Record this as F_2 for Trial 4 in Table 3.

5. Determine the weight of the unknown.

   a. Calculate the magnitude of Torque 2 ($F_2 d_2$). _Answers will vary._

   b. Solve for F_1 in Trial 4 as in Section C. _Answers will vary depending_
   on the weight of the unknown.

F. Results—Third-Class Levers

Table 3: Third-Class Levers

	Resistance Arm			Effort Arm		
Trial	F_1	d_1	$F_1 d_1$ Torque 1	F_2	d_2	$F_2 d_2$ Torque 2
1	_1.96_ N	0.400 m	_0.784_ N·m	_~7.8(4)_ N	0.100 m	_~0.784_ N·m
2	_1.96_ N	0.400 m	_0.784_ N·m	_~3.9(2)_ N	0.200 m	_~0.784_ N·m
3	_1.96_ N	0.400 m	_0.784_ N·m	_~2.6(1)_ N	0.300 m	_~0.784_ N·m
4	_????_ N	0.400 m	_????_ N·m	_????_ N	0.200 m	_????_ N·m

Discussion Questions

1. The mechanical advantage (M.A.) of a machine indicates how easy or hard it is to move the resistance. One way M.A. can be determined is by finding the ratio of the resistance to the effort. In this investigation, the ratio would be F_1/F_2. Complete the following table to determine the M.A. of second- and third-class levers using the forces recorded in Tables 2 and 3.

Table 4: Mechanical Advantage

Trial	Second-Class M.A.	Third-Class M.A.
1	_3.9(8)–4.0(0)_	_0.25(0)_
2	_2.9(9)_	_0.50(0)_
3	_2.0(0)_	_0.75(1)_

The digit in parentheses is significant.

   a. The mechanical advantage of a second-class lever is always ___greater___ than one. This means that using a second-class lever to raise an object is [harder] (easier) than simply picking it up.

   b. The mechanical advantage of a third-class lever is always ___less___ than one. This means that using a third-class lever to raise an object is (harder) [easier] than simply picking it up.

2. In the investigations with levers we were concerned with weight (or force) applied to the levers instead of mass.

   a. What is the difference between weight and mass? _Mass is a measure of the quantity of matter in an object, while weight is the force of gravitational attraction for the matter in an object._

   b. Why was force (i.e., weight) used in this investigation instead of mass? _The law of moments shows that the magnitudes of two opposing torques must be equal. To calculate torques, one must know the force acting on the lever arm. (See Investigation 14A.)_

3. Review the values of the resistance torques compared to the effort torques in Tables 2 and 3. How do their magnitudes compare? _Their magnitudes were equal._

4. Since the lever arm was in equilibrium for each trial, compare the directions of the resistance and effort torques. _The two torques are in opposite directions._

5. Examine the apparatus for the third-class lever test in Figure 3. Can you explain why it is necessary to hold down the fulcrum during the test? (Hint: Compare the downward force exerted by the test mass compared to the upward force exerted by the spring balance.) _The spring balance is exerting an upward force several times as large as the weight of the test mass. If the lever fulcrum was not held in place, the whole apparatus would be lifted together instead of just rotating the lever arm around the fulcrum._

Experimental Evaluation

6. Would it be possible to prove that the law of moments applies *exactly* to any given lever? Explain your answer. _No, you would have to make exact measurements, which is not possible. (See the investigations from Chapter 3.)_

7. (Optional) If you have not done so, read page 330 of your textbook. Discuss why it is not critically important that a law of science such as the law of moments produce exact results. _Answers will vary. Students should include the idea that scientific principles are often simplified to make them more understandable or useful. Point out to your students when reviewing this exercise that the law of moments as presented here concerns only the magnitudes of the vectors involved—the directions are intuitively understood._

8. (Optional) Scientific laws are used to predict various effects, but they do not explain what causes these effects. For example, the law of gravity can be used to predict the motion of most of the planets around the sun, but it says nothing about why the sun attracts the planets or how that attraction reaches to the planet. From questions 6 and 7, write in your own words two limitations of the laws of science. _____

a. Scientific laws can give only approximate answers; they are limited by the precision of measurement.

b. Laws do not explain the "why" of a phenomenon; they just describe it.

Second- and Third-Class Levers

Name _____

Date _____ Hour _____

Objectives

The purpose of this exercise is to

1. Demonstrate the mechanical advantage of an inclined plane.

2. Gain practice in mathematically solving for variables in a formula.

3. Investigate the behavior of physical quantities as a limit is approached.

Materials

Masking tape
String

Equipment

Board
Kinetic cart
Metric masses
Metric ruler
Spring balance (20 N)

Introduction

One of the most useful simple machines is the inclined plane. This has been in use since the earliest days of human history. It was used to construct huge structures such as the pyramids. It can be found in edge tools and weapons such as chisels and war axes. It was used by the American pioneers to fell trees and then to split the wood with wedges. Every screw and bolt has an inclined plane wrapped around a cylinder or cone. The inclined plane works by supporting some of the load as the load is moved through a distance by the effort. The more of the load that the inclined plane takes, the easier it is to move.

Simple machines are useful because they boost the effects of the user's efforts. This is called mechanical advantage (M.A.). As we have shown in previous investigations, you can find the M.A. of a machine by dividing the resistance force by the effort force $\left(\text{M.A.} = \dfrac{R}{E}\right)$. In a basic inclined plane, you would divide the weight of the object you were moving up the plane by the effort it took to move it. Inclined planes exhibit another rule that applies to all simple machines—the distance principle. This rule states that when using a simple machine, the reduction in the amount of force required to move a resistance is accompanied by a proportionately larger distance that the effort must act through. For an inclined plane, the M.A. can be calculated by dividing the length of the plane by the vertical distance that is gained as you move from the bottom to the top of the plane $\left(\text{M.A.} = \dfrac{L}{h}\right)$. For example, if a ramp is 3 m long and you rise 1 m as you walk from one end to the other, then the M.A. is $\dfrac{3 \, \text{m}}{1 \, \text{m}} = 3$. Once you know the M.A. of a specific inclined plane, you can use that

Introduction

The material presented is a reinforcement of the text material on inclined planes and mechanical advantage. A key concept to emphasize in this investigation is that the length of the inclined plane is measured along the surface of the ramp, not the length parallel to the ground. This may seem to be intuitively obvious, but many students get it wrong when they begin to apply trigonometric principles in more advanced courses. Another factor to address is that the forces "to move the load along the ramp" are calculated assuming no friction and that the loads are moving at constant velocity. Forces are higher (often much higher) in real world situations.

information to predict the effort required to move the resistance. In the example above, if the load to be moved is 150 lb., then the effort will be only 50 lb. $\left(E = \dfrac{R}{M.A.}\right)$, ignoring friction.

In this investigation, we will be using the experimental principles you have learned in the past to demonstrate the mechanical advantage of the inclined plane and exploring some mathematical properties of these relationships.

Pre-Laboratory Questions

Read the entire investigation. Answer the following questions prior to class on a separate sheet of paper. Use complete sentences.

1. Give two methods for determining the mechanical advantage of an inclined plane.

2. What is the rule that relates the magnitude of the effort and the distance it must act through in order to move the resistance?

3. If the M.A. of a ramp is 4 and its length is 12 m, what is the height of the ramp?

4. If an object weighs 400 N, how much effort will it take to push it up the ramp in question 3?

5. What are the units of M.A.?

6. In this investigation, does the kinetic cart have to be moving in order to demonstrate the mechanical advantage of the inclined plane? Explain your answer.

7. Why is it a good idea to average several readings of the same measurement together when collecting data?

8. If an inclined plane rises 2 m and is 4 m long, then it can be said that for every meter of upward motion, you must move <u>?</u> m along the inclined plane.

Procedures

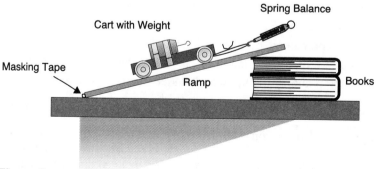

Figure 1

A. Setup

1. Tape a 1000. g mass to a kinetic cart using masking tape.

   In the next step, you will measure the weight of the cart and mass. One or two other individuals should make the same measurement without sharing the results until all have made the measurement. This ensures independence of the measurements and avoids bias. Use this method whenever the instructions say to independently make a measurement.

2. Zero the 20 N spring balance as discussed in Investigation 14B. Carefully hook the cart to the balance and measure the weight of the cart and mass to the nearest 0.1 N.

   a. If the cart does not have a convenient way to hook to the balance, tie some string around an axle in a loop and hook the balance into the loop. Make the loop large enough so that it extends beyond the end of the cart.

   b. Record the weights in the blanks:

   Your measurement: _____

   Partner 1 measurement: _____

   Partner 2 measurement: _____

   Average: _____

   c. Write the average weight in every blank in the "Cart Weight" column in the data table.

3. Independently measure the length of the board to be used as a ramp to the nearest 0.01 cm.

   a. After your partners have measured the board, enter the values in the blanks below and find their average.

   Your measurement: _____

   Partner 1 measurement: _____

   Partner 2 measurement: _____

   Average: _____

   b. Write the average measurement in every blank in the "Ramp Length" column in the data table.

4. When setting up the ramp, it is important to ensure that it does not move during the measurements. If this happens, the height will change, making the data invalid. Tightly roll up several lengths of masking tape so that the sticky surface is outward. Press the rolls of masking tape firmly onto the table along the base of the ramp. This will prevent the ramp from sliding away from the books.

Preparation

Equipment: All of these are used in physics courses.

1. Ramps can be made from 1 × 4 or 1 × 6 lumber cut to approximately 1.2 m lengths; $\frac{1}{2}$ or $\frac{5}{8}$ inch plywood is less likely to warp with age and can be easily cut to any width and length to conserve materials. Store planks flat when not in use.

2. Kinetic carts from science suppliers are ideal, but any wheeled object such as a roller skate, a toy wagon, or a truck can be used as long as its wheels rotate freely.

3. The metric mass sets can be substituted with lead shot or fishing sinkers, bricks, or stones.

4. The spring balances are essential, but they can be substituted with other types of portable scales such as those for weighing fish. Precision is generally lower with these, and the scales sold in the United States are usually in English units. You should strive to do all labs in metric units. Use of English units will require unit conversion. The balances must have a large enough capacity to weigh the cart with the 1 kg mass taped to it.

If your school has rigid apparatus supports and clamps, use of these will eliminate the need for step 5.

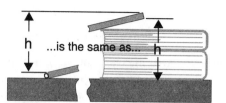

Figure 2

B. Trial 1

1. Set up the ramp on a stack of two books as in Figure 1. If the table has a square edge along its top surface, place the ramp parallel to and right at the edge of the table. This will make measuring the height easier.

2. Independently measure the height of the ramp perpendicular to the tabletop. Since the bottom surface of the ramp rests on the table, it is easier to measure the height from the tabletop to the underside of the raised end of the ramp. See Figure 2, above.

   a. Examine the lower end of your metric ruler before making this measurement. If there is a metal end cap on the meter stick or if the end has been damaged, measuring from the end will not give you an accurate measurement. Place a convenient mark on the meter stick such as 10.00 cm at the tabletop and measure from that point to the underside of the ramp. Subtract 10.00 cm from your reading to find the height.

   b. If the procedure in a. is not possible because the table has a rounded edge and your ruler's scale cannot be accurately read at the end, measure the height of the **upper** surface at the *base* of the ramp and the **upper** surface at the *top* of the ramp. Subtract the first measurement from the second to obtain the height.

   c. After your partners have measured the ramp height, enter the values in the blanks below and find their average.

   Your measurement: _____

   Partner 1 measurement: _____

   Partner 2 measurement: _____

   Average: _____

   d. Write the average measurement in the blank in the "Ramp Height" column for Trial 1 in the data table.

3. Find the M.A. of the ramp by dividing the ramp length by its height $\left(\text{M.A.} = \dfrac{L}{h} \right)$. Observe correct significant digits (SDs) if your teacher requires; otherwise, report the result to the nearest tenths place. Write this value in M.A. column for Trial 1 in the data table.

4. Estimate the effort required to hold the cart in equilibrium on the ramp using the M.A. determined in step 3. Recall from the introduction that $E = \dfrac{R}{\text{M.A.}}$. Divide the weight of the cart by the M.A. and enter this value in the "Predicted Effort" column for Trial 1 in the data table.

5. Independently measure the effort to hold the cart in equilibrium on the ramp. Place the cart on the middle of the ramp, hook the spring balance to the cart or the loop of string, and measure the force to the nearest 0.1 N.

a. After your partners have measured the effort, enter the values in the blanks below and find their average.

Your measurement: _____

Partner 1 measurement: _____

Partner 2 measurement: _____

Average: _____

b. Write the average measurement in the block under "Measured Effort" for Trial 1 in the data table.

C. Additional Trials

1. More trials can be taken using additional books. Repeat steps 1-5 under Trial 1 for taking and recording data.

2. If there is time, you may want to try the extreme cases of the ramp horizontal and the ramp vertical. These situations will be considered in the discussion questions.

Results

Data: Inclined Planes

Trial	Cart Weight	Ramp Length	Ramp Height	M.A.	Predicted Effort	Measured Effort
1						
2						
3						
4						
5						

Discussion Questions

1. Answer the following questions by referring to Figure 3.

a. What is the M.A. of the inclined plane? _The M.A. is 2._

b. Based on your answer in part *a,* for every meter that the load moves vertically, the load moves ___2___ m along the ramp.

c. If the height of the ramp were 10 m, what would be the length of the ramp? _The length would be 20 m._

d. If it requires 1000. N of force to move a load along the ramp, what would be the weight of the load? _The weight of the load would be_

_2000. N._

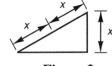

Figure 3

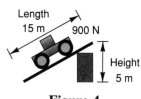

Figure 4

2. Answer the following questions by referring to Figure 4.

   a. What is the M.A. of the ramp? *The M.A. is 3.*

   b. In other words, for every 1 m the cart moves vertically, it moves _____*3*_____ m along the ramp.

   c. How much force would be required to hold the cart stationary on the ramp? *It would require 300. N to hold the cart stationary on the ramp.*

   d. How much work would be required to lift the cart vertically 5.0 m? ($W = F \cdot d$) *W = 900. N × 5.0 m = 4500 J*

   e. How much work would be required to push the cart 15 m along the ramp with 300. N of force? *W = 300. N × 15 m = 4500 J*

   f. Does the ramp reduce the work required to move the cart a certain vertical distance? Explain your answer. *No, the amount of work required to lift the cart and push it along the ramp to a point 5 m above its original position is the same.*

   g. What does the ramp reduce? *The ramp reduces the effort to move the cart.*

   h. What does the ramp increase when moving the cart? *It increases the distance the cart must be moved.*

4. (Optional) It is sometimes instructive to examine extreme cases, and you may have tested these in Part C of the Procedures, above. Let us examine the case when the inclined plane is vertical.

   a. If the ramp is vertical (length of the ramp equals the height of movement), what would be the M.A.? *The M.A. would be 1.* If you were to move a 1000. N load up this "ramp," you would use a *1000. N* effort.

   b. Is there any advantage to using a vertical ramp? *No, the effort is equal to the weight of the load.*

Chapter 14

5. (Optional) Suppose the ramp is horizontal. (The change in height from one

   end to the other is zero.)

   a. The M.A. of a 15 m ramp would be __$\frac{15\ m}{0\ m}$__. Does this value exist?

      ___No___

   b. To avoid dividing by zero, you can examine the M.A. as the height becomes smaller and smaller. Calculate the M.A. in the following cases. What will happen to the M.A. when the height becomes extremely small, so small that you cannot measure it any more ($h = 0$)?

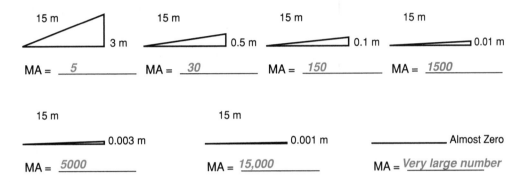

MA = __5__   MA = __30__   MA = __150__   MA = __1500__

MA = __5000__   MA = __15,000__   MA = __Very large number__

   c. Does a horizontal ramp provide any advantage to lift a load? _No, the_
      load is not lifted with a horizontal ramp.

Experimental Evaluation

6. Is it possible to obtain an exact measurement for the length of the board?
   No, all measurements involve approximations and estimates.

7. (Optional) Why would the force required to move the cart up the ramp at a constant speed be slightly larger than the force required to hold the cart still on the ramp? Give one of two possible reasons. _When the cart is_
   stationary, all forces are in equilibrium. In order to get it moving, it must be
   accelerated, which requires an unbalanced force. This force will be larger
   than the force required to hold it still. In addition, to keep the cart moving at
   constant speed, the force must be large enough to overcome the friction of
   movement. This will also be larger than the force required to hold the cart
   stationary.

Inclined Planes

15A TEACHER DEMONSTRATION

Pressure

Objectives

The purpose of this exercise is to demonstrate

1. The presence and effects of atmospheric pressure.

2. The relationship of water pressure to depth.

3. Some properties of flowing fluids.

Introduction

This exercise is based on the material presented in your textbook. You should recall that *pressure* is defined as the amount of force applied over a certain area (force/area). The SI unit for pressure is called the **pascal** (Pa). One pascal is equal to one newton per square meter ($1 \text{ Pa} = 1 \text{ N/m}^2$).

Demonstrations

I. Pressure

A. Air Pressure

Would you allow someone to place 14,000 lb. of weight on you? You probably wouldn't. Believe it or not, however, this is approximately the force of normal air pressure on an average-sized person. The total force that the air exerts on you can be calculated by multiplying the atmospheric pressure (air pressure at sea level is 14.7 lb./in.^{2}) by the number of square inches of your surface area (skin). This force does not crush us because God designed our bodies to function under these conditions. The matter in our bodies exerts a pressure in the outward direction equal to the force of the atmosphere pressing in on us. As long as these forces are balanced, we feel no ill effects. The pressures are said to be in a state of equilibrium. You probably have noted air pressure changes in your ears or sinuses. These sensations occur when the pressures on opposite sides of membranes in your body are not in equilibrium.

The relationships between gas pressure, temperature, and volume are described by two equations known as Boyle's law and Charles's law. You will be studying these laws in more detail in a later exercise. Boyle's law states that as the pressure exerted on a sample of gas increases, the volume will decrease, assuming constant temperature. In other words, a gas can be compressed by exerting pressure on it. Charles's law states that as the temperature of a sample of gas increases, its volume will increase, assuming constant pressure. These two laws acting together can produce dramatic effects on sealed objects containing a gas. For example, if the internal pressure of a non-rigid sealed object is raised because the temperature increases, the volume of the object will tend to increase.

Introduction

These demonstrations can be performed all in one class period or interspersed throughout the lectures on this chapter. The problems at the end are designed to familiarize students with the Pascal unit of pressure.

Materials

  Aluminum can
  Balloon, 10 inch
  Hard-boiled egg
  Hose
  Paper
  Soda bottle, 2-liter (2)
  Tape
  Thread

Equipment

  Beaker, 1000 mL
  Bunsen burner
  Dishpan
  Dowel rod
  Eyedropper
  Flask
  Hot mitt
  Knife edge clamp
  Meter stick
  Paper clips
  Support stand

Demonstration Procedures

In order to save class time, practice the following procedures ahead of time to ensure that they work!

I. Pressure

<u>*Suction*</u>

1. Preparation: Hard boil an egg and peel it prior to class. Keep the egg refrigerated.

2. Use a wide-mouthed Erlenmeyer flask whose aperture is just slightly smaller than the egg.

3. Drop a piece of burning paper into the flask and immediately place the hard-boiled egg in the mouth of the flask. The flame should go out, and the egg should slip into the flask as the gas inside the flask cools.

<u>*Crush the Can*</u>

1. Place about 30 cm³ (2 Tbsp.) of water into an empty aluminum soda can.

2. Heat the can over a Bunsen burner until the water boils and you see steam emerging from the top.

3. Using a hot mitt, immediately plunge the can upside down into a bowl containing 2 quarts of ice water. The purpose is to very quickly cool the metal sides of the can so that the steam inside will condense. As the volume of the gas decreases with the temperature, the sides of the can should crumple inward. You should see the effect immediately.

4. This demonstration doesn't always work the first time. Test it ahead of time to make sure you are familiar with the timing necessary to produce good results. If the can is not cooled quickly enough, the sides won't crumple and you will end up with a can half-full of ice water.

5. A more reliable demonstration uses a screw-top metal container such as a maple syrup can or brake fluid can that has been

1. **"Suction"**   Observe as your teacher performs the demonstration with the flask and the hard-boiled egg.

a What did the teacher do? <u>He placed a piece of burning paper in the</u> <u>bottom of the flask and placed a hard-boiled egg over the mouth of the</u> <u>flask.</u>

b. What happened? <u>The flame went out, and the egg slipped down</u> <u>inside the flask.</u>

c. Explain the results. <u>The burning paper heated the air inside the flask.</u> <u>The air expanded and flowed by the egg. After the flame went out, the</u> <u>egg created an airtight seal. The air inside the flask cooled and the</u> <u>pressure decreased, causing a higher pressure on the egg outside the</u> <u>flask than inside the flask. Eventually the pressure difference became</u> <u>great enough to force the egg through the mouth into the flask.</u>

2. **Crush the Can**   Observe as your teacher performs the demonstration with the aluminum can.

a. What did the teacher do? <u>He boiled water in the can and then turned it</u> <u>upside down in a container of ice water.</u>

b. What happened? <u>The can collapsed and was crushed.</u>

c. Explain the results. <u>When the water was boiling in the can, the air</u> <u>inside the can was also heated. When the can was turned over and</u> <u>placed in the ice water, the air inside the can was trapped and cooled</u> <u>very quickly. As the air cooled, the pressure decreased. The sides</u> <u>crushed in because the air pressure outside the can was greater.</u>

B. Air Pressure and Density

The density of an object determines whether it will float or sink in a fluid. If the density of the object is greater than the surrounding fluid, it will sink.

1. ***Atmospheric Buoyancy*** Observe as your teacher performs the demonstration with the balloon and the meter stick.

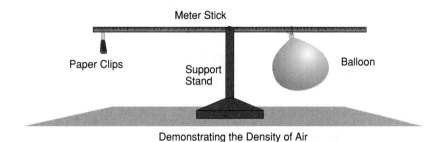

Meter Stick

Paper Clips

Support Stand

Balloon

Demonstrating the Density of Air

a. What did the teacher do? _First, he balanced an uninflated balloon on a meter stick balance with some paper clips. He then blew up the balloon, deflated it, and once again balanced the meter stick apparatus with the deflated balloon. He blew the balloon up again, tied it, and attached it to the balance._

b. What happened? _The side of the balance with the inflated balloon dropped._

c. How do you think the density of the air inside the balloon compared to the density of the air in the room? _The elastic balloon compressed the air inside of it slightly, making the air inside denser than the air outside in the room._

d. Explain the results. _Because it is denser, the sample of air inside the balloon has a greater weight than the quantity of the room air that it is displacing. The buoyant force of the room air is not great enough to hold it up, and it sinks._

e. Discuss why good experimental design required that your teacher inflate the balloon, deflate it, and place it on the balance before he performed the demonstration? _This step showed that the simple act of blowing up the balloon did not change the weight of the balloon in any way. This is a control._

thoroughly cleaned. Boil the water as before. Remove the heat; then screw the cap on and pour cool water over the can. It will crumple before your eyes.

Atmospheric Buoyancy

1. Attach a knife-edge clamp to a meter stick at the middle and place it on a support stand. Adjust the clamp's position until the stick balances. Check to ensure that there is enough clearance between the horizontal meter stick and the table for the inflated balloon to hang freely.

2. Attach an uninflated balloon to a piece of thread with a piece of tape and tape the other end of the thread to the meter stick 20 cm from the middle. Attach enough paper clips or other small weights to the other side of the balance with a loop of thread so that the balance is level. Tape the loop of thread to the meter stick so that it won't shift. The position of the weights on the stick is not important as long as it balances the weight of the balloon.

3. Remove the balloon and inflate it, without tying it off. Deflate it and reattach it to the balance to show that merely blowing up the balloon does not add any weight to the balloon.

4. Remove the balloon, inflate it almost completely, tie the end off, and reattach it to the thread with a piece of tape. The side with the balloon should descend.

Cartesian Diver

1. Fill an empty 2-liter soda bottle nearly full of water. It is essential that whatever bottle you use be flexible so that you can squeeze it.

2. Mark an eyedropper in 0.5 cm increments and fill it $\frac{1}{3}$–$\frac{1}{2}$ full of water. Test the buoyancy of the eyedropper in a large beaker full of water. The eyedropper should float in an upright position with the top of the dropper at or just below the surface of the water. If it floats too high out of the water, add more water to the dropper until you have it right.

3. Place the eyedropper into the water in the 2-L bottle and screw the cap on tightly.

4. Squeeze the bottle. As the pressure on the air inside the bottle increases, more water is forced into the eyedropper, compressing the air inside the diver. The level of the water in the eyedropper will rise, and the eyedropper will drop to the bottom of the bottle. The density of the eyedropper is related to the volume of the dropper and the weight of the dropper. The volume of the dropper includes the physical dropper itself plus the trapped air inside the dropper. As you squeeze the bottle, the mass of the dropper does not change but its volume decreases, increasing its density. The dropper sinks when it becomes denser than the surrounding water.

5. Release the pressure on the bottle. The effects will reverse themselves.

6. Fill the bottle to the top with water and repeat the demonstration. The experiment will work with just a little pressure

2. ***Cartesian Diver***   Observe as your teacher performs the demonstration with the Cartesian diver.

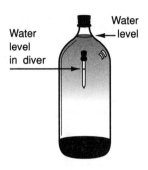

a. What did the teacher do? *He squeezed the plastic bottle and then released it.*

b. What happened? *The eyedropper sank to the bottom of the bottle. When he released the pressure on the bottle, the eyedropper rose to the top again.*

c. How did the density of the eyedropper change when the teacher squeezed the bottle? *The density of the eyedropper increased until it was greater than the density of the water.*

d. Explain the results. *As he squeezed the bottle, the pressure in the bottle increased. This forced more water into the eyedropper by compressing the air in the dropper bulb. As more water was forced into the eyedropper, its density increased until it was heavier than the water and it sank to the bottom. When the pressure was released, the air in the bulb expanded causing the water level in the eyedropper to decrease. The density of the dropper decreased below the water's density, and it floated back to the top.*

II. *Water Height and Gravity*

The pressure in a body of water differs according to the depth at which you measure the pressure in the water. The water molecules at the surface of the liquid experience only the pressure of the air above them. The water molecules at the bottom of the body of water are under more pressure because they experience the weight of all of the water molecules above them as well as the air pressure above the water. The pressure experienced is directly related to the height of the water above that point. This increase in pressure is one reason that water towers are built on hills and usually have leg supports to raise the tanks even higher. This is also why submarines can be crushed if they go below a certain depth.

1. **Deeper Means Higher**   Observe as your teacher pulls the tape off the plastic bottle.

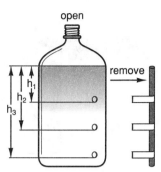

open

remove

a. Describe the bottle used in this demonstration. _It was a plastic bottle_ _with three holes arranged vertically from top to bottom._

b. What did your teacher do? _He unscrewed the cap and pulled the tape_ _off all three of the holes at the same time using a stick attached to the_ _three pieces of tape._

c. Describe what happened. _Water flowed out of the holes. The water_ _flowed slowest out of the top hole and fastest out of the bottom hole._

d. Explain the results. _Rate of flow is directly related to the pressure of the_ _water. The lower pressure at the top generated a lower flow, higher_ _pressure at the bottom of the bottle generated a higher flow, and the_ _middle hole was intermediate in both pressure and flow rate._

e. If your teacher had turned the bottle on its side before taking off the tapes, would the results have been the same? Explain. _No, all of the_ _holes would have been the same distance from the surface of the water, so_ _the water would have flowed out of all three holes at the same rate._

because the incompressible liquid transmits the pressure directly to the dropper instead of compressing the air at the top of the bottle.

II. Water Height and Gravity
Deeper Means Higher

1. Use a pencil to bore three small holes in an empty 2-liter soft drink bottle. Make sure the holes are all the same size. They should lie in a straight and vertical line with the holes 3 cm, 15 cm, and 27 cm from the bottom of the bottle.

2. Lay a dowel rod next to the holes and place pieces of strong tape over each hole and around the rod. When you pull on the rod during the demonstration, you want to uncover all three holes simultaneously.

3. Fill the bottle with water until the surface is 3 cm above the top hole.

4. Remove the cap; then simultaneously uncover the holes by pulling on the rod.

5. You could repeat this experiment, turning the bottle on its side so that all the holes are at the bottom of the water column. Keep the cap screwed on tightly.

1. Fill a dishpan with water and place it on the table.

2. Using another water source, fill a length of laboratory tubing or a hose completely with water. Keep your thumbs over both ends of the tube.

3. Place one end of the hose in the water in the pan and remove your thumb from that end. If you want to wait to begin the demonstration, have an assistant place a pinch clamp at the top bend of the tubing. Place the other end of the hose in an empty 1000 mL beaker placed on a chair or on the floor. Remove your thumb from that end (and unclamp the top end) when you want to begin the demonstration. Keep the top end submerged at all times.

4. When the lower beaker or container is nearly full, raise it above the level of the dishpan and have the students observe the siphon reversing directions. Do not let any air enter the tubing during the demonstration.

5. Demonstrate that changing the difference in height between the two containers changes the flow rate.

2. ***The Lower It Goes, the Faster It Flows***   Observe as your teacher demonstrates the use of a siphon.

a. Describe the apparatus used in this demonstration. *The apparatus consists of a long tube filled with water, one end of which was placed in a pan of water on the table with the other end emptying into a container placed below the level of the table.*

b. What happened? *The water flowed out of the pan through the tube and emptied into the other container.*

c. Explain the results.

(1) What kind of energy is associated with the height of an object? *Potential energy is associated with the height or condition of an object.*

(2) How does this kind of energy at the higher end of the siphon compare with the energy at the lower end? *The potential energy at the higher end is higher than the potential energy at the lower end.*

(3) What is happening to the energy of the water as it flows from the higher pan to the lower container? *It is losing potential energy.*

(4) What principle states that all processes naturally proceed toward the lowest energy and highest disorganization? *The second law of thermodynamics.*

d. If you reversed the positions of the containers halfway through the demonstration, what would happen? *The water would always flow from the higher container to the lower container.*

e. Would the results of this demonstration change if the bend in the tube was raised? *No, the only thing that affects the results of this demonstration is the relative heights of the containers.*

III. Moving Fluids

Both flowing air and flowing water exhibit many of the physical properties that are characteristic of all fluids. These properties are studied together under the heading **fluid pressure.** Bernoulli recognized that the pressure a moving fluid exerts is directly related to the speed at which that fluid is flowing. The faster the fluid is flowing over a surface, the lower the pressure that the fluid exerts on that surface. Air and water are fluids, so they both demonstrate this property. This simple observation has led to some amazing technology. Powered flight, sailing vessels, hydrofoils, motorboats, sail planes, kites, and Frisbees all depend on Bernoulli's principle.

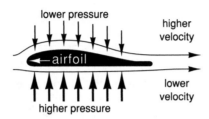

Observe as your teacher demonstrates the Bernoulli effect discussed in your textbook.

a. What did the teacher do? _He held a strip of paper just below his mouth_ _and blew across the top of the paper._

b. What did you observe? _The loose end of the paper strip rose._

c. Explain the results. _The moving air over the top of the paper was at a_ _lower pressure than the nonmoving air under the paper. The net upward_ _force caused the end of the paper strip to rise._

III. Moving Fluids

1. Cut a strip of paper 20 cm long by 6 cm wide. Lightweight paper will work best.

2. Hold one end of the paper so that it wraps around a forefinger and press it against your chin at the edge of your lower lip.

3. Forcefully direct your breath over the paper and it will rise in response to the lift generated.

Discussion Questions

A. Pressure

Molecules moving at the surface of a liquid must have a certain amount of kinetic energy to enter the gas above the liquid because the gas molecules, with much higher kinetic energies, are pressing down on the liquid surface. The force that a liquid must exert at its surface in order to become a vapor is called **vapor pressure.** Vapor pressure of a liquid increases as the liquid is heated. Water boils only when its vapor pressure equals or exceeds atmospheric pressure. At sea level, the air pushes down on the liquid surface at about 10^5 Pa. As you increase altitude (you are at a shallower "depth" in the atmosphere), the atmospheric pressure decreases. Because there is essentially no atmosphere in space, the pressure is very near 0 Pa. With this information answer questions 1 to 4.

1. Water boils at 100°C at sea level. Explain why water boils below 100°C at higher altitudes. _Boiling occurs when the vapor pressure equals the_ _atmospheric pressure. Because the atmospheric pressure is lower at higher_ _altitudes, vapor pressure will equal atmospheric pressure at a temperature_ _lower than 100°C._

2. Could liquid water exist in space outside a spacecraft? Explain. *If the* *air pressure is zero, liquid water would instantly vaporize.*

3. What would happen to the blood of an astronaut if he were not in a pressurized environment? *His blood would boil away.*

_____

4. A pressure cooker is sealed so that it generates pressure inside the pot higher than the surrounding atmospheric pressure. Explain why the water in a pressure cooker boils at a temperature higher than 100°C. *Because* *the steam pressure inside the pot is higher than normal atmospheric* *pressure, the temperature of the water must be higher for its vapor* *pressure to equal steam pressure.*

5. If the atmosphere applies 10^5 Pa of pressure on your skin, how much pressure does your skin apply to the atmosphere? *10^5 Pa*

6. Car brakes use liquids to transfer and amplify the force from your foot to the brake. Considering Pascal's principle, why is it dangerous to get air in the hydraulic piping of the brake system? *The air in the system would* *compress under pressure instead of transferring the pressure to the brakes.* *Braking power would be lowered.*

B. Working with Pressure (Pascals)

One pascal is defined as one newton applied over a square meter $\left(P = \dfrac{\text{Force}}{\text{Area}} \Rightarrow \dfrac{\text{N}}{\text{m}^2}\right)$. Recall that weight = mass × $g \Rightarrow \dfrac{\text{kg·m}}{\text{s}^2}$, where g is the acceleration due to gravity (9.8 m/s²).

Keeping these relationships in mind, answer the following questions.

1. If a breeze pushes on a two-square meter door with a total force of 60 N, how much pressure (in pascals) has been applied?

Formula: $P = \dfrac{Force}{Area} = \dfrac{F}{A}$

Substitute: $P = \dfrac{60\ N}{2\ m^2} = 30\ Pa$

2. The water in a ten-gallon aquarium weighs 360. N. How much pressure will be applied to the bottom of the aquarium if the bottom measures 0.30 m by 0.60 m?

Find the area of the base: *$0.30\ m \times 0.60\ m = 0.18\ m^2$*

Formula: $P = \dfrac{F}{A}$

Substitute: $P = \dfrac{360.\ N}{0.18\ m^2} = 2000\ Pa \approx 2.0 \times 10^3\ Pa\ (2\ SDs\ allowed)$

Objectives

The purpose of this exercise is to

1. Gain practice making measurements and calculating density.
2. Make predictions from theory and experimentally test the predictions.

Materials

Corn oil
Glycerol
Green food coloring

Equipment

Eyedroppers (2)
Graduated cylinder, 10 mL
Mass balance
Test tube brush
Test tubes (3)
Test tube rack

Introduction

The food coloring in the water makes this a vivid and fascinating investigation. The Experimental Evaluation section illustrates that science frequently does not give clear answers. This is a very important principle.

Introduction

The relative ease with which a fluid can support an object is called **buoyancy.** Buoyancy of an object is directly related to its density. You have read in your textbook about Archimedes' principle. Archimedes' principle states that an object is supported by a force that is equal to the weight of the fluid displaced. If you submerge a wooden block in water, as we did in Investigation 3D, and measure the volume of water displaced by the block, you will find that the weight of the water displaced was greater than the weight of the wooden block. This is the reason that the block float: the buoyant force upward is greater than the force exerted downward by the weight of the block. If an object has a density greater than water, the weight of the object is greater than the buoyant force and the object sinks. Finding the density of an object by measuring the weight and volume should allow you to predict whether an object will sink or float in water. A steel ship is able to float despite its great weight because it contains an enormous volume, most of which is air. Its overall density is much lower than that of water.

Density is a physical property of all matter. Different liquids have different densities. In this investigation you will be calculating and comparing the densities of corn oil and glycerol with the density of water. Based on your results, you will be able to predict if these substances will float or sink in the presence of the others.

Pre-Laboratory Questions

Read the entire investigation. Answer the following questions prior to class on a separate sheet of paper. Use complete sentences.

1. What is the buoyant force on an immersed object equal to?

2. In which direction does the buoyant force act?

3. To which property of an object or substance is buoyancy directly related?

4. Why does a steel ship float even though the density of the metal is much greater than that of water?

5. If you forgot the density of water, how could you determine it?

6. Why do you add green food coloring to the water in Part A of the procedure?

Procedures

A. Water

1. Place 5.0 mL of water in a test tube.

2. Add 1 or 2 drops of green food coloring into the water in the test tube. Set the tube aside. Record the density of water in the data table below.

B. The Density of Corn Oil

1. Find the mass of the 10 mL graduated cylinder. Record this in ① below.

2. Pour 5.0 mL of corn oil into the graduated cylinder. Add the last few tenths of a mL dropwise to avoid overshooting.

3. Find the combined mass of the graduated cylinder and the corn oil. Record this in ② below.

4. Find the mass of the corn oil by subtracting 1 from 2 and write the answer in ③ below.

②	Mass of the cylinder and corn oil		_____
①	Mass of the cylinder	−	_____
③	Mass of the corn oil	=	_____

5. Calculate the density of the corn oil and record that value in the data table (Density = mass/volume).

6. Pour the corn oil into a second test tube.

7. Clean the graduated cylinder using soap and a test tube brush and dry.

8. Record the density of corn oil calculated by two other groups in the data table.

9. Calculate and record the average density of corn oil for all three groups.

C. The Density of Glycerol

1. Record the mass of the 10 mL graduated cylinder in ④ below.

2. Pour 5.0 mL of glycerol into the graduated cylinder. Using a clean eyedropper, add the last few tenths of a mL dropwise to avoid overshooting.

3. Find the combined mass of the graduated cylinder and the glycerol. Record this in ⑤ below.

4. Find the mass of the glycerol by subtracting ④ from ⑤ and write the answer in ⑥ below.

   ⑤   Mass of the cylinder and glycerol   _____

   ④   Mass of the cylinder   − _____

   ⑥   Mass of the glycerol   = _____

5. Calculate the density of the glycerol and record that value in the data table.

6. Pour the glycerol into a third test tube.

7. Clean the graduated cylinder with soap and a test tube brush and dry.

8. Record the density of glycerol calculated by the two other groups in the data table.

9. Calculate and record the average density of glycerol for all three groups.

D. Order of Layers

1. Predict which substance will be the ...

   top layer   *corn oil*

   middle layer   *water*

   bottom layer   *glycerol*

2. Pour the corn oil into the test tube that contains the water. Do not shake the test tube.

3. Pour the glycerol from the graduated cylinder into the same test tube. Record the order of layers in the data table.

4. Clean all glassware with soap and water and dry thoroughly.

Data Table: Density

| Substance | Density (g/mL) | | | | Order of Layers (top, middle, bottom) |
	Your Group	Group 2	Group 3	Average	
Water	1.0	XXX	XXX	XXX	middle
Corn Oil	~0.91	~0.91	~0.91	~0.91	top
Glycerol	~1.3	~1.3	~1.3	~1.3	bottom

Discussion Questions

1. How can you predict whether a substance will float without placing it into water? *If its density is less than 1 g/mL, it will float.*

2. In both the Dead Sea and in the Great Salt Lake, a person is able to float on the surface and raise both hands and both feet out of the water. How is the water in these two lakes different from fresh water? *The water is extremely salty.*

3. Why does that affect your ability to float? *For any object, salt water will generate a greater buoyant force than the fresh water because salt water has a greater density.*

4. Gasoline has a density of 0.67 g/mL. Will gasoline float on top of a layer of water or sink underneath its surface? *Gasoline will float on top of a layer of water.*

5. What will happen if you try to use water to put out a gasoline fire? _____ *The gasoline will float on top of the water and continue to burn.*

Experimental Evaluation

6. Why were the densities for corn oil and glycerol determined by the three groups not exactly the same? *The calculated densities were not the same because the data was collected by different people, using slightly different quantities and possibly different instruments.*

7. Did your experiment match your predictions? *If everything was done correctly, yes.*

8. Did this investigation prove that *everything* with a density less than 1 g/mL will float in water and *everything* with a density greater than 1 g/mL will sink? Explain. *No, not everything was tested.*

9. (Optional) The density of a water strider is greater than 1 g/mL, yet it is able to walk on the surface of a pond. Why do you think that the insect can do this? *Surface tension of the water is as important as buoyancy in supporting the insect on the surface.*

10. (Optional) If the water strider were pushed beneath the surface of the water, what would happen to it? *It would sink.*

11. (Optional) This investigation assumed that the density of the tap water you used was 1.0 g/mL (the density of pure water). Do you think this is a correct assumption? Explain. *No, because of the chemicals added to tap water and and the minerals dissolved in it, the density is probably greater than 1.0 g/mL.*

12. (Optional) Is this assumption about the density of water acceptable for this investigation? Would it be acceptable for scientific research? Explain both questions. *The density difference between tap water and distilled water is not great enough to influence this investigation. For certain scientific research, a more accurate value for the density of the water might have to be determined.*

15C APPLICATIONS

Boyle's and Charles's Laws

Name _____

Date_____ Hour_____

Objective

The purpose of this exercise is to gain experience in solving problems involving changes in pressure, volume, and temperature of a sample of an ideal gas.

Introduction

While this is principally a math exercise, it will also give you some practical experience in deciphering word problems. The key to solving word problems is to focus first on what you are required to find. Then note what you are given or what is known. After you have correctly done these two steps, identifying the required formula is fairly easy. Gas law problems are straightforward proportions if you can identify which quantities go with which variables. Just remember that any words such as *initially, former, original,* or *before the change,* refer to quantities with a subscript of 1. Similarly, any words such as *final, new,* or *after the change,* refer to quantities with a subscript of 2. Unknown quantities may have either subscript. So it is important to list your known and unknown quantities at the beginning of the problem and assign them variables. (Computer programmers almost always assign variables at the beginning of their programs.)

It is more important to understand the physical process than to be able to "turn the equation crank" to get the correct answer. After each problem, look at the change in the given quantities and note how the unknown quantity responded. This is a good way to check your solution. If the change does not follow the gas law, then you probably have made an error.

A. Boyle's Law

Boyle's law states that as the pressure exerted on a given amount of a gas increases, the volume of the gas decreases. This kind of relationship between two such properties is called an inverse proportion. Boyle's law is expressed by the formula $P_1V_1 = P_2V_2$.

Example: 4.0 L of a gas is at a pressure of 500. mm Hg. If the pressure is doubled, what will be the new volume?

Follow these steps:

1. Known information: $V_1 = 4.0$ L, $P_1 = 500.$ mm Hg, $P_2 = 1000.$ mm Hg

2. Required quantity: $V_2 = ?$

3. Write the applicable formula: $P_1V_1 = P_2V_2$

4. Rearrange the equation and solve for the desired variable. In this case, you are trying to find V_2:

$$V_2 = \frac{P_1V_1}{P_2}$$

5. Substitute known values into the equation: $V_2 = \dfrac{500.\ \text{mm} \times 4.0\ \text{L}}{1000.\,\text{mm}}$

6. Solve the problem: $V_2 = 2.0$ L

Solve the following problems writing out the six steps given in the example. Assume that the temperature remains constant in each case.

1. 5.2 L of a gas is at 200. mm Hg pressure. What will be the new volume if the pressure is reduced to 100. mm Hg?

   a. *Known information:* $V_1 = 5.2$ *L,* $P_1 = 200.$ *mm Hg,* $P_2 = 100.$ *mm Hg*

   b. *Unknown quantity:* $V_2 = ?$

   c. *Write the applicable formula:* $P_1V_1 = P_2V_2$

   d. *Rearrange for* V_2: $V_2 = \dfrac{P_1V_1}{P_2}$

   e. *Substitute known values into the equation:* $V_2 = \dfrac{200. \ mm \times 5.2 \ L}{100. \ mm}$

   f. *Solve the problem:* $V_2 = 10.4 \ L \approx 10. \ L \ (2 \ SDs \ allowed)$

2. 8.0 L of a gas is initially at 400. mm Hg pressure. If the gas is allowed to expand to 10. L in volume, what is the final pressure?

   a. *Known information:* $V_1 = 8.0$ *L,* $P_1 = 400.$ *mm Hg,* $V_2 = 10.0$ *L*

   b. *Unknown quantity:* $P_2 = ?$

   c. *Write the applicable formula:* $P_1V_1 = P_2V_2$

   d. *Rearrange for* P_2: $P_2 = \dfrac{V_1P_1}{V_2}$

   e. *Substitute known values into the equation:* $P_2 = \dfrac{8.0 \ L \times 400. \ mm \ Hg}{10. \ L}$

   f. *Solve the problem:* $P_2 = 320 \ mm \ Hg \ (2 \ SDs \ allowed)$

3. What will be the new volume of a gas at the new pressure of 1500. mm Hg if the gas had an initial volume of 12 L at 750. mm Hg pressure?

   a. *Known information:* $V_1 = 12$ *L,* $P_1 = 750.$ *mm Hg,* $P_2 = 1500.$ *mm Hg*

   b. *Unknown quantity:* $V_2 = ?$

   c. *Write the applicable formula:* $P_1V_1 = P_2V_2$

   d. *Rearrange for* V_2: $V_2 = \dfrac{V_1P_1}{P_2}$

   e. *Substitute known values into the equation:* $V_2 = \dfrac{12 \ L \times 750. \ mm \ Hg}{1500. \ mm \ Hg}$

   f. *Solve the problem:* $V_2 = 6.0 \ L \ (2 \ SDs \ allowed)$

4. You currently have 24 L of a gas at 800. mm Hg pressure. If the *original* pressure of the gas was 400. mm Hg, what was its *original* volume?

    a. Known information: V_2 = 24 L, P_2 = 800. mm Hg, P_1 = 400. mm Hg

    b. Unknown quantity: V_1 = ?

    c. Write the applicable formula: $P_1V_1 = P_2V_2$

    d. Rearrange for V_2: $V_1 = \dfrac{V_2 P_2}{P_1}$

    e. Substitute known values into the equation: $V_1 = \dfrac{24\ L \cdot 800.\ mm\ Hg}{400\ mm\ Hg}$

    f. Solve the problem: V_1 = 48 L *(2 SDs allowed)*

B. Charles's Law

Charles's law states that as the temperature of a sample of gas increases, the gas volume increases, assuming that the pressure remains constant. This kind of relationship between two properties is called a direct proportion. Charles's law is expressed by the formula $\dfrac{V_1}{T_1} = \dfrac{V_2}{T_2}$, where T is measured in kelvins (K). Give a mathematical reason that you could not use the Celsius temperature. *If _____ Celsius temperatures were used, negative temperatures or even zero temperatures would be possible, which would make the Charles's law proportion invalid.*

    Example: A gas initially has a volume of 4.0 L at 200. K. If the temperature is doubled, what will be the new volume, assuming pressure remains constant?

Follow these steps:

    a. Known information: V_1 = 4.0 L, T_1 = 200. K, T_2 = 400. K

    b. Required quantity: V_2 = ?

    c. Write the applicable formula: $\dfrac{V_1}{T_1} = \dfrac{V_2}{T_2}$

    d. Rearrange the equation and solve for the unknown variable. In this case we are solving for V_2: $V_2 = \dfrac{V_1 T_2}{T_1}$

    e. Substitute known values into the equation:
$$V_2 = \frac{4.0\ L \times 400.\ K}{200.\ K}$$

    f. Solve the problem: V_2 = 8.0 L

Solve the following problems. Write out the six steps given in the example. Assume that pressure remains constant for each situation.

1. Given 5.2 L of a gas at 300. K, what will be the new volume if its temperature is reduced to 150. K?

   a. Known information: $V_1 = 5.2$ L, $T_1 = 300.$ K, $T_2 = 150.$ K

   b. Unknown quantity: $\qquad\qquad\qquad\qquad$ $V_2 = ?$

   c. Write the applicable formula: $\qquad\qquad$ $\dfrac{V_1}{T_1} = \dfrac{V_2}{T_2}$

   d. Rearrange for V_2: $\qquad\qquad\qquad$ $V_2 = \dfrac{T_2 V_1}{T_1}$

   e. Substitute known values into the equation: $\quad V_2 = \dfrac{150.\ K \cdot 5.2\ L}{300.\ K}$

   f. Solve the problem: $\qquad\qquad\qquad$ $V_2 = 2.6$ L (2 SDs allowed)

2. Given 8.0 L of a gas at 250. K, what will be the *change* in temperature $(T_2 - T_1)$ if the new volume after the change is 16 L?

   a. Known information: $V_1 = 8.0$ L, $T_1 = 250.$ K, $V_2 = 16$ L

   b. Unknown quantity: $\qquad\qquad\qquad\qquad$ $T_2 = ?$

   c. Write the applicable formula: $\qquad\qquad$ $\dfrac{V_1}{T_1} = \dfrac{V_2}{T_2}$

   d. Rearrange for T_2: $\qquad\qquad\qquad$ $T_2 = \dfrac{T_1 V_2}{V_1}$

   e. Substitute known values into the equation: $\quad T_2 = \dfrac{250.\ K \cdot 16\ L}{8.0\ L}$

   f. Solve the problem: $\qquad$ $T_2 = 500\ K = 5.0 \times 10^2$ K (2 SDs allowed)

   g. Determine change in temperature: $\qquad$ $\Delta T = (T_2 - T_1) =$
   $\qquad\qquad\qquad\qquad\qquad\qquad\qquad$ $500\ K - 250\ K = +250\ K$

3. Determine the new volume of a sample of gas at 600. K if its initial volume was 12 L at 400. K.

   a. Known information: $V_1 = 12$ L, $T_1 = 400.$ K, $T_2 = 600.$ K

   b. Unknown quantity: $\qquad\qquad\qquad\qquad$ $V_2 = ?$

   c. Write the applicable formula: $\qquad\qquad$ $\dfrac{V_1}{T_1} = \dfrac{V_2}{T_2}$

   d. Rearrange for V_2: $\qquad\qquad\qquad$ $V_2 = \dfrac{T_2 V_1}{T_1}$

   e. Substitute known values into the equation: $\quad V_2 = \dfrac{600.\ K \cdot 12\ L}{400.\ K}$

   f. Solve the problem: $\qquad\qquad\qquad$ $V_2 = 18$ L (2 SDs allowed)

4. The volume of a gas at 400. K is 16 L. If the original volume was 10. L, what was the original temperature?

   a. *Known information:* $V_1 = 10. L, T_2 = 400. K, V_2 = 16 L$

   b. *Unknown quantity:* $T_1 = ?$

   c. *Write the applicable formula:* $\dfrac{V_1}{T_1} = \dfrac{V_2}{T_2}$

   d. *Rearrange for T_1:* $T_1 = \dfrac{V_1 T_2}{V_2}$

   e. *Substitute known values into the equation:* $T_1 = \dfrac{10. L \cdot 400. K}{16 L}$

   f. *Solve the problem:* $T_1 = 250 K$ *(2 SDs allowed)*

Temperature, Heat, and Thermal Energy

Objective

The purpose of these demonstrations is to help the students understand the differences between temperature, heat, and thermal energy through practical experiences.

Introduction

The terms *temperature, heat,* and *thermal energy* are often used incorrectly. However, each has a specific definition. **Temperature** is a measure of the average kinetic energy of the molecules in a substance. The temperature is not dependent on the number of particles present (the mass of the substance). The concept of "measure" relies on a numerical system that is directly proportional to the kinetic energy. *Average* kinetic energy implies that not all of the particles of matter are necessarily moving at exactly the same speed. Some of the molecules are moving faster than the average and some slower. **Thermal energy** is the measure of the total kinetic energy of all the particles of the substance. Thermal energy is therefore dependent on the total mass of the object. Although *heat* and *thermal energy* are often used interchangeably, **heat** refers only to the *transfer* of thermal energy from one place to another. You can discuss how much heat was given off or absorbed by a substance, but it isn't proper to discuss how much heat is contained in a substance.

Procedures

I. Temperature

A. Sensory Perception

When your skin comes in contact with an object or substance, your nerve endings seem to give you a sense of how hot or cold the object or substance is. However, these sensory perceptions are dependent on many different factors and they can easily deceive us. With prolonged contact, the sensors lose their responsiveness and you no longer feel the initial temperature difference so intensely. This can be illustrated with a frog. If the frog is dropped into very hot water, it will immediately leap out of the pan. However, if the frog is placed in lukewarm water and the water is heated slowly, the frog will not notice the change in temperature and will remain in the water until the hot water kills it.

Watch as one of your classmates places one index finger in a cup of cold water and the other in a cup of hot water.

How does he describe the intensity of the sensation of temperature after leaving his fingers in the cups for five minutes? *The initial perceptions of cold and hot are no longer so strong.*

Introduction

This set of demonstrations is designed to supplement a lecture. Most of these demonstrations can be easily done at home. Distinguishing between the terms temperature, heat, and thermal energy may be difficult for many students. Understanding the distinction is fundamental to understanding many physical processes, however, and should be stressed.

Materials

Food coloring
Ice
Styrofoam cups (8 oz), 5

Equipment

Beakers 250 mL (3)
Bunsen burner
Burner lighter
Flask
Glass tube
Stopper, one-hole
Tongs
Tripod
Wire Gauze

Preparation

1. You will need boiling water for several of the demonstrations. Heat enough water before class so that you don't have to wait for it to boil before each section.

2. It will facilitate the demonstrations if you have a liter or so of water that you have allowed to come to room temperature. You can be sure that several samples taken from this store will actually be at the same temperature without having to measure it each time.

*Have three beakers of water
at different temperatures:
17–20°C, 30–33°C, and
44–47°C. Have a student
come to the front and be
soaking his index fingers in
the hotter and colder water
for at least five minutes
while you are lecturing.
Have him place both fingers
simultaneously into the
warm water and describe
his sensations of hot and
cold.*

How does he describe the sensation of temperature when he places both index fingers in the cup of water at room temperature? *The finger originally placed in the cold water feels warm. The finger originally placed in the hot water feels cool.*

Is your fingertip a reliable temperature indicator? *No*

Questions

1. If you spend too much time in the snow without proper protection, your feet will start feeling very cold. What happens to the sensation of coldness if you ignore the feeling and stay outside? *Your feet no longer feel as cold.*

2. Have your feet warmed up or are you getting inaccurate sensory information from your feet? *Your senses are no longer giving you accurate information.*

3. Could this "lack of feeling" be dangerous? Explain. *If you continue to ignore the cold, you will eventually get frostbite.*

Measuring Temperature
*Fill a flask approximately
half-full with colored water.
Carefully insert a clear glass
tube into a one-hole stopper
using soap and water or
glycerol and water as a
lubricant. Place the stopper
firmly in the mouth of the
flask. The glass tube will
provide an avenue for
expansion of the liquid. Heat
the flask gently with a
Bunsen burner. You should
observe the water level
rising.*

B. Measuring Temperature

Our senses do not provide an objective way to measure temperature. The Facet on pages 360–61 in your textbook provides the history of the development of the modern temperature scales and thermometers that allow us to measure temperature objectively and with great precision. Liquid thermometers indicate temperature by the liquid level in a fine tube calibrated in degrees. The level depends on the liquid volume as it expands and contracts in response to an increase or decrease of the average kinetic energy of the fluid. The kinetic energy of a distinct, physical object can be calculated easily, but the average kinetic energy of the *particles* in a substance cannot be measured directly in joules. By using a calibrated scale to measure the expanding fluid in a thermometer, we can *infer* the magnitude of the average kinetic energy of a substance without actually measuring it.

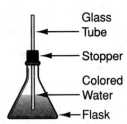

Glass
Tube

Stopper

Colored
Water

Flask

Observe the level of water in the tube as your teacher heats the demonstration flask. What did you observe? *The water in the tube should rise.*

Questions

1. Both Gabriel Fahrenheit and Anders Celsius divided their scales between two temperatures they believed to be fixed into 100 divisions. State the fixed points used for each scale. *Fahrenheit used the freezing point of a saturated salt solution and what he thought was normal body temperature.*

Celsius used the freezing and boiling points of pure water.

2. Why do you think Fahrenheit used mercury instead of pure water as the liquid in his thermometer? *Pure water freezes at 32°F. A water* _____

   thermometer would be useless at temperatures below that. _____

3. Does a thermometer directly measure particle kinetic energy? _____

   No, the indication it provides is an inference of average particle kinetic _____

   energy. _____

4. Upon what physical property does a thermometer depend? *It depends* _____

   on the expansion and contraction of a liquid as its particles' average kinetic _____

   energy increases and decreases. _____

5. When you measure temperature, does the reading imply that all of the molecules of that substance are moving at exactly the same speed? Explain.

   No, the temperature is only an indicator of the average kinetic energy. Some _____

   molecules are moving slower and some are moving faster. _____

II. Heat and Thermal Energy

Several principles are important when talking about heat and thermal energy. First, all matter has thermal energy, even substances that we consider "cold." Unless the substance is at absolute zero, the molecules have some kinetic energy. Second, when two objects or substances touch, their molecules collide with each other transferring kinetic energy to the other substance. Therefore, heat is actually flowing in both directions. However, the net heat flow is from the hotter object or substance to the colder one. When both objects are the same temperature or the temperature of the two substances is constant, they are said to be in *thermal equilibrium*. Heat transfer has not stopped at that point; it merely proceeds at the same rate in both directions.

When a substance is undergoing a phase change (melting or boiling), it is possible to add heat without increasing the temperature of a substance. The added heat provides the energy to disrupt the various bonds that hold the molecules together in the less energetic state.

A. Heat

Observe the two cups of water that your teacher presents to the class. One cup is near the boiling point of water; the other is at room temperature.

1. What is visibly different about them? *One of the cups is steaming,* _____

   and one is not. _____

2. As the steam rises, what is being transferred to the air? *Heat* _____

3. Why is the heat moving in this direction? *The air is at a lower* _____

   temperature than the water, and heat flows from higher temperature to _____

   lower temperature. _____

4. Is there any heat flow associated with the cooler cup of water? *yes* _____

5. Which direction(s) is the heat flowing? *Heat is flowing from the water to* _____

   to the air and from the air to the water. _____

Heat and Thermal Energy
Heat
Place two Styrofoam cups of water in front of the students, one near boiling and one at room temperature. An important concept to emphasize in this section is that when two bodies (such as water and air) come to thermal equilibrium, there is not a cessation of heat flow but that the rate of heat flow is the same in both directions. This is called dynamic *equilibrium.*

6. Is there any net heat flow? Explain. _No, the heat flow is the same in both directions._

7. What is this condition called? _It is called thermal equilibrium._

Thermal Energy and Mass
Follow the directions for Trials 1 and 2 in the demonstration. Use of a Styrofoam cup will minimize heat loss. You will need to measure the temperatures of both the boiling water and the water at room temperature.

B. Thermal Energy and Mass

Trial 1: Your teacher will mix 50 mL of boiling water with 50 mL of water at room temperature in a Styrofoam cup.

1. Enter the temperatures of the hot and cold water as given by your teacher in the data table.

2. Make a prediction of the temperature of the mixture.

3. Enter the actual temperature of the mixture as measured by your teacher.

Trial 2: Your teacher will mix 75 mL of boiling water with 25 mL of water at room temperature in a Styrofoam cup.

1. Enter the temperatures of the hot and cold water in the data table as given by your teacher.

2. Make a prediction of the temperature of the mixture.

3. Enter the actual temperature of the mixture as given by your teacher.

Table 1: Thermal Energy and Mass

	T_{hot}	m_{hot}	T_{room}	m_{room}	Predicted T of Mixture	Actual T of Mixture
Trial 1		50 g		50 g	*	
Trial 2		75 g		25 g	**	

*Because the volumes are equal, the prediction should be a temperature exactly between the two extremes.

**Because the volume of the hot water is three times that of the cold water, the predicted temperature should be at a point closer to the hot temperature.

Questions

1. Was the actual temperature of the mixture in Trial 2 higher or lower than in Trial 1? _It was higher._

2. Why were the actual temperatures different? _In Trial 1, the amounts of hot water and cool water were equal. In Trial 2, more hot water than cool water was added to the cup._

3. In which trial was more thermal energy added to the mixture? _More thermal energy was added in Trial 2._

4. Was the temperature of the hot water in each trial different? _no_

5. Explain how the amount of thermal energy was increased. _Thermal energy increases with mass. When a greater mass of hot water was added, more thermal energy was added._

6. What is the relationship between temperature and thermal energy?
Temperature measures the average kinetic energy of the molecules.
Thermal energy measures the total kinetic energy of all particles in the mass of a substance.

C. Thermal Energy and Phase Changes

1. Boiling

Observe the temperature as your teacher applies heat for several minutes to water that is already boiling.

Temperature

Initial   _____*_____

1 min.   _____

2 min.   _____

3 min.   _____

4 min.   _____

5 min.   _____

  a. Can thermal energy be added to an object or substance without increasing its temperature? _yes_____

  b. When can this happen? _It happens when the substance is_____

_undergoing a phase change._____

  c. What is the added thermal energy accomplishing? _It provides the energy_

necessary to disrupt the attractive forces that hold the substance in the

_phase with lower kinetic energy._____

2. Freezing

Trial 1: Your teacher will mix 50 mL of ice-cold water with 50 mL of water at room temperature.

  a. Enter the temperatures of the room-temperature water and the cold water in Table 2 as given by your teacher.

  b. Make a prediction of the temperature of the mixture.

  c. Enter the actual temperature of the mixture as given by your teacher.

Trial 2: Your teacher will mix 50 g of ice with 50 mL of water at room temperature.

  a. Enter the temperatures of the ice and the water in the data table as given by your teacher.

  b. Make a prediction of the temperature of the mixture.

  c. Enter the actual temperature of the mixture as given by your teacher.

Table 2: Thermal Energy in Different Phases

		T_{cold}	m_{cold}	T_{room}	m_{room}	Predicted T of Mixture	Actual T of Mixture
Trial 1	Ice Water		50 g		50 g	*	
Trial 2	Ice		50 g		50 g	**	

Sidebar:

Thermal Energy and Phase Changes
Boiling
This can be performed as you are lecturing. The temperature should not change during the boiling process.

*The boiling point of water will vary according to altitude. The value should be close to 100°C and should not change as long as the water is boiling.

Freezing
Prepare a slush of coarsely crushed ice and water in equal amounts. After coming to equilibrium, both the water and the ice should be at or just above 0°C. Use the water in Trial 1 and 50 g of the ice (well drained) in Trial 2. You may want to measure the 50 g of ice directly in the cup by using the tare feature of the balance or by accounting for the mass of the cup in the measurement.

*Because the volumes are equal, the prediction should be a temperature exactly between the two extremes.

**Because the heat of fusion for the ice is so great, the predicted temperature should be close to the freezing point of water. Students may forget this and enter the same answer as for the ice water trial. Do not require the students to calculate this answer.

Questions

1. Which trial resulted in a higher temperature? <u>*Trial 1 resulted in a*</u>
   <u>*higher temperature.*</u>

2. How did the temperatures of the ice water in Trial 1 and the ice in Trial 2
   compare? <u>*They were about the same.*</u>

3. Does the ice-cold water have any thermal energy? <u>*Yes, everything*</u>
   <u>*that is not at absolute zero has some thermal energy.*</u>

4. Which contains less thermal energy, a certain mass of water at 0°C or the
   same mass of ice at 0°C? <u>*The ice will contain less thermal energy because*</u>
   <u>*the molecules have less kinetic energy when they are in the solid state.*</u>

5. Why was the temperature lower in Trial 2? <u>*The net heat flow from the*</u>
   <u>*warmer water into the ice was used to melt the ice without giving any*</u>
   <u>*increase in temperature.*</u>

Discussion Questions

Write the correct term (*temperature, heat,* or *thermal energy*) in the blanks
in the following questions.

1. <u>*Heat*</u> involves the flow of energy from a hot object to a cooler one.

2. Ice may be cold, but it still has some <u>*thermal*</u> energy.

3. A measure of the average kinetic energy of the particles of a substance is
   called its <u>*temperature*</u>.

4. Fifty grams of lead will have more <u>*thermal energy*</u> than 1 g of lead at
   the same temperature.

5. Fifty grams of lead at 75°C will give off more <u>*heat*</u> to the
   atmosphere than 1 g of lead at the same temperature.

6. Hot coffee cools off because <u>*heat*</u> is transferred from the
   coffee to the air.

7. A large iceberg will have more <u>*thermal energy*</u> than a small ice cube,
   although they may have the same <u>*temperature*</u>.

8. (Optional) Thermal energy is defined as the total amount of kinetic energy
   in the particles of an object. On the surface, this definition appears to
   answer the question "What is thermal energy?" However, this explanation
   contains an undefined term, *energy*. Do scientists know what any type of
   energy *is* or merely how it *behaves*? <u>*Scientists can only observe and*</u>
   <u>*describe how energy behaves. As we have discussed before, it is*</u>
   <u>*impossible to define energy in more basic terms.*</u>

People frequently think that science enables us to fully understand nature. In
fact, it often describes only how nature operates. This is knowledge that God has
given us to enable us to "subdue the earth and have dominion over it." We
should use science as a tool to further God's purposes.

16B INVESTIGATION
Specific Heat

Objective

The purpose of this investigation is to determine the specific heats of several different metals.

Materials

Paper towels
Styrofoam cups, 8 oz (3)

Equipment

Beaker, 1000 mL
Bunsen burner and lighter
Mass balance
Metal samples (3 different metals)
Stirring rod
Thermometer
Tongs
Tripod
Wire gauze

Introduction

As you learned in your textbook, the **specific heat** (c_{sp}) of a pure material is a distinct physical property. Although there are several ways to define specific heat, one common definition is the amount of thermal energy (calories) needed to raise the temperature of 1 gram of the material 1°C. You remember that temperature is a measure of the average kinetic energy of the individual molecules in a material. The amount of kinetic energy given to the molecules by a certain amount of thermal energy depends on the strengths of the chemical bonds within molecules and the attractive forces between molecules. Thus, each material has a different specific heat because these forces are different for each substance. For example, one gram of water requires the input of 1.00 cal of thermal energy to raise its temperature by 1°C. An identical mass of silver needs only 0.05 cal to experience the same change in temperature.

A material with a high specific heat must absorb a large amount of energy for its temperature to rise one degree Celsius. It also releases large amounts of heat for every degree that it cools. A substance with a low specific heat requires a relatively smaller addition of thermal energy for its temperature to rise the same amount, and it releases a smaller amount of heat for every degree that it cools. In other words, materials that have high specific heats hold more thermal energy for every gram of mass than materials with low specific heats.

This investigation is based upon the law of the conservation of energy. When two substances at different temperatures come into physical contact with one another, thermal energy will flow from the one whose particles have greater kinetic energies (higher temperature) to the one whose particles have lower kinetic energy (lower temperature). When the average kinetic energy of both substances has become equal, the net flow of heat stops. Both substances then exist at a temperature somewhere between the original temperatures. In

Introduction

If students use metal cylinders that are about the same size, it is easier for them to visualize that some metals hold more heat. Using shot or metal turnings will give more accurate results, but the visual benefit is lost. Likewise, the use of made-for-the-purpose calorimeters can be more accurate, but the primary lesson is lost in trying to calibrate the calorimeter. Many high-school students will actually get better results using Styrofoam cups than a calorimeter. This is an investigation in which increasing accuracy obscures the main point.

Preparation

Set aside enough water for this investigation ahead of time so that it will come to room temperature. This ensures that T_1 (water) is the same for all the samples and makes the calculations easier. Water running from the tap changes temperature over time.

General Comments

1. Specific heat specimens can be obtained from a scientific supply company. Other household materials can be substituted: steel bolts, iron nails, lead sinkers or shot, copper plumbing fittings, or a length of copper wire rolled tightly (be sure to strip the insulation first).

2. The water in the Styrofoam cups should completely cover the hot metal specimen. The investigation calls for 50 mL

3. You will obtain more accurate results if the mass of the metal is at least 40 percent of the mass of the water in the cup.

4. Emphasize to the students that the basis for this investigation is that the heat lost by the metal equals the heat gained by the water.

5. If a gram balance is not available, a spring scale calibrated in newtons can be used. Multiply the weight by 102 to obtain the mass in grams.

6. We are assuming for the sake of simplicity that no heat is lost to the Styrofoam cup or to the air.

7. Demonstrate to the students step 9 in the procedure. There must be a fine balance between getting most of the hot water off the sample and how fast the sample cools down while you are blotting it.

8. One way to avoid getting the metal wet while heating it is to place the sample in a small loosely stoppered test tube. Let the sample heat for 10-15 minutes, remove the stopper, wipe the test tube, and pour the metal into the calorimeter. You will want to use this method if you are using several small pieces of metal (like lead sinkers) instead of one large piece.

addition, the total amount of thermal energy lost by the hotter substance equals the total amount of thermal energy gained by the colder substance. We will use these principles to determine the specific heat capacity of a metal using an insulated device called a *calorimeter*. From its name you can tell that this instrument allows the measurement of heat flow.

The basic idea behind calorimetry is that heat gained or lost by a substance can be calculated if one knows the mass of the substance, the change in temperature of the substance, and its specific heat capacity (c_{sp}). This is expressed in the equation

$$Q = c_{sp} \cdot m \cdot \Delta T$$

where Q is the heat gained or lost, m is the mass in grams, ΔT is the change in temperature ($T_2 - T_1$), and c_{sp} is the specific heat capacity of the substance.

In calorimetry, you begin with a known quantity of water (m_{water}) at a known temperature ($T_{water\ 1}$). A heated piece of a known amount of metal (m_{metal}) at a known temperature ($T_{metal\ 1}$) is placed into the water in the calorimeter, and the system is allowed to come to thermal equilibrium. When you measure the final temperature (T_2), which is the same for the water and the metal, you can determine the change in temperature (ΔT) for both. We know that the heat gained by the water (Q_{water}) in the calorimeter must be equal to the heat lost by the metal ($-Q_{metal}$) because the total thermal energy in the system cannot change. Therefore,

$$Q_{water} + Q_{metal} = 0$$

$$Q_{water} = -Q_{metal}$$

or

$$(c_{sp} \cdot m \cdot \Delta T)_{water} = -(c_{sp} \cdot m \cdot \Delta T)_{metal}$$

From this expression, you can solve for the unknown, the c_{sp} of the metal.

$$c_{sp\ metal} = \frac{(c_{sp} \cdot m \cdot \Delta T)_{water}}{-(m \cdot \Delta T)_{metal}}$$

We know that the c_{sp} of water is 1.00 cal/g·°C, so this expression is often simplified to

$$c_{sp\ metal} = -\frac{(m \cdot \Delta T)_{water}}{(m \cdot \Delta T)_{metal}} \cdot \frac{cal}{g \cdot °C} \cdot$$

Answers to Pre-Laboratory Questions

1. The specific heat of a substance is the amount of thermal energy that must be added to 1 gram of a substance to raise its temperature 1°C.

2. A substance with a high specific heat can hold more thermal energy per gram.

3. The law of conservation of energy states that when two substances are in contact, the heat lost by one substance must equal the heat gained by another. If all variables are known except for the unknown specific heat, you can solve for the unknown variable.

4. The pieces of metal are immersed in boiling water until they reach the same temperature as the water.

5. Blotting the metal sample removes the residual boiling water that could affect the temperature of the calorimeter.

6. If the calorimeter loses water mass, the mass for water in the equation will be incorrect and there will be errors in the calculations.

7. The water in the calorimeter gains heat.

Pre-Laboratory Questions

Read the entire investigation. Answer the following questions prior to class on a separate sheet of paper. Use complete sentences.

1. Define *specific heat.*

2. Which is able to hold more thermal energy per gram, a substance with high or low specific heat?

3. How does the law of conservation of energy help you find the specific heat of the metals in this investigation?

4. How do you determine the initial temperature of the pieces of metal?

5. Why do you blot the metal pieces before placing them into the calorimeter?

6. Why is it important to not splash water out of the calorimeter when placing the metal into it?

7. Which material in the calorimeter gains heat in this investigation?

Procedures

Calorimetry

1. Enter the names of the different metal samples in the "Metal" column in Tables 1, 2, and 3, below.

2. Put 400 mL of water into the 1000 mL beaker. This water volume does not have to be exact.

3. Place the beaker on the wire gauze on the tripod, light the Bunsen burner, and begin heating the water to a boil.

4. Use the mass balance to find the masses of the different metals. Measure to the nearest 0.01 g. Record their masses opposite their names in Table 2.

5. Place all three metal samples into the boiling water.

Do not drop the pieces of metal into the beaker. Use tongs to lower them gently into the water to avoid breaking the bottom of the beaker.

Leave the pieces of metal in the water for 10 minutes.

6. Label three 8-oz Styrofoam cups with the names of the metals being tested and add 50.0 mL (50.0 g) of water at room temperature to each cup.

7. Measure the temperature of the water in each cup and record these values opposite the name of the corresponding metal in Table 1 for T_1 (water).

8. Measure the temperature of the boiling water with a thermometer and enter this value in Table 2 for T_1 (metal).

9. **Perform this step as rapidly as possible.** Remove a piece of metal from the boiling water with tongs, quickly blot it dry on a paper towel, and carefully place it into the cup labeled with the matching name without splashing water out of the cup.

10. Stir the water in the cup with a stirring rod (not the thermometer) every thirty seconds and note the temperature on a piece of scrap paper.

11. When the temperature remains the same for three consecutive readings, thermal equilibrium has been established. Record the temperature in Table 1 for T_2 (water) and T_2 (metal).

12. Repeat steps 9 through 11 for the remaining samples of metal.

13. Calculate ΔT_{water} for each metal and complete Table 1.

14. Calculate ΔT_{metal} for each metal and complete Table 2.

15. Calculate the specific heat of each of the different metals by using the last equation given in the introduction. Record your results opposite the metals' names in Table 3.

16. Record the results from two other groups in Table 3 and find the average for each metal.

Results

Table 1: Heat Gained by Water

Metal	T_1	T_2	ΔT_{water} $(T_2 - T_1)$	Mass (m_{water})	$m_{water} \cdot \Delta T_{water}$
				50.0 g	
				50.0 g	
				50.0 g	

Table 2: Heat Lost by Metal

Metal	T_1	T_2	ΔT_{water} $(T_2 - T_1)$	Mass (m_{metal})	$m_{water} \cdot \Delta T_{water}$

Table 3: Specific Heats

Metal	$c_{sp\ metal}$			
	Your Group	Group 2	Group 3	Average

Discussion Questions

1. State a formula for finding the amount of heat any material will gain or lose with a certain temperature change. $\underline{Q = c_{sp} \cdot m \cdot \Delta T}$

2. Calculate Q for the following conditions:

Material	m	ΔT	c_{sp} (cal/g·°C)	Q (in cal)
Copper	1.0 g	3.0°C	0.09	*0.27 cal*
Copper	10.0 g	−2.0°C	0.09	*−1.8 cal*
Glass	1.0 g	−10.0°C	0.20	*−2.0 cal*
Glass	3.0 g	5.0°C	0.20	*3.0 cal*
Aluminum	10.0 g	2.0°C	0.22	*4.4 cal*
Aluminum	2.0 g	−2.0°C	0.22	*−0.88 cal*

3. What is the difference between temperature and thermal energy?

   Temperature is proportional to the average kinetic energy of the particles of a substance. Thermal energy refers to the total amount of kinetic energy in the entire mass of a substance.

4. Although all the metals had the same T_1, did all the metals contain the same amount of thermal energy? *No*

5. On a cool evening following a warm day, which would give off more heat to the atmosphere above it, the ocean ($c_{sp} = 1.00$ cal/g·°C) or the ground ($c_{sp} < 0.5$ cal/g·°C), as each cooled 5°C? Explain your answer. *The ocean would give off more heat for two reasons: it has a higher specific heat and its mass is greater.*

6. Which would make a better coolant for a car engine, water ($c_{sp} = 1.00$ cal/g·°C) or alcohol ($c_{sp} = 0.58$ cal/g·°C)? Explain your answer. *Water makes a better coolant because for the same mass, it will absorb more of the heat given off by the engine.*

Experimental Evaluation

7. You made some assumptions regarding the apparatus and the procedure in order to make the calculations easier. Name one. *Answers will vary.*

   Accept any of the following: that no heat was lost to the Styrofoam cup or to the air, that no heat was added to the cup from hot water clinging to the metal, and that no water was lost from the cup after the metal was placed in it.

8. Would these assumptions tend to make your results higher or lower than their standard values? Explain. _Unaccounted heat loss tends to lower c_{sp} because it tends to lower ΔT_{water}. Unaccounted heat gain tends to raise c_{sp} because it tends to raise ΔT_{water}. If water were lost from the cup, c_{sp} would be raised—less water to be heated leads to higher ΔT_{water}._

9. Did everybody obtain the same results for the same metals? Explain why or why not. _The results varied slightly because of differences in instruments, differences in samples, and differences in taking measurements._

10. The specific heat for silver is 0.03 cal/g·°C. Do you think this is an exact value or a close approximation? Explain. _Since all measurements are estimates, you can't say that this is an exact value._

Objectives

The purpose of this exercise is to

1. Develop a practical definition of electricity.
2. Observe the properties of static electrical charges.

Materials

Balloon
Oat cereal piece
Office tape
Paper
Plastic bag
Silk fabric (or fur), small piece
Thread

Equipment

Glass rod
Metal rod
Plastic rod
Support stand and ring

Introduction

Suppose you were asked to define *electricity*. You would probably say that it referred to electrical charges, electrons, electric current, or some other term with the root word *electron*. However, defining the word *electricity* using the root word *electron* does not add any new information. This problem arises because nobody can answer the question "What is electricity?" To bypass this difficulty, scientists simply describe how electricity behaves or operates. This approach is called an **operational definition** since it answers the question "What are the properties of electricity?" rather than "What is electricity?"

The Greek philosopher Thales (630?-546 B.C.) was the first person to systematically investigate electrical phenomena. He found that amber (fossilized tree sap), when rubbed, would attract a variety of objects like fluff, feathers, and dried leaves. William Gilbert (1544-1603) called this property *electricity* since the Greek word for amber was *elektron*. With this information, electricity can now be given a preliminary operational definition. Electricity is that property of attraction that results when objects, such as amber, are rubbed. During this investigation we will expand our operational definition by observing other properties of electricity.

Introduction

This investigation can take the place of an introductory lecture to static electricity. Electricity is one of the most abstract areas in physics because nobody has observed an entity called electricity, objects called electrons, a thing called charge, and so on. For many students these terms are never really defined; consequently, they begin the study of electricity with mysterious terms. For example, can you define a negative charge? Does it mean that something is missing? Scientists understand electricity solely on the observed effects with the faith that something underlies these effects. This investigation is designed to lead students to understand that terms like negative charge and electron describe only visible effects. In one sense electricity is a total mystery to scientists. On the other hand, they have described very accurately how it behaves.

The term electricity tends to restrict understanding to electrons. The definitions used are purposely constructed to help the students understand that the phenomenon of electricity involves charges rather than electrons. Students will later observe that electricity frequently involves positive and negative charges in motion. Examples include ionic solutions, electrochemical reactions, and solid state electronics.

Pre-Laboratory Questions

Read the entire investigation. Answer the following questions prior to class on a separate sheet of paper. Use complete sentences.

1. Why is it difficult to define electricity?

2. When scientists cannot define a term with more basic terms, how do they deal with this problem?

3. What is another scientific term you have studied that cannot be properly defined?

4. Describe one method for creating an electrical charge on an object.

5. What device detects the presence of a static electrical charge described in this investigation?

6. What process physically transfers charges from one object to another?

7. Name the process that produces a temporary charge in an object when another charged object is brought near it.

Procedures

As you perform the following steps, answer the associated questions and record your observations in complete sentences. Try to completely describe your observations in your statements.

A. Frictional Effects

1. Tear five or six small pieces of paper (1 cm^2) and place them on the tabletop.

2. Touch the plastic rod to the table or floor. Bring it close to the pieces of paper without actually touching them and observe what happens.

    Observation: *Nothing should be apparent if the rod was discharged properly.*

3. Now rub the rod with a silk or fur cloth and bring the rod close to the pieces of paper. Describe what happens.

    Observation: *The pieces of paper were attracted to the rod. Students may report that the paper was forcibly rejected from the rod after touching it, although that is not important at this point.*

4. What had to be done for the rod to attract the paper? *The rod had to be rubbed with a cloth.*

    Did the rod have to touch the paper for attraction to occur?

    Observation: *The rod did not have to touch the paper in order to attract it.*

B. Charge

1. Touch the metal rod to the table or floor and bring it close to the paper bits without touching them. Describe what happens.

   Observation: *The metal rod did not attract the paper.* _____

2. Rub the metal rod with a fur or silk cloth and bring it near the pieces of paper. Describe what happens.

   Observation: *The metal rod was not able to attract the paper bits* _____

   whether it was rubbed or not. _____

3. Obtain a 5 cm piece of clear tape. Fold one of the ends over onto itself to form a nonsticky handle about $1/_2$ cm long. Stick the tape down firmly to the table.

4. Using your "handle," pull the tape up quickly and bring it near to the pieces of paper. Describe what happens.

   Observation: *The tape attracts the bits of paper.* _____

Summary: The ability to attract that is acquired by objects through rubbing them is called *charge*. Notice that charge is detected only when *two* objects interact. The influence of charge can be exerted at a distance; it is not necessary for the two objects to actually touch each other.

C. Interactions

1. Forming handles as before, stick two 10-cm pieces of tape onto the table.

2. Quickly pull up the pieces of tape and bring them close together without touching. Describe what happens.

   Observation: *The two pieces of tape move away from each other* _____

   (repel one another). _____

3. Both pieces of tape received their charges in the same way—both were pulled up from the table. You can rightfully assume that they have the same charges or **like charges.** State a property of like charges from your observation in step 2.

   Property: *Objects with like charges repel one another.* _____

4. Forming handles as before, stick two pieces of tape onto the table, one on top of the other (piggyback).

5. Pull both pieces of tape off of the table together and immediately separate them.

6. Bring the pieces of tape together without touching and describe what happens.

   Observation: *The two pieces of tape draw together (attract each other).* _____

   _____

5. The office tape is intended to be clear-type Scotch tape.

6. This investigation is best performed on a day with low humidity.

7. Keep the students focused on each question in order. The tendency will be to jump ahead or do steps out of sequence.

8. If an electroscope is available, demonstrate it as part of the lecture in preparation for this investigation.

7. The two pieces of tape received their charges in different ways (one from the table and the other from the first piece of tape). You can rightfully assume that they have different charges or **unlike charges.** State a property of unlike charges from your observation in step 6.

Property: *Objects with unlike charges attract one another.*

Summary: It is now possible to describe two ways in which pairs of charges can behave: *Like charges repel, while unlike charges attract.*

From our observations, we can now extend the operational definition we started with to include not only the interactive property of *attraction* but also *repulsion*.

D. Charge Detector

An *electroscope* is one device used to detect the presence of charges. Traditionally, it is a device consisting of a glass jar or flask with an insulator top penetrated by a metal rod. Inside the jar are two thin leaves of metal attached to the rod so that they can swing freely. Your teacher may show you an electroscope or you may be using one for this investigation. A simple yet effective charge detector can be made with two pieces of tape and a support stand. For the purpose of this investigation, we will assume that you are using the latter apparatus.

1. Charge two 10-cm pieces of tape using the piggyback method as in Section C.

2. Stick both pieces to the support stand near each other so that they hang freely as in Figure 1, below.

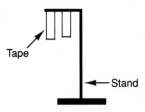

Figure 1

3. Charge a third piece of tape on the table and bring it near both pieces on the charge detector. Describe what happens.

Observation: *One piece of tape is attracted, while the other is repelled.*

4. Remove the pieces of tape from the charge detector.

E. Number of Charges

1. Take two fresh 10-cm pieces of tape and label one **A—Table** and the other **B—Top**. Charge both pieces of tape and stick them to the support stand. When charging or recharging the tapes, always place *A* on the table and *B* on top of *A* as in Section C. It may be necessary to periodically recharge or replace the pieces of tape in this section.

2. Charge various items by rubbing them with the piece of silk or by rubbing them on your hair, shirt, or anything else that will generate friction. Use such things as combs, pens, balloons, Lucite rods, and Bakelite rods, and determine their interaction with tape *A* and tape *B*. Record your results as "attract" or "repel" in the data table.

Chapter 17

3. Did any charged object attract or repel both pieces of tape at the same time?

No

Write a statement that summarizes the possible interactions with tape *A* and tape *B*.

Observation: *A charge either attracts A and repels B or repels A and attracts B.*

Summary: Scientists believe that only two charges exist since there are only two states.

Data Table: Electrical Interaction

Charged Object	Interaction (Repel/Attract)	
	Tape A	Tape B

F. Charge by Induction

Up to this point we have produced charges by rubbing or physically transferring charges from one point to another. An uncharged object can acquire a charge when a charged object is brought near to it, even if they don't actually touch. This process is called **induction.** A charge is *induced* when the charged object attracts opposite charges (or repels like charges) in a nearby object, producing one kind of charge on the near surface and the opposite charge on the far surface. Two areas of opposite charges must exist on the second object because it was originally neutral and the charges initially were canceling each other out. Induction is temporary, lasting only as long as the original charged object is present.

1. This demonstration will require a laboratory faucet or a standard sink faucet with the aerator nozzle removed.

2. Establish a very thin stream of water flowing out of the faucet.

3. In Section E, you noted that different kinds of charges can be produced on different objects. Take the same objects used in Section E, charge them again, and bring them near to but not touching the stream of water one at a time. Describe what happens.

Observation: *The stream of water is deflected toward the charged object.*

Does the type of charge make any difference in the results? *No, all cause the stream to deflect.*

4. Bring a charged rod near the stream of water. Describe what happens.

Observation: _The stream of water is deflected toward the rod._

If the rod is negatively charged, what must be the charge on the side of the stream of water closest to the rod? Explain. _The water must have a positive charge on the side nearest the rod because opposite charges attract._

What is the charge of the water stream on the side away from the rod? How do you know this? _Charges on neutral objects come in pairs. The side away from the rod must have a negative charge because there must be negative charges present in order to neutralize the positive charges on the side facing the rod._

5. Suspend a piece of toasted oat cereal (e.g., Cheerios) by a thread from the support ring. Bring a charged rod near it (do not allow it to touch!) and describe what happens.

Observation: _The cereal is attracted to the rod._

Assume the rod had a negative charge. Explain why the cereal was attracted to the rod. _The negative charge on the rod repelled the negative charges on the cereal and attracted the positive charges, creating a positively charged region on the side of the cereal closest to the rod. Since opposite charges attract, the cereal was pulled toward the rod._

G. Charge by Conduction

Another way in which a charge may be produced is by using induction to force charges to move from one object to another in contact with it. If the two objects are separated, they will both have a permanent charge. This process is called charging by **conduction.**

1. Bring the charged rod near the suspended piece of cereal. Allow the cereal to touch the rod. Describe what happens.

Observation: _The cereal was attracted to the rod as before. When the cereal touched the rod, it stuck for a moment and then was forcibly repelled away._

2. Try to touch the now-charged cereal with the rod. Describe what happens.

Observation: _The rod and cereal repel each other. The cereal cannot be touched by the rod._

Assume the rod has a negative charge. Attempt to explain your observations. _The rod induced a charge in the cereal as in Section F. When the cereal and rod touched, negative charges moved to the cereal because opposite charges attract. The cereal now has a net negative charge and repels the negatively charged rod (like charges repel)._

Discussion Questions

Many people have difficulty understanding electricity and other areas of science because many scientific concepts cannot be defined in distinct, unambiguous terms. We have seen this before with concepts such as energy, gravity, and force. Electricity cannot be defined apart from other electrical terms. This is why scientists resort to operational definitions.

1. What is an operational definition? *An operational definition is a definition developed from a description of how something works or operates.*

2. Give an operational definition for the following terms:

    a. Charge— *Charge is the property of attraction or repulsion acquired by some substances through friction, induction, or conduction.*

    b. Electroscope— *An electroscope is a device with metal leaves that is used to detect charges.*

    c. Like charges— *Like charges are the same kind of charge, indicated by the fact that they repel each other.*

    d. Unlike charges— *Unlike charges are different kinds of charges, indicated by the fact that they attract each other.*

    e. Law of charges— *Like charges repel, while unlike charges attract.*

Scientists make a number of observations and then state generalizations based upon those observations. In this investigation you made some of the same observations made by the early scientists. You will be asked to make some generalizations based on the indicated observations.

3. Refer to Section A. What did you observe about the relationship between friction and static charges? *Friction is capable of placing a charge on an object.*

4. Refer to Section B. What can you say about acquiring charges on metal and nonmetal objects? *Nonmetal objects seem to be able to acquire and hold charge, while metal objects do not.*

5. Refer to Sections C-E. Give a reason scientists believe there are only two kinds of charges. *For any given type of charge, there are only two kinds of interactions with other charges—either attraction or repulsion. It seems reasonable that there are only two kinds of charges.*

Objects can be charged by conduction or induction. When the cereal piece moved to the rod, it was charged by induction; and when the cereal was repelled by the rod, it had been charged by conduction. The root *duct* has the meaning of a "channel," "passageway," or "path." The prefix *con-* means "with," and the prefix *in-* means "not" or "without." Putting these pieces together, you can see where *conduction* means "a process using a pathway," and *induction* means "a process not using a pathway."

6. Using this information, explain the difference between acquiring a charge by conduction and by induction. *An object is charged by conduction when a source of charge physically touches the object so that the charges can move from one object to the other. An object can be charged by induction when a source of charge is brought near and the attraction and repulsion of charges shifts the charges on the object without providing a path for charges to be transferred.*

7. The word *static* normally means "stationary" and, therefore, can be confusing when the word is associated with static electricity. In some cases the charges are stationary, while in other cases the charges move. Give an example of each that you observed in this investigation. *Objects were given charges by friction, which involved the transfer of charges from one object to another. Then, as long as no other object touched it, the charges tended to remain for a period of time.*

8. Experiments with static electricity work poorly on humid days. Explain the adverse effect of high humidity using the fact that water vapor combines with substances in the air and on surfaces to form electrically charged ions. *The ions formed by the water vapor combine with static charges, which quickly neutralize the charges on objects.*

17B INVESTIGATION
Circuits

Objectives

The purpose of this exercise is to

1. Demonstrate the properties of current electricity.

2. Demonstrate open circuits, closed circuits, and short circuits.

3. Compare series and parallel circuits.

Materials

Masking tape
Salt
Steel wool
Sugar
Wire, various lengths

Equipment

Alligator clips (2)
Batteries, 1.5 V (4)
Battery holders (optional) (4)
Beakers, 250 mL (3)
Compass
Conductivity apparatus (see Investigation 2B)
Insulated shorting wire, heavy
Knife switch
Miniature lamps, 6 V (4)
Miniature lamp base (4)
Terminal board (optional)
Voltage test meter (optional)

Introduction

Be sure to assign the reading of the introduction after you have covered the material in class.

This investigation is organized by stations. Small schools or home schools could set up the stations one at a time using the materials and equipment specified. Doing so will require more time and direction by the teacher to ensure that the apparatus is correctly assembled.

If time is limited, you may selectively omit one or more stations.

Station D is important because it introduces the relationship between current and magnetism. The optional stations introduce series and parallel circuits.

Introduction

Static electricity deals with charges that are normally considered stationary, although they can jump as a spark, leak into the air on a humid day, or be transferred between objects. *Current electricity* deals with charges that are in continual motion. For a charge to be in motion, two things must be present: a driving force (electrical potential energy) and a path or circuit.

Three types of circuits are the open circuit, the closed circuit, and the short circuit. A closed circuit consists of an energy source (battery or generator), wires or other conductors that form a continuous path, and a load (an object that uses or dissipates most of the energy transferred in the circuit). The load can be a light bulb, speaker, motor, or heating element on a stove, as well as many other devices. An open circuit (which is not really a circuit) lacks the continuous path because there is a gap in the conductor, either purposely made (an open switch) or unintentionally (a break in a wire). A short circuit bypasses the load, so the energy from the driving force is expended only in the wire. This produces very high currents that cause the wire to get hot and melt due to the resistance in the wire.

We will also look at two simple circuit configurations mentioned in your textbook, series circuits and parallel circuits. In series circuits, all electrical charges pass through all electrical components one at a time in a series. The electrical potential energy of the source is used step-wise in each component until it is completely gone at the last load. In *parallel circuits,* the charges take different paths through the various loads. If you arrange the loads side by side in a diagram, the electrical paths through them are parallel. The total electrical potential energy from the source is applied to each component all at the same time.

Pre-Laboratory Questions

Read the entire investigation. Answer the following questions prior to class on a separate sheet of paper. Use complete sentences.

1. What is the difference between static electricity and current electricity?

2. What must exist for current electricity to occur?

3. List the parts of a basic electrical circuit.

4. What kind of device allows us to purposely open a circuit?

5. Can any object be a conductor in a circuit? Explain your answer.

6. What do we call a substance that can conduct electricity in a solution?

7. Name another action-at-a-distance force other than the electrostatic force that is related to electricity.

Procedures

This investigation will be performed at different stations unless you are given other instructions by your teacher. Read the instructions for each station carefully before you begin. After you have completed the actions at a station, be sure the battery is disconnected and the station is returned to the condition you found it before proceeding to the next station. The teacher will inform you of how much time you have at each station. Work quickly and quietly. Record the data during the class period and answer the discussion questions at a later time.

I. Closed Circuits

Station A

1. Materials include a battery, several lengths of wire, and a miniature light bulb.

2. Experiment with different ways to connect the battery, the wires, and the bulb so that the bulb lights.

   In the Results section for Station A, make sketches of the configurations that worked and those that did not. Note details such as the locations where the wires touched the light bulb and which terminal of the battery is connected to a given wire.

3. Disconnect the wires from the battery.

4. Answer Discussion Questions 1-4.

Station B

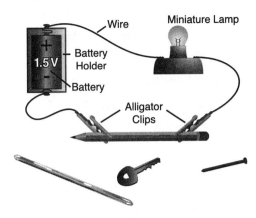

Figure 1

1. Materials include a battery, wires with alligator clips on the free ends, a miniature light bulb in a base, and various objects to be included in the circuit.

2. Attach the wires to the battery terminals as shown in Figure 1.

3. Insert various objects into the circuit by attaching alligator clips to the ends of the objects as shown in Figure 1.

4. Note whether the lamp lights with the object in the circuit. Record whether the object is a conductor or a nonconductor in the Station B data table in the Results section.

5. Remove the object from the clips and disconnect the wires from the battery.

6. Answer Discussion Questions 5-7.

Station C

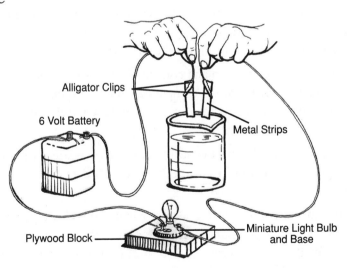

Figure 2

1. Materials include a battery, the conductivity apparatus used in earlier investigations, and three beakers containing distilled water, salt water, and sugar water.

Preparation

Preparations for this lab are extensive but fairly straightforward.

1. Cut 16- to 18-gauge wire into 30-cm lengths sufficient to make the connections at all of the stations. Strip 2-3 cm of insulation from each end of the wires.

2. If you are using standard $1\frac{1}{2}$ V D-cell batteries or 9 V batteries, it will be far more convenient when making connections to use battery holders. These are small plastic boxes that have electrical contacts and connections so you can hook up circuits to the batteries easily. Usually, the large 6 V batteries have connectors with screw posts or spiral wires.

3. Alligator clips, knife switches, miniature lamps, and lamp bases may be purchased at hardware stores or electronic shops such as Radio Shack.

4. Be sure that the miniature lamps you purchase are rated for the maximum voltage they will be subjected to or they will blow. For most stations, 6 V lamps will be sufficient.

5. For Station B, use objects such as copper plumbing fittings, wood, cloth, silverware, plastic ware, glass, paper, and nails.

6. The solutions for Station C may be prepared using 30 g each of sugar and salt dissolved in 100 mL of distilled water. Assemble the conductivity apparatus used in Investigation 2B and include the metal electrodes.

7. Station D requires a variety of voltages. This can be accomplished using a model train DC transformer. (Ensure that the lamps can

2. Connect the free ends of the wires to the battery. Dip the metal electrodes into the beaker containing distilled water and note if the solution conducts.

3. Rinse the electrodes between each test and determine the conductivity of the other solutions in turn.

4. Disconnect the wires from the battery and rinse the electrodes.

5. Record your observations in the table for Station C in the Results section.

6. Answer Discussion Questions 8-11.

Station D

This station illustrates a simple device called a **galvanoscope**. A galvanoscope indicates the presence of an electrical current by deflecting a magnet. You will alter the amount of current passing through the circuit by adding more batteries to the circuit.

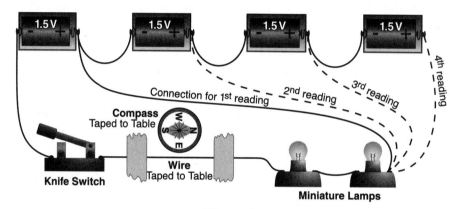

Figure 3

1. Materials include four batteries connected in series or a variable DC power source, a circuit consisting of wires, a switch, several miniature lamps and bases, and a magnetic compass taped to the table.

2. Verify that the switch is open and connect the two free ends of the wires to the first battery. Verify that the compass needle is parallel to the wire next to it. If you are using a transformer, position the control to the $^1/_4$ position (3 V for a 12 V transformer).

3. Shut the switch and observe the needle position (in degrees from north) on the compass. Record your results in the Station D data table in the Results section.

4. Open the switch and connect a second battery in series according to the directions provided by your teacher. The total voltage is the sum of the voltages for the two batteries. If you are using a transformer, move the control to the halfway point.

5. Shut the switch and note the position of the compass. Record your results as before.

6. Repeat steps 2-5 for a third and fourth battery (or the $^3/_4$ and full positions on the transformer).

7. Open the switch and disconnect the wires from the batteries.

8. Complete the graph of voltage versus angle of deflection for Station D in the Results section. You will have to provide the scales for voltage and angle to make the graph as large as possible.

II. Open Circuits

Station E

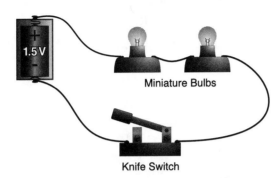

Miniature Bulbs

Knife Switch

Figure 4

1. Materials include a battery, wires, a switch, and two miniature light bulbs in bases.

2. Verify that the switch is open and connect the free ends of the wires to the battery.

3. Shut the switch and observe that the lamps light.

4. Unscrew and remove one of the lamps and observe what happens. Reinstall the lamp and verify that the lamps light again.

5. Open the switch and disconnect the wires from the battery.

6. Answer Discussion Question 12.

III. Short Circuits

Station F

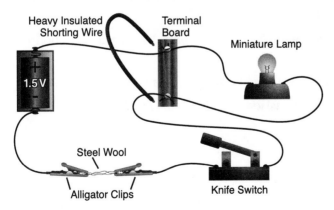

Heavy Insulated Shorting Wire

Terminal Board

Miniature Lamp

Steel Wool

Alligator Clips

Knife Switch

Figure 5

1. Materials include a battery, a circuit consisting of wires, a terminal board with two screws, a miniature light bulb in a base, and two alligator clips with some steel wool between them.

General Comments

1. Go over the layout of this investigation with your students before beginning. It is somewhat different from previous exercises. Show them where they will be recording data and ensure that there are no questions before starting.

2. Emphasize to your students that they will not have time to both record the data and complete the discussion questions in the lab period.

3. Inform students that they should try at least three different configurations for Station A.

4. Frequently monitor the activity at Station D since it is technically the most complicated station.

5. The two optional stations (H and I) will be most beneficial if students can measure the voltages specified in the investigation. Be sure the multimeters/voltmeters are set up correctly and demonstrate how to use them.

6. After the lab is completed, demonstrate to the students in a general way how to set up and enter data in the galvanoscope graph for Station D.

2. Verify that the switch is open and connect the free ends of the wires to the battery.

3. If not already done, pull a few strands of steel wool from the pad and insert them into the circuit between the two alligator clips.

4. Shut the switch and observe that the bulb lights.

5. Touch the two ends of the piece of heavy insulated wire to the screws at points A and B in Figure 5. Record what happens to the lamp and the steel wool under Station F of the Results section.

6. Open the switch and disconnect the wires from the battery.

7. Answer Discussion Questions 13-15.

Station G

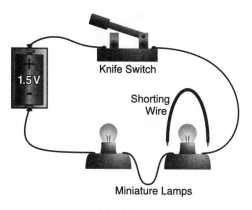

Figure 6

1. Materials include a battery, a circuit consisting of wires, two miniature lamps connected to a switch, and an additional insulated wire.

2. Verify that the switch is open and connect the free ends of the wires to the battery.

3. Shut the switch and observe that the bulbs light.

4. Touch the two ends of the heavy insulated wire to both terminals of one of the lamp bases as in Figure 6.

5. Describe what happened to *both* lamps under Station G in the Results section.

6. Open the switch and disconnect the wires from the battery.

7. Answer Discussion Questions 16 and 17.

IV. Types of Circuits (Optional)

Station H (Series Circuit)

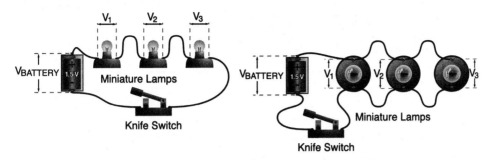

Figure 7   **Figure 8**

1. Materials include a battery and a circuit consisting of three miniature lamps connected in a string (series) with a switch. There may be a voltage test meter at this station also. (See Figure 7.)

2. Check that the switch is open and connect the free ends of the wires to the battery.

3. Shut the switch and note that all three lamps are lighted.

4. Unscrew each bulb one at a time, note what happens to all of the lamps, and screw it back in.

5. Take the test leads of a voltmeter and measure the voltage of the battery. Record this value in the blank labeled "$V_{battery}$."

6. Measure the voltage across each lamp by touching the terminals on the lamp bases with the test leads. Record each voltage reading in the blanks labeled "V_1," "V_2," and "V_3," below.

7. Add up the lamp voltages and enter the sum in the blank labeled "$V_{circuit}$," below.

Answers will vary for Question 7.

V_1 _____ $V_{battery}$ _____

V_2 _____

V_3 _____ $V_{circuit}$ _____

8. Open the switch and disconnect the wires from the battery.

9. Answer Discussion Questions 18–20.

Station I (Parallel Circuit)

1. Materials include a battery and a circuit consisting of three miniature lamps connected in a ladder arrangement (parallel) with a switch. There may be a voltage test meter at this station also. (See Figure 8, above.)

2. Verify that the switch is open and connect the free ends of the wires to the battery.

3. Shut the switch and note that all three lamps are lighted.

4. Unscrew each bulb one at a time. Note what happens to all of the lamps and screw the bulb back in.

5. Take the test leads of a voltmeter and measure the voltage of the battery. Record this value in the blank labeled "$V_{battery}$."

6. Measure the voltage across each lamp by touching the terminals on the lamp bases with the test leads. Record each voltage reading in the blanks labeled "V_1," "V_2," and "V_3," below.

V_1 _____ $V_{battery}$ _____

V_2 _____

V_3 _____

7. Open the switch and disconnect the wires from the battery.

8. Answer Discussion Questions 21-23.

Results

Station A

Sketch the circuit configurations that you tried when you attempted to light the lamp. Include both those that worked and those that did not.

Station B
Data Table:
Determining Conductivity

Object	Conductor? (Y/N)

Station C
Data Table:
Solution Conductivity

Solution	Conducts? (Y/N)
Distilled Water	N
Salt Solution	Y
Sugar Solution	N

Station D

Directions for graph: Determine the maximum voltage used at this station and write the value at the right end of the horizontal scale (Voltage). Subdivide the scale in equal parts starting at 0 V at the left end. Determine the maximum angle of deflection of the compass from the zero point (north) and write this value at the top of the vertical scale (Angle). Subdivide the vertical scale into equal parts starting at 0° at the bottom. Plot the ordered pairs of points (Volts, Degrees) for the readings in the data table below. Connect the points with a smooth curve.

Data Table: Galvanoscope Voltage vs. Deflection Angle

Volts	Deflection

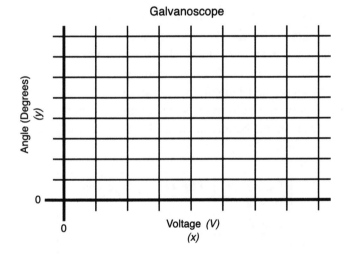

Galvanoscope

Station E

No results are to be recorded.

Station F

Describe your observations when you short out the lamp.

Lamp: *The lamp should be extinguished.* _____

Steel Wool: *The steel wool should first glow red and possibly melt,* _____ *opening the circuit.*

Station G

Describe your observations when you short out one of the lamps.

Shorted Lamp: *The shorted lamp should be extinguished.*

Nonshorted Lamp: *This lamp should glow brighter when the first is shorted out.*

Discussion Questions

Station A

1. What are the three components of a basic electrical circuit? *The three parts are an energy source (battery), conductors (wire), and a load. Students may also include a switch, but this is not one of the three essential components.*

2. What is the function of an electrical load? *The load is the device or component that uses or dissipates the energy supplied by the energy source.*

3. Considering a lamp as an electrical load, it converts energy from the battery into _____*light*_____ and _____*heat*_____.

4. The electrical path within a light bulb is not always immediately obvious. Look at Figure 9. Notice that as with all loads, there is a point where charges enter the bulb and a point where they can exit (Diagram A). These points are connected by the filament conductor (Diagram B). To ensure that no charges bypass the filament, there is an insulating material between the contact points on the bulb base. State whether the bulb would light when the two wires from the battery are placed at the following pairs of points on the bulb in Diagram C:

Contacts	Lights	Stays Dark
W & X		X
X & Y	X	
W & Z	X	
Y & Z		X

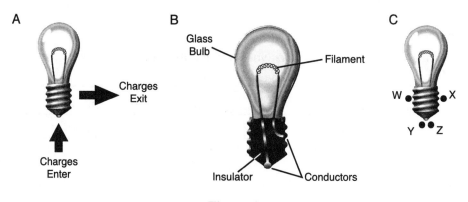

Figure 9

Station B

5. Make a generalization about the conductivity of metals and nonmetals based on your observations at Station B. *Metals conduct electricity, and nonmetals do not conduct electricity.*

6. Do the observations you made prove your generalization or merely suggest it? Explain your answer. *The data only suggests it since not all possible objects were tested.*

7. It is believed that the valence electrons of metal atoms are relatively free to move around, giving them the ability to conduct heat and electricity. What could be said about the freedom of valence electrons in nonmetal substances? *They are not free to move around.*

Station C

8. State whether testing the following resulted in an open or a closed circuit:

    a. Distilled water: *Open circuit*

    b. Salt solution: *Closed circuit*

    c. Sugar solution: *Open circuit*

9. What made the one solution conduct while the other two did not? *The salt solution had charged particles in solution, which caused the solution to act as a conductor. The other two solutions did not have current-carrying charges in solution.*

10. In Figure 10, draw arrows indicating the direction the ions will move when the charges shown are applied to the electrodes.

Figure 10

11. When a metal is inserted into a direct current circuit, electrons flow only in one direction—from the negative contact to the positive contact. Considering your answer to question 10, when ions in solution are part of a direct current circuit, how many directions can they move in? *They move in two directions.*

Station D

No questions for Station D.

Station E

12. Describe why the second lamp went out when the first lamp was unscrewed. *Unscrewing the lamp produced an open circuit, preventing the charges from flowing through the second lamp.*

Station F

13. When you touched the two screws with the insulated wire, explain what happened to the lamp. Discuss the relative resistance to the flow of charges of the wire and the bulb filament. Which is easier for the charges to flow through? *The bulb was extinguished because it was easier for charges to pass through the insulated wire than the filament.*

14. Why did the steel wool get hot (and possibly melt)? *The resistance to the high flow of charges through the fine steel wool produced enough heat to cause the metal to glow.*

15. Many years ago when electrical fuses were commonly used in houses, some people replaced a burned out fuse with a penny to restore a circuit, especially if they did not have a replacement fuse. Why was this an unsafe practice? *The penny acted just like the wire in the rest of the circuit, so there was no protection from short circuits.*

Station G

16. When the first bulb was shorted by the insulated wire, why did it go out? *The insulated wire has less resistance to the flow of charges compared to the lamp filament, so they went through the wire rather than through the bulb.*

17. Explain why the second bulb did not go out. *With the shorting wire in place, there was still a complete circuit for the second bulb, so it continued to burn.*

Station H (Optional)

18. What happened when each lamp was removed from the circuit? *The other two lamps went out.*

19. How does $V_{battery}$ compare to $V_{circuit}$? *They are the same.*

20. Make a general statement summarizing the relationship of the energy produced in a circuit and the energy used by the loads in the circuit. *Answers will vary. Students should say essentially that the energy produced by the battery is equal to the total energy used by the loads.*

Station I (Optional)

21. What happened when each lamp was removed from the circuit? *The* _____
    other two lamps remained lit.

22. How does $V_{battery}$ compare to V_1, V_2, and V_3? *They are all equal.* _____

    _____

23. How did the individual brightness of each lamp compare to the individual
    brightness of the lamps at Station H? Explain your observation. *The lamps* ____
    were brighter at Station I than at Station H because there was a greater
    voltage across each lamp at Station I.

18A INVESTIGATION

Magnetic Fields: Bar Magnets

Objective

The purpose of this exercise is to determine the shape, direction, and strength of the magnetic field around a bar magnet.

Materials

Card stock
Iron filings
Paper
Paper clips
Tape

Equipment

Bar magnets (2)
Lodestone (optional)
Magnetic compasses (5)

Introduction

Magnets can exert a force on certain objects without physically touching them. How these action-at-a-distance forces get from the magnet to an object is an area of intense speculation about the nature of space and matter. Although the process is not understood, the effects of these forces can be described with great precision and their presence can be easily seen by sprinkling iron filings around a magnet. The curved lines formed by the iron filings picture a two-dimensional *cross section* of the three-dimensional **magnetic field** surrounding the magnet. A field is the region of space in which a force acts. A magnetic field is the force field generated by the magnet that will affect another magnet, iron, or any other magnetic material.

These imaginary lines of force are used to visualize the direction and strength of the field, and they have certain properties characteristic of all fields. For example, the closer together the lines are, the stronger the field. Field lines never cross one another. If they did, it would mean that the field points in more than one direction at the point of intersection—a physical impossibility. Magnetic field lines always start at a north magnetic pole and end in a south magnetic pole. Some magnetic field lines ending in a magnet could theoretically originate at an infinite distance away. Practically speaking, though, there are many closer sources of magnetic fields (the earth, power lines, etc.).

Introduction

The concept of a field is developed in more detail. While field theory is best studied in advanced calculus, you can convey to your students that fields can be represented by vectors at every point in the field. Most diagrams show a two-dimensional representation of magnetic fields. Emphasize that magnetic fields are three-dimensional. A nice educational aid is available from science suppliers consisting of a clear container filled with oil containing suspended iron filings. You can insert a magnet into a central receptacle and observe the filings orient themselves around the magnet in three dimensions.

Pre-Laboratory Questions

Read the entire investigation. Answer the following questions prior to class on a separate sheet of paper. Use complete sentences.

1. How does the magnetic attraction get from the matter in a magnet to an iron nail?

2. Describe a field of force such as an electrostatic or a magnetic field.

3. What is a magnetic field?

4. What determines the strength of a magnetic field?

5. Where do magnetic field lines originate? Where do they end?

6. How will you make the field lines visible in this investigation?

7. How will you determine the direction of the magnetic field?

Procedures

A. Field Strength

If you could count the number of field lines passing through an imaginary plane with an area of 1 cm², you could determine the strength of the field. This is not possible, although there exist mathematical methods to calculate field strength. In this investigation, we will use a more physical approach to indicate field strength.

Figure 1

1. Mark a bar magnet every 1 cm from the south pole to the middle. Do the same from the north pole. Label the sections, starting with *A* at the ends and proceeding to the center of the magnet as in Figure 1.

2. Test the strength of the magnetic field at each section, one at a time, by determining how many paper clips will hang from that section of the magnet. Hold the magnet with one hand and add the paper clips one at a time with the other until no more can be supported by the magnet.

3. Enter these numbers in the data table in the Field Strength section of the Results.

B. Field Direction

The direction of any field is indicated by arrows drawn parallel to the field lines. The direction of the field is completely arbitrary (not determined by some supreme authority). Scientists have agreed that the direction of a magnetic field (the ways the field lines point) is the same direction that the north end of a magnet suspended in the field would point.

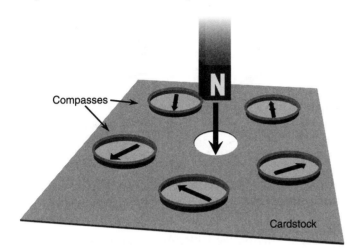

Figure 2

1. Tape the five compasses to a piece of cardstock so that they are equally spaced around a hole just large enough to allow the bar magnet to pass through. (See Figure 2.)

2. Holding the card horizontal, allow the compass needles to come to rest. Slowly pass the magnet vertically down through the hole in the card. Note which pole is entering first and the orientation of the compass needles.

3. Have an assistant finish pulling the magnet through the hole from underneath the card. Note the direction of the compass needles as this process is completed.

4. Draw the orientation of the compass needles when the north end of the magnet is in the hole on Diagram A in the Field Direction section of the Results. After drawing the compass needles, sketch the direction of the field. Follow the same instructions when the magnet is exactly halfway through the hole for Diagram B and when the south end of the magnet is in the hole for Diagram C.

Preparation

1. Some laboratories do not have small compasses. In this case, larger compasses can be used. If you do not have sufficient compasses for all of your lab teams, they can use one compass per team as follows. Mark five locations equally spaced around the hole in the card. For each position of the magnet, observe the compass at each of the marked locations.

2. Iron filings can be inexpensively purchased in 1 kg or 1 lb. quantities from science suppliers. For small schools and home schools, it is possible to obtain sufficient magnetic particles for this demonstration from local soil or sand deposits. Drag a strong magnet through the sand. It will pick up magnetite and ferrite particles, which can be scraped into a container.

3. Lodestones can be obtained from most science suppliers.

C. Field Lines

We have already discussed the use of field lines to describe the shape of a magnetic field. Recall that field lines are a mental concept or model to help us understand the field theory. Magnetic particles tend to line up parallel to the forces in a field. Your eyes and brain interpret this arrangement of particles as lines.

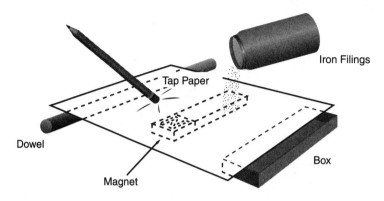

Figure 3

1. Lay one bar magnet flat on the table. Arrange objects around the magnet about the same thickness as the magnet to support the sheet of paper. You can use items such as the top and bottom of the magnet box, wooden dowels, or notebook paper pads. (See Figure 3.)

2. Center the sheet of paper on top of the magnet.

3. Carefully sprinkle the iron filings onto the paper at the location of the magnet. Do not pour the filings in a pile. As more particles are trapped by the field, tap the paper with a pencil to help the particles become oriented with the field. Use enough filings so that all parts of the field can be seen.

4. Sketch the shape of the lines around Diagram A of the single bar magnet in the Field Lines section of the Results.

5. When finished, lift the paper straight up, bend it into a trough, and return the filings to the container.

6. Place two bar magnets so that their opposite poles are in line with each other but separated by about 3 cm.

7. Arrange the paper supports and center the sheet of paper over the gap between the ends of the magnets.

8. Repeat step 3 and sketch the shape of the field on Diagram B. Be sure to label the poles on the diagram.

9. Return the iron filings to the container. Rotate one of the magnets so that two like poles are now close to each other. Replace the paper sheet.

10. Repeat step 3 and sketch the shape of the field on Diagram C. Label the poles on your diagram.

11. Return the filings to the container and clean up any stray particles on the desk.

D. Lodestone (Optional)

Lodestones are natural magnetic ores of iron consisting of a mixture of iron oxides. As with any magnet, lodestones have a north and a south pole.

1. Examine your lodestone sample. Note its shape, color, texture, and relative density.

2. Using a magnetic compass, locate the north and south poles.

3. Sketch your lodestone, including the location of the poles in the designated space in the Results section.

Results

A. Field Strength

Data Table: Field Strength

Section	Number of Paper Clips	
	North End	South End
A		
B		
C		
D		
E		
F		
G		
H		
I		
J		
K		

B. Field Direction

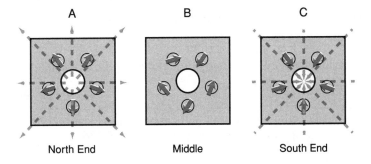

A	B	C
North End	Middle	South End

Magnetic Fields: Bar Magnets

C. Field Lines

D. Lodestone

Sketch your sample of lodestone in this space.

Discussion Questions

1. Where on a bar magnet is the field strongest? Where is it weakest? *The field is strongest at the ends (or poles) of the magnet. It is weakest in the middle of the magnet.*

2. Does the strength of the magnet taper off gradually, or does it seem to be concentrated at certain locations? *The magnet has concentrations of force at the ends. Most of the length between the ends has little or no magnetic strength.*

3. In what direction does the field point around the north end of the magnet? *The field points away from the north end.*

    In what direction does the field point at the south end? *The field points toward the south end of the magnet.*

    In what direction does the field point in the middle of the magnet? *The field direction is indeterminate.*

4. (Optional) Is there any external indication of the location of the poles on a lodestone? Explain. *No, the rock is irregular in shape. No texture or color clues indicate the magnetic poles.*

5. How do the fields interact between opposite poles? *The field lines bend toward the other pole.*

   How do the fields interact between like poles? *The field lines bend away from the other pole.*

6. State two ways that the drawings of field lines on a flat piece of paper misrepresent an actual magnetic field.

   a. *A field is three-dimensional.*

   b. *A field is continuous—it is not made of distinct lines.*

Magnetic Fields: Bar Magnets

18B INVESTIGATION
Electromagnets

Objectives

The purpose of this exercise is to

1. Review the principles of electromagnetism.

2. Investigate the properties of electromagnets.

3. Practice graphing and evaluating data.

Materials

Iron filings
Masking tape
Notebook paper
Wire (insulated), long length (1)
Wire (insulated), short lengths (3)

Equipment

Bar magnets (2)
Batteries, 6 V (3)
Knife switch
Machine bolt
Nails
Rods (glass, plastic, wood)

Introduction

Be sure to discuss the information in Sections 18A and 18B of the textbook before performing this investigation. Emphasize the different types of magnetic materials. You may want to mention a class of materials called diamagnetic *that could almost be considered anti-magnetic. When placed in a magnetic field, they actually weaken the field. Such materials include bismuth, copper, and salt. You may also want to review Ohm's law to show how current is proportional to voltage. Emphasize that it is the current that produces the magnetic field and not the voltage.*

Introduction

In 1823 William Sturgeon created the first working electromagnet by wrapping wire around a metal bar. No one suspected that these devices would someday guide protons down the path of particle accelerators at nearly the speed of light, hold superheated plasma in invisible containers, or probe the intricate structures of the brain to detect disorders. Today, electromagnets perform all of these functions and more.

You will recall from your textbook that an electromagnet consists of a solenoid (a coil of wire connected to an energy source) surrounding a material that concentrates magnetic lines of force (the core). Some materials are not much better than air at concentrating magnetic lines of force, while others are very effective at concentrating them. Materials that have this property are called *ferromagnetic,* and they tend to make strong electromagnets. In addition to the core material, the strength of an electromagnet depends on the number of wraps (or turns) of the wire around the core as well as the amount of current passing through the wire. Ohm's law states that for constant resistance, the current in a circuit is directly proportional to the voltage applied to the circuit. We will assume that the wire used in this investigation has a small but constant resistance. Therefore, if the voltage is doubled, the current will be doubled.

Pre-Laboratory Questions

Read the entire investigation. Answer the following questions prior to class on a separate sheet of paper. Use complete sentences.

1. Describe the structure of an electromagnet.

2. Give two of the three ways discussed that an electromagnet can be made stronger.

3. Why is it necessary to limit the time that the switch is shut when testing the strength of the electromagnets?

4. What term describes the tiny regions in a ferromagnetic material that give the material its magnetic character?

5. Review the procedure for testing the number of wraps in Part II. If both electromagnets are connected to 6 V batteries, which one will actually have a higher current flow, the one with ten wraps of wire or the one with fifty wraps? Explain.

6. Define *extrapolation* and *interpolation*.

Procedures

I. Domains

The domain theory of magnetism states that ferromagnetic material is composed of very small areas that act like magnets with a north and a south pole (see diagram A in Figure 1). Normally, these areas are not in line, so they cancel each other's magnetic effects (diagram B). However, when placed in a strong magnetic field, these domains become oriented more or less in the same direction, forming a magnet (diagram C).

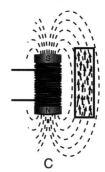

A   B   C

Figure 1

Loose iron filings can illustrate the behavior of domains.

1. Take two bar magnets and lay them side by side with the north poles aligned.

2. Place nonmagnetic spacers around the magnets to support the sheet of paper.

3. Place a piece of notebook paper over the magnets and sprinkle iron filings over the magnets.

4. Note the orientation and concentration of the field lines around the pair of magnets. Sketch your observations around the pair of N–N magnets in the Domains section of the Results.

5. Return the iron filings to the container and turn one of the magnets so that the magnets are in a N–S orientation. Replace the sheet of paper.

6. Again sprinkle the iron filings over the magnets and note the orientation and concentration of the field lines. Sketch your observations around the pair of N–S magnets in the Domains section of the Results.

7. Return the iron filings to the container.

8. Which orientation produced the stronger and more distinct north and south poles? *The students should observe that the N–N orientation produced the largest and most distinct magnetic poles.*

II. Electromagnets

In this part of the investigation, you will construct an electromagnet by wrapping the long insulated wire around the machine bolt, which will act as the core. To make the magnet as efficient as possible, ensure that the wraps are tight and snug against one another. If it is necessary to double the layers of coils, carefully continue the wrapping in the same direction on top of the first layer, working back to the starting point on the bolt.

A. Number of Turns

1. Make an electromagnet by wrapping the long wire around the bolt ten times. Leave about 40 cm free at the end of the wire before you start wrapping. Tape the wire to the bolt to hold it in place. Allow the remaining wire to hang free—do not cut it off.

2. Connect one end of the wire to the 6 V battery and the other end to the switch. Check that the switch is open and connect a short piece of wire from the switch to the other terminal on the battery.

Note: You may be using batteries with a voltage other than 6 V. The procedures may be followed as written for any voltage battery.

3. Scoop the nails into a pile.

Perform the next step as quickly as possible. Remember that while the switch is shut, there is essentially a short circuit through the electromagnet coil since there is very little resistance in the wire. The battery will drain rapidly, and the wire will heat up. Open the switch as soon as the maximum number of nails can be picked up.

4. Shut the switch to energize the electromagnet and pick up as many nails as possible. Select an open area and open the switch to drop the nails so that they can be counted.

5. Count the nails collected and enter this number in Table 1 for Trial 1, 10 wraps.

Preparation

1. The main limiting resource for this investigation will be the number of batteries. DO NOT USE 12 V AUTO BATTERIES! We chose 6 V batteries because they can produce the relatively high current flow needed to produce the desired magnetic field strength. If the cost is prohibitive, you can use up to three or four 1.5 V batteries in battery holders and use paper clips instead of nails.

2. You may also perform the investigation as a teacher demonstration. You can do the domain demonstration on the overhead using a transparency and have the students record the data from your wrap, voltage, and core-type demonstrations in front of the class.

3. To make the core materials demonstration work best, you should try to obtain core samples that are all about the same diameter. The bolts should be chosen so that they are slightly larger than the other materials. The wood core can be a section of the appropriate diameter wood dowel. The glass and plastic can be rods from an electrostatic demonstration kit. You can also tape glass stirring rods together. Other metal cores can be substituted from a specific gravity kit. These can be particularly interesting when demonstrating paramagnetism (Al) and diamagnetism (Cu).

4. You should obtain a spool of 18- to 22-gauge insulated single-strand copper wire from a home improvements store. Prior to class, wrap a bolt with fifty turns of wire to see how much will be required.

Add 80 cm to this length and cut the required number of wires for the number of teams in your class. If you will be doing the entire voltage section of the investigation with three batteries, you will need three 30-cm sections per lab team. Strip 2-3 cm of insulation off all wire ends.

5. Batteries should be obtained in bulk from discount stores. Try to obtain the ones with screw-on terminal caps. Test all batteries before class to verify that they have sufficient voltage. It is always wise to have spares available.

6. Knife switches are a convenience but not essential for this investigation. You may just connect a wire to a battery as necessary to energize the electromagnet.

7. Nails should be ungalvanized, uncoated, steel nails approximately one to three inches long. Obtain enough so that each lab team will have sufficient nails for the high voltage test. Perform the investigation yourself prior to the lab period to see how many will be needed.

6. Repeat steps 3 and 4 twice more, recording the numbers in Table 1 for Trials 2 and 3.

7. Compute the average for the three trials and enter this value in Table 1.

8. Perform this section (steps 1-7) again with twenty, thirty, forty, and fifty wraps. You do not have to unwrap the previous turns; just add the new wraps to the existing electromagnet.

9. In addition to Table 1, record the average results for fifty wraps in the "1 Battery" row of Table 2 and the "Bolt" row of Table 3 in the Results.

B. Voltage

1. Check that the switch is open. Disconnect the wire to the negative terminal of the battery you used in the previous section. Attach one of the short segments of wire to this terminal and connect the other end to the positive terminal of a second 6 V battery. Connect the free wire of the electromagnet to the negative end of the second battery. You now have two 6 V batteries connected in series with a total voltage of 12 V. Enter the total voltage of the batteries used in the "Batteries" column of Table 2.

2. **Perform this step quickly to avoid damaging the batteries and melting the wire insulation.** Scoop the nails into a pile, shut the switch to energize the electromagnet, and pick up as many nails as possible. Open the switch to drop the nails in an open space.

3. Count the nails and enter this number in the "2 Batteries" row of Table 2.

4. (Optional) If available, connect a third 6 V battery in series with the second battery according to step 1 of this section. You now have three batteries in series with a total of 18 V.

5. (Optional) **Observe the precaution of step 2.** Determine how many nails can be picked up at 18 V. Enter this number in the "3 Batteries" row of Table 2.

C. Core Type

1. Without unwrapping the wire, carefully remove the bolt from the fifty-turn solenoid. You may have to rotate the bolt to loosen it from the wire.

2. Disconnect the second and third batteries and reconnect the free wire of the solenoid to the first battery.

3. Scoop the nails into a pile as before. Leaving the core empty, shut the switch to energize the solenoid. Touch the solenoid to the pile of nails and pick up as many nails as possible. Open the switch to drop the nails in an open area and count them. Enter this number in the "Air" row in Table 3.

4. Repeat step 3 for the remaining core types that you were provided. Complete Table 3.

When you are finished, disconnect all wires and set the short lengths aside. Carefully unwrap the bolt and coil the wire according to your teacher's instructions. Return all equipment and materials to their designated locations.

Results

   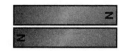

Table 1: Electromagnets and Number of Wraps

Number of Wraps	Number of Nails			
	Trial 1	Trial 2	Trial 3	Average
10				
20				
30				
40				
50				

Table 2: Electromagnets and Voltage

Batteries	Number of Nails
1 (V)	
2 (V)	
3 (V)	

Table 3: Electromagnets and Core Type

Core Type	Number of Nails
Bolt	
Air	
Wood	
Glass	
Plastic	

Discussion Questions

1. State the three variables tested and describe how each variable affected the strength of the electromagnet. *The three variables tested were the number of wire wraps, the voltage applied, and the type of core. Electromagnetic strength increased with greater number of wraps, greater voltage, and use of a ferromagnetic core.*

2. Plot the data from Table 1 using the number of wraps as the *x* value and the average number of nails as the *y* value. Draw a best-fit line through the resulting points.

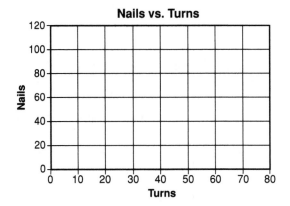

3. Extend the line in the graph from the last datum point to the edge *using a dashed line*. Read the *y* value corresponding to eighty turns on the *x*-axis along this extended line. According to your graph, how many nails could be picked up with eighty turns? _____

Estimating values that are greater than the actual range of data collected is called **extrapolation.** Scientists often obtain information from extrapolations.

a. What did you have to assume about the shape of the line in order to make your extrapolation? *The student had to assume that the straight line continued.*

b. How accurate would your extrapolation be if your assumption was incorrect? *The extrapolation would be wrong.*

c. What must scientists ensure when making extrapolations of their data? *Scientists must make sure that their assumptions are reasonable based on what is already known, not on bias or prejudice.*

d. What are scientists doing when they conclude that a series of similar fossils of increasing complexity in a geologic column are the evolutionary ancestors to a living organism? *They are making an inappropriate extrapolation based on unscientific assumptions.*

4. According to the graph, how many nails could be picked up with thirty-five turns? _____

Estimating values between tested data points is called **interpolation.** Interpolation is a valuable mathematical tool used when one must estimate an unknown value between two known ones.

5. Which do you think would be more accurate, extrapolation or interpolation? Explain. *Interpolation is likely to be more accurate because the relationship of the data is more predictable between known data points than assuming a relationship beyond known data points.*

6. What is the domain theory of magnets? *The domain theory of magnets* *states that magnetic force is produced by tiny regions within ferromagnetic* *materials that contain a north and south pole. When these regions are* *aligned in the same direction, magnetism is produced.*

7. When electrical current passed through the coil, what happened to the domains in the bolt? *The domains in the bolt aligned with the external* *magnetic field.*

8. When the switch was opened, what do you think happened to the domains in the bolt? *Most of the domains gradually shifted out of alignment back* *to their original orientation.*

Experimental Evaluation

9. A magnetic field of force can be defined as the strengths and directions of the magnetic forces around the magnet. What is the weakness with this definition? *The term* magnetic forces *is not defined because it uses a* *form of the word* magnet *and incorporates the ideas of "strengths and* *directions" (part of the definition of* force*), so nothing has actually been* *defined.*

10. Several of the cores did not form an effective electromagnetic field. Do you think this proves that there are no domains in these materials? Explain.
It does not necessarily prove that there are no domains. The methods used *in this investigation may not detect very weak domains in the materials.*

11. Domains are described as theoretical. Why are domains not described as facts or laws? *Domains cannot be observed or measured directly. They are* *part of the mathematical model of magnetism.*

Objective

The purpose of these demonstrations is to show some of the basic properties of waves.

Introduction

In this demonstration we will be considering some properties of **mechanical waves,** those that travel through a medium. Examples of mechanical waves include water waves, seismic waves, and sound waves. Mechanical waves depend on a disturbance of the particles of the medium to transmit their energy. It was demonstrated by Robert Boyle that sound waves do not travel in a vacuum chamber (a chamber that has had all of the air removed). This is in contrast to light waves, which do not require the presence of any matter for their propagation.

You know that sound waves travel through air, but you also will recognize through practical experiences that sound waves are able to travel through solids as well. The effectiveness of a doctor's stethoscope depends on the fact that sound energy is transmitted better through solids than through air. He cannot hear your heart beating when he is standing next to you. However, when the stethoscope makes physical contact with you, the sound waves are effectively transmitted through the instrument to the doctor's ears. Before the stethoscope was invented, the doctor would place his ear on a patient's chest to help in his diagnosis. When you are underwater, you can still hear garbled sounds that your friend is making even if you can't clearly understand the words. Many marine species use sound waves both as a means to communicate with each other and as sonar to locate prey. Generally the more rigid a substance is, the more effective it is at transmitting sound energy. Water transmits sound better than air, but solids are more effective than water.

Mechanical waves can be classified as either **transverse** or **longitudinal.** Any wave can be fully described by stating its amplitude, wavelength, and frequency. The **amplitude** of the wave refers to the size of the disturbance caused by the source of the wave. The **wavelength** describes the distance between one crest and the next (alternately, it describes the distance from one trough to the next or, in a standing wave, the distance between alternate nodes). The **frequency** of the wave states how many times a complete wave passes a point in one second. The meaning of these terms will become clearer during the demonstrations.

Answers to Pre-Laboratory Questions

1. A mechanical wave is a rhythmic disturbance that transmits energy through matter. Light is an example of a wave that is not a mechanical wave.

2. Wavelength is the distance between the same point on two sequential waves. Amplitude is the distance the wave crest or trough departs from the neutral position. Frequency is the number of waves that pass a point in one second.

3. A longitudinal wave is a wave in which the direction of deflection of the matter through which it is traveling is parallel to the direction that the wave energy is traveling. Light is also an example of a wave that is not a longitudinal wave (light is a transverse wave).

4. A pulse is a single wave-like disturbance.

5. A standing wave produces resonance in an object.

Equipment
Slinky, full-sized

Demonstration Procedures For most of these demonstrations, you will need to use a full-sized Slinky that is either secured to the wall at one end or held firmly by a student. A metal slinky will probably work better than a plastic one. It should be extended to a length of about 10 m so that much of the slack is removed. The Slinky could also be laid on the floor and the transverse waves generated by moving the end side to side rather than up and down. A length of soft, heavy rope will also serve well in these demonstrations if it is kept fairly taut.

Pre-Laboratory Questions

Read the entire demonstration. Answer the following questions prior to class on a separate sheet of paper. Use complete sentences.

1. What is a mechanical wave? Give an example of a wave that is *not* a mechanical wave.

2. Describe wavelength, amplitude, and frequency.

3. What is a longitudinal wave? Give an example of a wave that is *not* a longitudinal wave.

4. What is a pulse?

5. What is one result of a standing wave in an object or substance?

Demonstrations

A. Transverse Waves

1. Observe what happens when one end of the Slinky is rapidly elevated once and brought back down. A one-time event that causes a wavelike disturbance is called a **pulse.** Describe your observations. <u>*A bump*</u>
   <u>*formed in the Slinky, which traveled to the other end and back again.*</u>

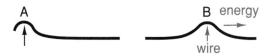

Figure 1

In Figure 1, the arrow below *A* shows that the movement of a particle in the wire is in the upward direction, perpendicular to the length of the wire. However, the movement of the wave itself (the movement of the energy) is parallel to the length of the wire. You can see the "bump" moving along.

2. In diagram B in Figure 1, draw an arrow (labeled "wire") representing the direction that a particle in the wire moved and an arrow (labeled "energy") representing the direction that the energy was originally moving.

3. Draw a picture of the return wave below, labeling the direction of displacement of the wire and the energy flow.

This type of wave is called a **transverse** wave since the particles in the wire are deflected perpendicularly to the path of the energy. Light and some seismic waves are examples of transverse waves. The rebounding of the wave is called a **reflection.** In this case, the reflected wave is a mirror image of the original wave. Notice that although the energy is transmitted down the Slinky, the Slinky returns to its original position after the wave has passed. Mechanical waves require matter to transmit energy, but there is little or no net movement of matter along with the wave itself.

B. Longitudinal Waves

1. Observe what happens when your teacher gathers together a section of the Slinky and then releases it. This is called a compression wave.

2. Describe your observations. *A section where the coils are close together*

   (wave of compression) moves down the Slinky and back again.

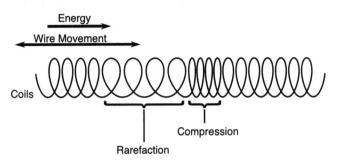

Figure 2

The arrows in Figure 2 indicate the direction of the wire motion and of the energy. This type of wave is called a **longitudinal** wave since the particles are deflected parallel to the same direction as the movement of energy. Sound and some seismic waves are examples of longitudinal waves. Notice in Figure 2 that adjacent to the compression, the particles of matter in the medium are farther apart than in the medium at rest. These regions are called **rarefactions.**

C. Describing Waves

The waves demonstrated thus far are called **pulses** since they were caused by only one vibration. Many waves are generated by an ongoing source of vibrations.

1. Observe as your teacher generates a constant source of transverse vibrations in the wire. You should be able to observe a resulting wave similar to that below. Notice the crest, the trough, the amplitude, and the wavelength. The Greek letter λ (lambda) is used to represent the wavelength.

2. Notice that the amplitude refers to the amount of displacement from the neutral position and is equal to one-half the distance between the top of the crest and the bottom of the trough. The crest and the trough have the same amplitude but in different directions.

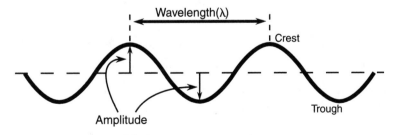

Figure 3

A. Transverse Waves
To generate a pulse, move the free end of the Slinky up and down one time sharply. Try not to allow any additional displacement below the original starting point of your hand so that the pulse looks like a hump. The inversion of the reflected pulse will be much more distinct.

B. Longitudinal Waves
To generate the wave, gather up about one foot of the Slinky in your hand and release it suddenly. You can generate a train of compression waves as follows: Attach a wooden dowel or a paint stirring paddle with tape to one loop of the Slinky so that it projects like a handle. Rhythmically move the handle longitudinally to form a train of longitudinal waves.

D. Standing Waves

If a constant train of waves moves down the wire and is reflected with the same frequency and amplitude, a **standing wave** develops (see Figure 4 below). Standing waves produce the phenomenon of *resonance*. In a standing wave, the stationary points are called **nodes** and the alternating crests and troughs are called **antinodes.** Standing waves occur not only in wires but also in water and sound waves. Altering the frequency of the wave creates different standing waves.

1. Watch as your teacher alters the frequency of the vibration of the slinky to create different standing waves. What do you notice as the frequency increases? *The number of nodes increases.*

2. How does this affect the wavelength? *The wavelength decreases.*

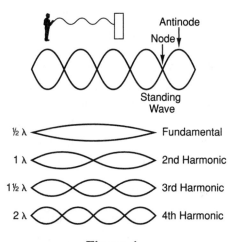

Figure 4

Musical pitches are distinguished by their frequencies. The different standing waves or resonances that are formed by a musical instrument are called its **harmonics** or **overtones.** An instrument produces the fundamental pitch loudest but also produces many overtones at the same time. It is these different combinations of harmonics that give each type of instrument, and indeed each individual instrument, its own unique sound.

E. Wave Speed

1. Notice the speed of a single wave pulse as it moves down the Slinky. Your teacher may ask you to use a stopwatch.

2. Watch as your teacher increases the amplitude of the pulse. Did the greater amplitude change the speed? *No*

3. Watch as your teacher sends a train of waves through the Slinky. Did the increased frequency of waves increase the speed of the waves? *No*

4. What can be concluded from these observations? *The speed of a wave is not dependent on either the amplitude of the wave or its frequency.*

5. What do you think determines the wave speed? *The medium through which it travels is the only thing that affects the speed of a wave.*

F. Interference

When two waves meet, the resulting wave at any point is the sum of the amplitudes of the two individual waves. This is called **interference.** If two crests meet (or two troughs), the resulting wave will have an amplitude at that point greater than either of the individual waves. This is called **constructive interference.** If a crest and a trough meet, the two waves will offset each other. This is called **destructive interference.** If the crest and trough are of exactly the same amplitude, at the point where they meet, the wave will be cancelled out completely. This principle is used effectively to create high quality headphones for pilots by eliminating virtually all static in radio transmissions.

Your teacher will have two people produce transverse waves on each end of the Slinky according to his directions. Observe and draw the resulting waves at the point where they coincide, labeling the direction of deflection and the direction of the energy flow.

Discussion Questions

1. Define the following terms:

   Wave *A wave is a disturbance that transfers energy through space or matter.*

   Transverse wave *A transverse wave is a wave in which the particles move in a direction perpendicular to the direction of the path of energy.*

   Longitudinal wave *A longitudinal wave is a wave in which the particles move in a direction parallel to the direction of the path of energy.*

   Reflection *Reflection is the rebounding of a wave from a surface.*

   Pulse *A pulse is a wave form that results from only one vibration.*

   Standing wave *A standing wave is the wave form resulting from the interference of a train of waves and their reflections traveling in the same path at the same frequency and amplitude.*

   Harmonics (overtones) *Harmonics are different standing waves related to a fundamental that can exist in the same medium.*

   Interference *Interference is the overlapping of two waves at the same place and time.*

E. Wave Speed
1. Generate a single pulse. The second time, increase the amplitude of the pulse. The third time, send two pulses close together, a small amplitude pulse followed by a large amplitude pulse. The fact that the larger pulse does not overtake the smaller will demonstrate that the amplitude does not affect the wave speed.

2. This is a tricky demonstration because it is hard to visually distinguish between the speeds of waves that have different amplitudes. Waves with large amplitudes always appear to go faster. Stretch the Slinky as far as possible to increase its length and have the students count the time out loud as the wave is traveling. You could also assign several students to time the waves with stopwatches.

1. Have a student hold each end of the Slinky. Try to create a constructive interference by having both students simultaneously create waves by deflecting their end of the Slinky in the same direction. Try to create destructive interference by having both students simultaneously create waves by deflecting their end of the Slinky in opposite directions.

2. Emphasize that the waves actually pass through each other. The students may not be able to tell whether the waves pass through or bounce off each other. Solve this by having one student generate a large pulse while the other generates a small one. Students will be able to track the pulses through the interference point.

Constructive interference *Constructive interference results when displacements of overlapping waves are in the same direction, resulting in a crest or trough of greater amplitude than either of the original waves.*

Destructive interference *Destructive interference results when displacements of overlapping waves are in opposite directions, resulting in a crest or trough of lesser amplitude than either of the original waves.*

2. Was it proved that all waves that were generated in this demonstration traveled at the same speed in the Slinky? Explain. *No, the wave speed was only approximated.*

3. Could you prove that all mechanical waves travel at the same speed through the Slinky? Explain. *No, all waves would have to be tested, and that would be impossible.*

4. An important aspect of waves is that the medium (Slinky, water, air, vacuum, etc.) determines the speed of the wave and not the amplitude or the frequency. Is this statement a proven fact, a statement supported by many observations, or a guess? Explain. *This is a statement supported by repeated demonstrations. One cannot test all waves under all conditions.*

19B TEACHER DEMONSTRATION
Properties of Sound

Objective

The purpose of these demonstrations is to illustrate several of the properties of sound waves.

Introduction

Vibrating matter can produce sound waves. As you have learned in this course, sound travels as longitudinal waves. When a wave hits your eardrum, your middle and inner ear convert that mechanical energy to electrochemical energy. The electrical impulses are transmitted to your brain, where they are interpreted as sound. Sound waves can illustrate properties that are common to all kinds of waves.

Pre-Laboratory Questions

Read the entire demonstration. Answer the following questions prior to class on a separate sheet of paper. Use complete sentences.

1. What equation can you use to calculate the speed of a sound wave, given its frequency and wavelength?

2. What phenomenon causes the change of the perceived pitch of a sound source moving relative to the hearer?

3. Which medium transmits sound energy better, water or air, and why?

4. What instrument will your teacher use to demonstrate the reflection of sound waves?

5. What is the bending of waves around a corner called?

Procedures

A. Pitch, Wavelength, and Frequency

Recall that the speed of a sound wave in any medium is constant for that medium. The speed $(\frac{\text{meters}}{\text{second}})$ = frequency $(\frac{\text{cycles}}{\text{second}})$ × wavelength $(\frac{\text{meters}}{\text{cycle}})$. As a formula, $v = f\lambda$. If v is to stay constant, as the frequency increases the wavelength must decrease.

1. Watch as your teacher places a ruler so that it extends beyond the edge of the table and then thrums the end to start it vibrating. He will vary the length of the ruler extending beyond the edge as he thrums it.

2. What do you notice about the sound as he continues thrumming it while sliding more of the ruler onto the tabletop (shortening the overhanging portion)? *The pitch of the sound gets higher.*

3. If you shorten the length of material that is vibrating by sliding more of the ruler onto the tabletop, you generate shorter wavelengths. Since the speed of sound in air is constant, this results in a higher frequency sound wave. Your brain perceives a sound wave with a higher frequency as a higher pitch. Shortening the length of a vibrating string on a violin by pressing your finger onto the fingerboard generates a higher pitch for the same reason.

B. Sound Transmission

What kind of medium transmits sound the best? A sound wave travels because a disturbance in some particles creates a similar disturbance in the particles directly adjacent to them. Naturally, the closer the relationship of the particles to each other, the more efficiently the disturbance will be transmitted. For the sake of illustration, imagine a room that is full of people who are standing about six inches apart. If someone stepped into the doorway from outside the room and gave the person closest to him a good shove, that person would be displaced and would in turn displace the person next to him. This would create a wave of displacement in the group of people, but the effect would lessen the farther it traveled into the room. Now imagine the same room fully packed with people, with no space between them. The same shove from the doorway would displace a lot more people, and the wave of disturbance would travel farther. A gas contains molecules that are far apart compared to the molecules in a liquid. The molecules in a solid are even more closely associated. This is why solids conduct sound energy much better than liquids or air.

1. Listen as your teacher or a partner taps a pencil eraser on the table. Then place your ear on the table and listen again to the same tapping.

2. Which medium produces a louder, clearer sound (makes a better conductor)?
   The solid table conducted the sound much better.

C. Doppler Effect

Describe the pitch of sound as a fast-moving car approaches you, passes close by, and then recedes from you. *The pitch of the sound starts high then gradually lowers until the car is nearly opposite you. At that point, the pitch drops suddenly and continues to drop but more slowly as the car recedes.*

If the car is traveling at a constant speed, its engine produces sound waves that are at a constant frequency. The speed of the sound waves emitted by the engine in air is essentially constant. However, due to the motion of the car, the spacing of the waves is closer in front of the moving car than it would be if the car were standing still. In the time that it takes to make a new wave, the car moves forward, shortening the distance between the previous wave and the new wave. As we saw in Section A, a shorter wavelength yields a higher pitch. Similarly, the spacing of the waves is greater directly behind the moving car because the car has moved away from the previous wave in the time it takes to make a new wave. Therefore, the wavelength is longer and the pitch sounds lower than at the sound's source.

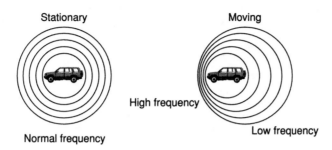

Stationary

Moving

High frequency

Normal frequency

Low frequency

graduated cylinder is slightly longer than one-fourth of the wavelength of the tuning fork you will be using. If you are using this method, try it out before class so that you will know approximately how much water you will need to add. The accuracy of your measurement depends on stopping as soon as you reach the resonating point.

D. Speed of Sound in Air

The speed of a sound wave in air can be calculated by employing the principle of *resonance*. If you direct a pure tone of a single wavelength from a tuning fork into a cylinder, a standing wave will result inside the cylinder. When the standing wave is successfully established, you will hear a distinct increase in the volume of the sound. This resonant condition is established only when the length of the air column in the cylinder is in a specific proportion to the wavelength of the sound. A cylinder with one end closed off will resonate when its length is one-fourth of the wavelength. A cylinder open on both ends resonates when its length is one-half of the wavelength. If you know the frequency and the wavelength of the wave, you can calculate the speed of the wave by using the equation from Section A, $v = f\lambda$. The frequency is marked on the tuning fork, and the wavelength can be calculated by measuring the length of the resonating cylinder.

1. Watch and listen as your teacher demonstrates a resonating cylinder.

2. What did you notice when the resonance was successfully established?
   The volume of the sound increased.

3. What is the frequency of the tuning fork (Hz)? *Answers will vary.*

4. What is the length of the air column in the cylinder (m)? *Answers will vary.*

5. What is the calculated wavelength (m)? $\lambda = 4 \times L$ *(closed cylinder)* or $\lambda = 2 \times L$ *(open cylinder)*

6. What is the calculated speed of sound in air? *About 332 m/s ± 33 m/s (10%)*

2. Use a large graduated cylinder half-full of water and a glass tube 3-4 cm in diameter. Lower the tube into the water, bring the vibrating tuning fork over the end of the tube, and continue lowering the tube into the water. The water surface forms a closed reflecting end. A benefit of this method is that it allows you to pass through the resonating point and come back to it simply by raising or lowering the tube. Measure the length of the tube above the water surface and calculate the wavelength as above. There is a slight error introduced because a small amount of air vibrates above the cylinder as well. We will disregard this error in these calculations.

3. Although glass resonates better, you could use heavy construction paper or manila folders to construct two tubes approximately 2-3 cm in diameter, one fitting tightly inside the other. Tape a piece of cardboard over one of the ends to create a reflecting surface. Strike the tuning fork over the open end and slide the tubes together or apart until you detect the resonating point.

E. Forced Vibrations

Sound waves are generated by vibrations, but they can also cause vibrations. If you struck a tuning fork next to a violin string tuned to the same frequency, the string would begin to vibrate as well. If you dampened the tuning fork, the string would continue to sound for a short time. Sources of sound often vibrate at many different frequencies simultaneously. When they cause nearby objects to vibrate that have only certain resonant frequencies, those frequencies become reinforced and can change the perceived quality of the original sound.

1. Listen as your teacher rings a buzzer, first by itself in air and again after bringing it very close to or touching various objects.

4. You could use resonating tubes from a science supply company, open-ended glass cylinders designed to resonate at only one frequency. They will resonate at a length of one-half wavelength. You could strike two tuning forks in sequence, one with the correct frequency and one incorrect. This will demonstrate that resonance occurs only under specific conditions.

E. Forced Vibrations
Various DC or AC powered buzzers are available from science suppliers, and they can be obtained from some home improvement stores. As always, Radio Shack and other electronics supply stores should be checked for solid state electronic buzzers.

F. Reflection
The cone can be constructed from heavy cardboard, or you can use a megaphone. Some schools may have parabolic dishes for other physics demonstrations that would be very effective in this case. We have all used our hands as makeshift megaphones when trying to hear someone from a distance. This also tends to focus the sound waves so that they are traveling in the desired direction. Point out that our external ears also function in this way.

2. Describe what happened in the cases where the sound quality changed noticeably. *The combined quality of the buzzer and object changed as certain tones became more noticeable.*

3. Why did this happen? *The sound waves coming from the buzzer forced the object to vibrate as well. The sound waves added by the object to those of the buzzer created a different sound.*

F. Reflection

Sound waves, like all waves, reflect off hard surfaces. This is why echoes occur. A sound source will emit sound waves in all directions simultaneously if the path of the waves is unobstructed. A great increase in loudness can be produced if all of the sound waves can be made to travel in the same direction.

1. Watch and listen as your teacher rings a buzzer, first by itself and then inside of a cone.

2. What do you notice when the mouth of the cone is pointed toward you? *The sound is louder than before.*

3. Can you explain why this occurs? (Hint: There are two properties of sound illustrated in this example.) *The sound waves are reflected by the cone so that they are all traveling toward you. The cone is also forced to vibrate with the same frequency, adding to the total number of sound waves.*

4. What do you notice when the mouth of the cone is pointed away from you? *The sound is softer than before.*

5. Can you explain why this occurs? *When the cone is pointed away, most of the sound waves are traveling away from you.*

6. According to your textbook, what is the process called that produces an increase of energy in a sound? *This process is called amplification.*

G. Diffraction

Do waves travel only in straight lines? If you will think about it, you will realize that sound waves are able to bend around corners. After all, you are able to hear a conversation taking place just around the edge of an open door. This property of all waves is called *diffraction*.

1. Listen as your teacher rings a buzzer, first in the room and then from around a corner.

2. What happened to the sound volume when the buzzer is moved around the corner? *Its volume was diminished.*

3. Why can you still hear the sound? *The sound waves bend around the corner and move to the hearer.*

4. Why is the volume of the indirect sound lower? *Most of each sound wave continues in a straight line from the source. Only a small portion of each wave is diffracted, and it becomes spread out over a large area, reducing its intensity.*

Wave Properties

Objective

The purpose of this exercise is to demonstrate visually the various properties of all waves.

Introduction

All mechanical and electromagnetic waves exhibit the following properties: straight line propagation, reflection, refraction, diffraction, and interference. **Straight line propagation** means that waves will move in a straight line in a uniform medium. This is the basis for ray theory, which you will study in Section 20C of your textbook. **Reflection** is the rebound of a wave off a barrier. **Refraction** is the bending of waves as they move from one medium to another. It is the result of the different speeds of the waves in the different media. **Diffraction** is the bending of waves as they move around a corner. **Interference** is the interaction of waves as they pass through each other.

These properties can be observed using a device called a ripple tank. A ripple tank is a shallow, typically rectangular, panlike container with a glass bottom. Waves (ripples, actually) are generated by rapidly dipping an object into the water. When a strong light is beamed vertically through the tank, the waves can be projected either onto the ceiling or the floor as alternating light and dark bands. If the light is above the tank, the light area below the tank corresponds to a wave crest and the darker area corresponds to a wave trough. If the light source is below the tank, this pattern is reversed. The reason for this effect is that the curved surface of the wave acts as a lens, either concentrating the light or dispersing it, depending on the direction of light.

Wave generation can include point sources (using a tiny ball or pencil tip) or plane sources (using a bar or ruler). Reflection off a plane surface will be demonstrated by placing a long block in the tank. Refraction will be demonstrated by changing the characteristics of the medium (water depth), and diffraction will be clearly displayed as a wave is observed to bend around an obstruction. The last demonstration will graphically show how destructive interference and constructive interference occur between two wave systems.

Introduction

If you performed the teacher demonstrations in Chapter 19, the demonstrations in this exercise will be a good review using a visually stimulating medium. This demonstration is written assuming you have procured a ripple tank from a science equipment supplier. There is no question that buying one with all the attachments will provide the most effective demonstration. Commercial units include wave reflection dampers at the edges of the tank, variable speed wave generator motors with a variety of tips for producing required wave forms, high intensity lights, projection systems, and various shaped wave barriers. It is possible to construct a very effective system, particularly if you or an acquaintance is talented in the workshop. Science suppliers offer the motor, lights, and projection systems as individual components that can be added to a home-built tank. You may purchase only those items needed. Attempting to project the wave forms from the overhead projector using a glass baking pan and a pencil as a wave generator is a distant third choice in desirability, but it is possible to convey some of the concepts in this demonstration using these items.

Pre-Laboratory Questions

Read the entire investigation. Answer the following questions prior to class on a separate sheet of paper. Use complete sentences.

1. Define each of the following terms:
   a. Straight-line propagation
   b. Reflection
   c. Refraction
   d. Diffraction
   e. Interference

2. Describe a ripple tank.

3. Frequency of a wave is directly proportional to wave _?_ and inversely proportional to wave _?_ .

4. How will the medium be changed to demonstrate refraction?

5. What do you call the points in a pattern of superimposed wave trains that exist where destructive interference occurs?

Procedures

A. Straight-Line Propagation

In this demonstration, you will observe how waves move, or propagate, through a *uniform medium,* that is, a medium that does not change in character or properties from point to point.

1. Observe as your teacher creates a single pulse in the ripple tank using a small object. This pulse is assumed to originate at a point, so its position is called a *point source.*

   a. All points experiencing displacement associated with a single wave are together called a *wave front.* What is the shape of the wave front associated with a point source? *The wave front is circular.*

   b. If you followed a single point on the wave front of a point source from the moment it was formed until it hit the side of the tank, what kind of figure would it trace? *The point would trace a straight line.*

2. Observe as your teacher now generates a single pulse using a straight bar. The pulse now originates along a linear object, so its starting position is called a *line source.*

   a. What is the shape of the wave front on the long sides of the bar? *The wave front is straight.*

   b. What kind of figure is traced over time by a single point on the wave front? *The point traces a straight line.*

3. State a generalization regarding the path that points on a wave front follow. *Points on a wave front follow a straight line.*

B. Wave Speed

If you performed Investigation 19A, you should have noted that wave speed in a medium seemed to be constant without regard to amplitude or frequency of the wave. In this section you will make observations that will either support or contradict that conclusion.

1. Using a stopwatch, note the time it takes a normal pulse in the ripple tank to travel to the edge of the tank. $t =$ _____

   a. Your teacher will give you the distance the pulse traveled. Calculate the speed of the pulse. $d =$ _____

   $v =$ _____

   b. Your teacher will next produce a single large pulse. Measure the time required for this pulse to reach the edge of the tank and calculate the velocity. $t =$ _____

   $v =$ _____

   c. Observe while your teacher creates a rapid series of pulses simulating a high frequency source. Pick a wave front and determine the time of travel and speed as before. $t =$ _____

   $v =$ _____

2. What can you conclude about the speed of any wave through a given medium? *The speed of a wave through a medium appears to be constant.*

C. Frequency and Wavelength

An essential relationship exists between frequency and wavelength for any wave in a given medium. You know that $v = f\lambda$. Recall that the wavelength of a wave depends on the duration of the original displacement that caused the wave, so λ does not depend on the medium or any other factor associated with the wave (it is an independent variable). Note that since wave velocity is a constant and wavelength is an independent variable, frequency must be dependent on the other two quantities. To show this relationship more clearly, the velocity formula is often rewritten as a frequency formula: $f = \dfrac{v}{\lambda}$.

1. As wavelength increases, frequency *decreases* .

2. If the wavelength decreases to half the original, the new frequency will be ___*double*___ the original.

3. If the wavelength triples, the new frequency will be ___*one-third*___ the original frequency.

4. Mathematically, this relationship is known as a(n) ___*inverse*___ proportion.

5. Observe the ripple tank as your teacher starts with a low-frequency train of waves and slowly increases the frequency. What happens to the wavelength of the ripples? *Their wavelength becomes shorter.*

Preparation

1. One day prior to the demonstration, fill a large container with sufficient water to fill the ripple tank to the proper depth. Let this water stand overnight so that any dissolved gases will come out of solution. This will avoid the development of bubbles in the water during the demonstration.

2. Set up the ripple tank according to the manufacturer's instructions.

3. If your ceiling is light-colored and smooth, it is generally more effective to project the waves onto the ceiling by placing the lamp under the tank. If this is not possible, place the tank apparatus over a large sheet of paper on the floor and project the waves onto the paper from above. As mentioned in the introduction, some systems have screens and projection systems to throw an image onto a wall.

4. The wave generator should be a variable speed motor with the ability to hold two point sources (small wooden or plastic balls) and a line source (a wooden or plastic bar). If you are forming waves manually, make a holder so that two points will touch the water simultaneously for Section G.

5. If you are making your own ripple tank barrier components, they can be made from sheet Plexiglas and other dense materials (wood will float!) with basic shop tools. The barriers must be thick enough or wide enough to stand above the working depth of the water. You will need a long, narrow, rectangular barrier for Section D. The circular barrier for Section D can be made from a washed tuna

D. Reflection

For this demonstration, your teacher will insert a series of barriers in the ripple tank. Using several wave sources, he will reflect the trains of waves off the barriers at various angles.

1. Describe the pattern of the reflected waves when the source is parallel to the reflecting surface. *The waves are also parallel to the source and reflecting surface.*

2. With the reflecting surface oriented at a 45° angle to the direction of wave travel, describe the orientation of the reflected wave fronts compared to the original waves. *The reflected wave fronts are perpendicular to the original wave fronts.* Sketch this observation in the Results section under Reflection, Diagram A.

3. How does the angle of the incoming wave to the barrier compare to the angle of the reflected wave? *The two angles appear to be equal.*

4. Observe as your teacher generates reflections with a point source. What is the shape of the reflected wave fronts? *They are shaped like arcs or portions of circles.*

5. In the Results section under Reflection, Diagram B, sketch the wave fronts resulting from a plane wave reflecting off a circular object.

E. Refraction

It is difficult to show refraction as a wave passes from one medium to another in a ripple tank because the two liquids would have to be in contact, yet separated. Instead, your teacher will simulate the effect that a shoaling bottom (becoming shallower) along a shoreline has on an approaching wave.

1. Observe as your teacher generates a continuous train of waves that move from the normal depth of the tank across the Plexiglas plate.

2. Compare the speed of the waves over the plate to the waves still in the "deeper" water of the tank. *The shallow water waves should appear to be moving slower—they lag behind the deep-water waves.*

3. Compare the wavelengths of the waves over the plate to the waves still in the "deeper" water. *The wavelengths should appear shorter with the wave fronts closer together.*

4. It appeared that for the waves above the plate, both wavelength and the wave speed changed in the same direction. Does this violate the wave velocity formula? Explain your answer. *No, the formula assumes a uniform medium. The change in depth over the plate alters the medium.*

5. Sketch your observation in the Results section under Refraction.

Name _____

Date _____ Hour _____

F. Diffraction

A characteristic of all waves is the ability to undergo diffraction. In fact, diffraction is one of the key differences in behavior between particles and waves. The model of the electron was greatly complicated when it was discovered that this so-called elementary sub-atomic *particle* exhibited the property of diffraction. Diffraction occurs whenever a wave front intersects the edge of a barrier. Part of the wave is reflected, part moves on in the original direction, and some of the energy is deflected as the wave wraps around the edge of the barrier.

1. Observe as your teacher generates a train of wave fronts that intersect a single barrier. Sketch your observations in the Results section under Diffraction, Diagram A.

2. Next observe as a train of waves intersects two barriers placed nearly end-to-end forming a small gap. What is formed on the side of the gap opposite the wave source? *A series of semicircular waves are formed.*

3. What kind of wave source does diffraction through a small opening simulate? *The diffraction through the opening simulates a point source.*

4. Sketch your observations in the Results section under Diffraction, Diagram B.

5. (Optional) If you imagine the opening in question 3 reduced in size to a point, make a generalization about every point on a wave front. *Every point on a wave front is a point source for a wave.*

G. Interference

You learned in Chapter 19 that two waves intersecting each other will interfere in some way but will pass through each other unchanged. When two trains of waves are superimposed on each other, the results can be very complex. In the demonstration of interference, on the projection of the ripple tank pattern, you will note bright areas, dark areas, and places that are of intermediate intensity (gray). Recall from Investigation 19A that a standing wave was characterized by nodes (points that did not move) and antinodes (points that alternately were crests or troughs). When two wave trains are superimposed, the bright and dark areas are the antinodes, while the gray areas are the nodes as the two trains interfere constructively and destructively. The diagram below is a typical interference pattern formed by the wave fronts of two point sources.

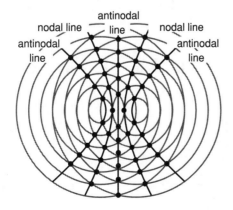

demonstrate reflection from them at this time. A parabolic reflector is particularly interesting because all waves from a line generator will be reflected to exactly one point. This information will be built upon later in the chapter.

2. The intent of steps 1-3 is to show the students the law of reflection, which will be discussed in a later section in the text. Start with the barrier parallel to the wave generator. Change its angle until it is at a 45° angle to the wave train.

3. Use a curved barrier or a tuna fish can to demonstrate reflection from a convex surface.

E. Refraction

1. Place the Plexiglas plate in the tank so that the waves will travel along its length. Run the line generator at a low speed. Students will see that the waves over the plate are slower and closer together than in the deeper water. You can bend the waves by placing the plate at an angle to the incoming waves.

2. Point out to the students that many factors can change the medium's characteristics, including temperature, pressure, density, depth, the existence of dissolved or suspended matter in the medium, or even a change in chemical composition.

F. Diffraction

1. Place a barrier so that half of the wave front from a line wave generator will pass and half will be reflected. Point out to the students how the waves bend at the edge of the barrier, moving into the "shadow zone" behind the barrier.

1. Observe the ripple tank projection as two point sources are vibrated to form the interfering wave patterns and note the location of the points of constructive and destructive interference.

2. Note the pattern of the ripples on the surface of the water in the tank. Observe that there are exceptionally high and low points as well as points where the water surface is essentially motionless.

3. Which of the points represent constructive interference? *The points having exceptionally high or low spots in the water represent constructive interference.*

4. Explain why some points on the surface of the water appear motionless. *The waves passing through these points are interfering destructively, so there is no displacement. These are the nodes of the standing waves.*

Results

A.–C. (No results required)

D. Reflection

A

Angled Plane Reflection

B

Circular Reflection

E. Refraction

Refraction Across a Plate

F. Diffraction

General Comments

1. Have the students make schematic sketches of the principal ripples in the Results section. Tell them to ignore the reflected ripples from the sides of the tank as well as the shadows of the wave generator components.

2. One or more of these demonstrations can be performed again later in the chapter when discussing optics to reinforce those concepts.

A	**B**
Single-Edge Diffraction	**Diffraction Through a Gap**

G. (No results required)

Virtual Images

Objective

The purpose of this investigation is to

1. Determine the distance of an object and its virtual image from a plane mirror.

2. Determine the relationship between the angle of incidence and the angle of reflection.

Materials

Cardboard
Paper
Tape
Wooden block

Equipment

Plane mirror
Protractor
Straight pins

Introduction

As you have learned from your text, mirrors are capable of generating various types of images depending on the shape of the mirror. Images have several characteristics that have to be evaluated in order to classify them. Before we discuss these, recall that an image is formed in the brain from optical organs (eyes) that must receive and focus incoming light rays. If these light rays arrive in the eyes in the correct angular relationship so that they form a pattern that is recognizable, an image will be formed of an object, whether or not that image really exists in the perceived location. This is the fundamental difference between real images and virtual images. A **real image** can be formed and focused on a surface at a specific location, with or without the presence of a mind to perceive it. A **virtual image** can only be perceived by the mind—it does not really exist.

The reason we see a virtual image is that our eyes and our mind assume that light always travels in a straight line. We know through logic that the light rays forming the image were reflected at the mirror, but our mind perceives the light as coming from behind the mirror. Without logical clues, we could not perceive the difference between a real object and a virtual image. Have you ever been confused by a mirror maze? It is difficult to tell what is real and what is not. Interior decorators use the illusion of virtual images to good effect to make rooms appear larger than they actually are.

Single plane (flat) mirrors can produce only virtual images. These images appear to exist on the opposite side of the mirror from the object forming them. They also appear to be the same size as the object (taking perspective into account), they are upright, and they appear to exist at the same distance from the mirror as the object. Other kinds of images (formed by curved mirrors) can be either virtual or real. They also can have additional properties. They can (1) be formed in front of the mirror, (2) be inverted compared to the object, and (3) appear smaller or larger than the object.

Introduction

This investigation is an easy introduction to ray optics. Be sure to cover the differences between real and virtual images. It may lead to some interesting philosophical discussions.

General Comments

1. It is difficult for the students to know which pins in the mirror to line up. Walk the students through steps 1 through 8 as a group and make sure everybody has drawn his line correctly.

2. The use of pins with colored heads helps the students to differentiate the different pins in the mirror.

In this exercise you will verify the properties of images formed by plane mirrors using some principles of *ray optics*. One of these principles is that a ray of light will reflect off any polished surface at an angle that is equal to the angle at which it approached the surface. This is called the *law of reflection*. Recall from your text that the angle of incidence and the angle of reflection are measured from the *normal* to the reflective surface.

Pre-Laboratory Questions

Read the entire investigation. Answer the following questions prior to class on a separate sheet of paper. Use complete sentences.

1. What is a virtual image?
2. What is a real image?
3. When you see the reflection of an object in a plane mirror, where does your brain tell you the image of the object is?
4. What is a *normal*?
5. How do you measure the angles of incidence and reflection?

Procedures

A. Virtual Image

1. Draw a line that divides a piece of paper in half and label the line **L.**

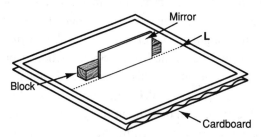

2. Tape the paper onto a piece of cardboard.

3. Use several small pieces of tape to secure a small plane mirror to a wooden block. Place the reflective edge of the mirror on line **L.** (The mirror may be a *front surface* or *rear surface* mirror, which will make a difference as to where the mirror is placed.)

4. Stick a pin into the paper about 3 cm in front of the center of the mirror.

5. Write a small **O** (for Object) by the base of the pin. This will help you to distinguish this pin from the other pins.

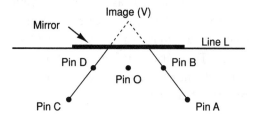

6. Place another pin about 3 cm in front of and 7-8 cm to the right of pin **O.** Label this pin **A.**

7. With one eye closed, bring your eye down to the level of the cardboard and sight along a line that passes from pin **A** to the reflection of pin **O** in the mirror. Mark this line of sight by placing another pin into the paper at a point between pin **A** and the image of pin **O.** Label this pin **B.**

8. Remove the mirror and pins **A** and **B** from the paper and draw a line through points **A** and **B.** Extend the line 8-10 cm past line **L.**

9. Place the mirror back on line **L.**

10. Place pin **C** about 3 cm in front of and about 7-8 cm to the left of pin **O.** Repeat steps 7 and 8 aligning pin **D** between **C** and the image of pin **O** in the mirror.

11. Remove the mirror and pins **C** and **O.** Draw a line through **C** and **D,** extending it until it intersects line **AB.**

12. The point where lines **AB** and **CD** intersect is the apparent location of the virtual image. Label this point **V.** Draw a line connecting point **O** to **V.** This line should be perpendicular to line **L.** Measure the distance from point **O** to line **L** and from line **L** to **V.** Record these values in Table 1.

B. Angles of Incidence and Reflection

1. Label the points where lines **AB** and **CD** intersect line **L** as points **E** and **F,** respectively.

2. Draw line segments from point **O** to points **E** and **F** to form **OE** and **OF.**

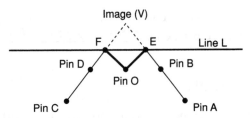

3. Use a protractor to draw a normal (a line perpendicular to line **L**) at points **E** and **F.** Label these lines **EG** and **FH.**

4. Measure the incident and reflected angles: $\angle r_1$, $\angle i_1$, $\angle r_2$, and $\angle i_2$. For example, the incident angle, $\angle i_1$, is $\angle OEG$, while the reflected angle, $\angle r_1$, is $\angle AEG$. Extending the lines with a pencil makes it easier to measure the angles. Record your results in Table 2.

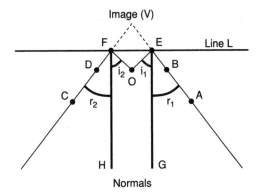

Results

Table 1: Image Distances

	Distance
Pin **O** to mirror	
Image (**v**) to mirror	

Table 2: Angles

Angle	Measurements
$\angle i_1$	°
$\angle r_1$	°
$\angle i_2$	°
$\angle r_2$	°

Discussion Questions

1. What is the relationship between the distance from the pin to the mirror and its image to the mirror? *They should be about the same distance.*

2. What is the relationship between the angles of incidence and reflection ($\angle i_1$ and $\angle r_1$)? *They should be about the same measurement.*

3. If you had used a convex curved mirror, would the angle of incidence and reflection still have been equal? *Yes, they would still have been equal.*

Experimental Evaluation

4. How sure are you that point **V** is the position of the virtual image of pin **O**? *Answers will vary.*

5. How could you improve your confidence for your solution? *You could project one or more additional lines of reflection to confirm the position.*

6. List some sources of error in this investigation. Be specific. *Answers can include errors in sighting along pins, errors in placing pins, errors in drawing lines, and errors caused by rear surface mirror reflections.*

Objective

The purpose of this investigation is to

1. Demonstrate the difference between the terms *focal point* and *image point*.

2. Determine when a convex lens will form real and virtual images.

3. Determine the effect on a real image when the distance between the object and the lens is altered.

Materials

Candle
Matches
Paper
Tape

Equipment

Candle holder
Convex lens
Lens holder
Meter stick
Meter stick supports (2)
Screen
Screen holder

Introduction

Light changes speed as it passes from one medium into another. If the light ray is at any angle other than 90° to the boundary between the media, its direction will change. This bending of light is called **refraction.** The phenomenon of refraction is used principally in optical lenses. There are many different kinds of lenses. In this investigation you will be using a convex lens, one that is thicker in the middle than at the edges.

Before you begin this investigation, some terminology needs to be presented to help you understand the process of forming an image with a lens and the properties of lenses. Some terms are very similar to those used for curved mirrors. The *lens plane* is the imaginary plane passing through the edges of the lens and its optical center. The *principal axis* is an imaginary line perpendicular to the lens plane passing through the optical center of the lens. Lenses are classified by their *focal lengths*. Examine the diagram of the theoretical object in Figure 1. Light rays parallel to the principal axis will converge at a point on the axis called the *principal focus*. The focal length is the distance of the principal focus or *focal point* from the optical center of the lens. Only rays of light originating from an object at an "infinite" distance are mathematically parallel. In reality, no object is infinitely far away or else you would not be able to see it (remember the inverse square law for intensity), but we can use this concept to define the focal length of the lens.

Now examine the diagram of the real object in Figure 1. All real objects are closer than an infinite distance from the lens, so objects will be in focus at locations other than at the focal point. The distance at which the image of a point

Introduction

Be sure the students know the difference between image point and focal point, and image distance and focal length. The focal point can be confused with the image point because of the similarity of terms. The focal point is determined by the convergence of light rays from an object at an infinite distance. Astronomical objects such as the stars are far enough away that we can assume that they are optically at infinity and that light rays from them are parallel. Real objects on earth are considerably closer, and their light rays are not parallel as they enter the lens. The points on the object do not come into focus at the focal point of the lens but at the image point. Students will observe this in Section C of the investigation. For practical purposes, the focal point is used to classify the lens and the image point determines the usefulness of a lens in a given application.

Preparation

1. The equipment includes parts of any standard kit called an optical bench, which can be ordered inexpensively from science supply companies. Supports come in different heights. Make sure when you are ordering that the various pieces of equipment are designed to be used together.

2. It is possible to perform the same procedures without the lens, screen, and candle supports, but the results will not be as

accurate. The supports are valuable because they are steady and they have pointers to indicate their exact position on the meter stick.

3. If you choose not to use the supports, it will be necessary to hold the lens in your hand, perpendicular to the table and parallel to the screen. You may need two people, one to hold the lens steady and one to adjust the screen.

4. You may want to arrange the equipment on the meter sticks beforehand to save time.

General Comments

1. Part A is done best by focusing on distant, bright objects outside such as buildings, stationary vehicles, or other distinct objects.

2. Make sure to measure distances from the center of the lens (the lens plane), not from the center of the curved faces.

3. Darkening the room while the candles are lit will help the students see when the images are sharp.

4. You may want to place a sheet of paper underneath the burning candles to catch wax drips. Depending on the surface of the table, the wax may be hard to remove without damaging the finish.

on an object is in focus is called the *image distance*. For an image to be *in focus*, all rays from any given point on an object intercepted by the lens must converge to a point in the image.

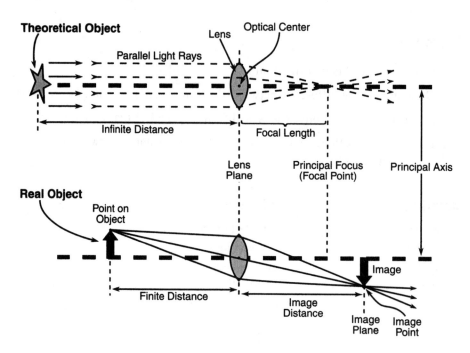

Figure 1

In this investigation you will be using a device called an *optical bench*. It consists of a meter stick supported by two stands and clip-on supports holding a lens, a projection screen, and a light source. Your teacher will explain how to assemble the components. Some questions you should keep in mind during the exercise are

1. What is the focal length of the lens?

2. When an object is placed near the lens so that the light rays striking the lens are not parallel, does the lens form a virtual image or a real image?

3. What is the size of the image in relation to the object?

4. If a real image is formed, what is the image distance?

5. If a real image is formed, is the image right-side up or upside down?

You will see that the answers to these questions depend on the distance between the object and the lens.

Pre-Laboratory Questions

Read the entire investigation. Answer the following questions prior to class on a separate sheet of paper. Use complete sentences.

1. What is refraction?

2. What causes refraction?

3. How can you determine the focal point of a lens?

4. Define the term *image distance*.

5. Would you expect to be able to see an image at any place besides the image distance?

6. Name a device that produces a virtual image that appears larger than the real object.

Procedures

A. Determine the Focal Point of the Lens.

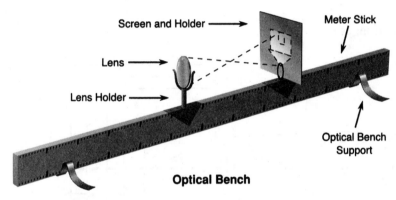

Figure 2

1. Clean the lens with lens paper or a soft cloth. Insert the lens and the screen into their supports. Set the meter stick into its support legs and clip the screen on top of the meter stick at the 50.0 cm mark. Clip the lens support onto the meter stick between the screen and the zero mark (see Figure 2).

2. Point the meter stick toward a distant object (>10 m away, preferably a brightly lighted object outside the building) and slide the lens along the meter stick until you obtain the sharpest image possible of the object on the screen.

3. Record the positions on the meter stick of the screen and the lens in Table 1. Subtract the lens position from the screen position to obtain the focal length of the lens.

4. Slide the lens support in either direction until the image is no longer in focus. Have different people on your lab team repeat steps 2-3 for two other distant objects.

5. Find the average focal length for your lens.

6. Turn the lens and support around on the meter stick so that the light from the last object is passing through the lens in the opposite direction. Check the focal length again. Do you find any difference? *Unless the lens is greatly asymmetrical, there should not be a significant difference.*

7. Was the image of the object on the screen right-side up or upside down? *It was upside down.*

8. How did the size of the image compare to the actual size of the object? *The image was much smaller than the actual object.*

Table 1: Focal Length

	Screen Position	Lens Position	Focal Length (mm)
Trial 1	mm	mm	mm
Trial 2	mm	mm	mm
Trial 3	mm	mm	mm
Average			mm

B. Real Images

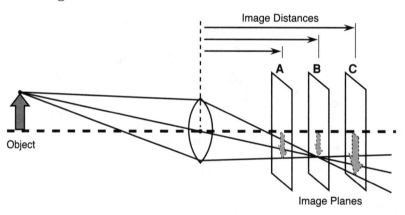

Figure 3

Examine Figure 3. Imagine light rays emitted by the tip of the arrow at the left striking the lens. Three of these rays have been drawn for you. If you assume that the thickness of the lens is negligible, the ray through the center of the lens is not deflected by the lens. The upper and lower rays are called the **limiting rays** because rays farther from the center ray than these fall outside the lens and cannot be focused. The limiting rays are refracted as they pass through the lens and converge (come together). The image of the arrow tip will be in sharpest focus at the point where the rays converge. This is called the *image point*. All points on the object that are a specific distance from the lens will produce an image at the same distance from the lens. These image points are in a single plane called the *image plane* (see Figure 1).

One interesting optical feature should be noted. If the object is not flat but has a lot of depth along the optical axis, not all the points are the same distance from the lens and their images will not all fall on the same image plane.

Therefore, only part of the image will be in focus. Also notice that light rays will still fall on the screen if it is moved away from the image plane. For a limited distance on either side of the image plane, you can still obtain an image, but it will not be in sharp focus.

Refer to Figure 3 to answer the following questions.

1. Are all light rays coming from the tip of the arrow parallel? *no*_____

2. What rays define the maximum amount of light that can be focused by a lens from any given point on an object? *These rays are called limiting rays.*

_____

3. At which screen position do the rays from the arrow tip converge to a point? *They converge at B.*_____

4. What do all of the image points that are in focus form at that position? *All points in focus form the image plane.*

C. Image, Image Distance, and Object Distance

The distance 2*F,* where *F* is the focal length of the lens, is an important position. You will observe the effect on the image and the image distance as you move the object through this point.

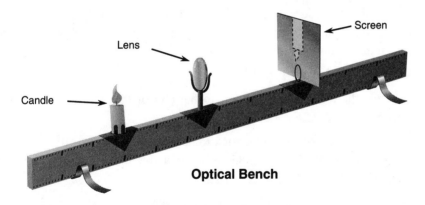

Optical Bench

Figure 4

1. Object Distance: 2.5F (typical of a camera lens)

1. From the data you gathered in Section A, calculate 2*F* for your lens. Use the average focal length calculated by your group.   2*F* = _____mm

2. Clip the lens in its holder at the 50.0 cm point on the meter stick.

3. Insert a candle into the candle holder and clip it on the meter stick at a distance approximately 2.5*F* from the lens.   2.5*F* = _____mm

4. Clip the screen and its holder onto the meter stick on the other side of the lens.

5. Light the candle.

6. Slide the screen along the meter stick until you obtain the sharpest image possible.

7. Note the distance of the screen from the center of the lens. This is D_I, the image distance. Record the image distance in Table 2 in terms of F by dividing D_I by F.

8. Notice whether the image is larger or smaller than the object and whether it is erect (upright) or inverted. Fill in the blanks in the data table for "2.5F."

2. Object Distance: 2F (typical of a photocopy machine)

1. Repeat the procedure, placing the candle exactly at 2F.

2. Enter the data in the data table.

3. Object Distance: 1.5F

1. Repeat the procedure, placing the candle halfway between F and 2F.

$$1.5F = \underline{\hspace{2cm}}mm$$

2. Enter the data in the data table.

4. Object Distance: 0.5F (typical of a slide projector)

1. Slide the candle slowly from the 1.5F position through the 1F position. Move the screen as necessary to keep the image in focus as much as possible. What appears to happen to the image as you approach 1F?
   The image becomes very large and is not able to be focused any longer.

2. Repeat the procedure, placing the candle at 0.5F from the lens. Slide the screen to obtain the clearest or brightest image possible. (It may be difficult to obtain any image.)

3. **Verifying the Image Type**

   a. Move the lens and its support to the end of the meter stick. Clip the candle at the 0.5F distance from the lens.

   b. Move the end of the meter stick to the edge of the table. To best do this step, the candle flame should be easily visible through the middle of the lens from the end of the meter stick.

   c. Close one eye and slowly move your head toward the lens while looking at the candle. Stop when the candle is in sharp focus.

   d. Estimate the distance of the image relative to the position of the lens. Calculate the D_I/F distance and enter it for Image Distance under 0.5F (in parentheses).

   e. What is the orientation of the image? *The image is upright.*

   f. How does the image size compare to the actual candle flame? *The image is larger.*

   g. Where does the image appear to be relative to the lens? *Answers may vary, depending on the focal length of the lens.*

   h. What kind of image is this? *It is a virtual image.*

4. Enter the data in the data table.

D. Virtual Images: Magnifying Glasses/Binoculars

You have seen that when an object is closer to a convex lens than one focal length, it will form a virtual rather than a real image. In a virtual image, the light rays from the object do not actually converge to a point. This is why a virtual image cannot be projected onto a piece of paper. The image does not exist at any point in space.

1. Magnifying glasses work by fooling your eye into accepting a virtual image that is larger than the real object. Hold the lens close to ($<1F$) the letters on this page. Describe their image size compared to their actual size.

   They look larger than actual size.

The rays entering your eyes from the magnifying lens make a wider angle than the rays would from the same points of the actual object. Your brain interprets this as the object being closer than it actually is.

2. The image formed in binoculars appears magnified but for a slightly different reason. Binocular objects are always greater than $2F$ away from the lens. In order to produce a useful upright image, the eyepiece is designed so that the pupil of the eye intercepts the outgoing light rays inside the $1F$ distance from the eyepiece. The image is virtual within this distance.

Results

Table 2: Effects of Object Distance

Position of Object	2.5F	2F	1.5F	0.5F
Image distance (D_I/F)	< 2F	2F	3F	(?)*
Type of image (real or virtual)	Real	Real	Real	Virtual*
Image size (larger/smaller)	Smaller	Same	Larger	Larger*
Image orientation (erect/inverted)	Inverted	Inverted	Inverted	Erect*

These can be determined only by looking through the lens at the candle.

Discussion Questions

1. Explain under what ideal conditions the focal point and focal length are the same as the image point and the image distance. *They are the same when the object is essentially at an infinite distance so that the light rays coming from it are parallel.*

2. Explain how the sun can be used to find the focal point of a convex lens.

   You can focus an image of the sun onto a piece of paper. Because the sun is so far away, the image distance and focal length are essentially identical.

3. What happens at the image plane that makes it an important location?
   The light rays coming from the object converge at the image plane. This is the only point at which you can obtain a sharp image.

4. Your eye functions as a lens. Which should fall on the retina of your eye, the focal point or the image point? *The image point should fall on the retina.*

5. Considering your answer to number 4, why is looking directly at the sun dangerous for your eyes? *This would focus too much energy at one spot on your retina, which could be damaging to your vision.*

6. Many broad-leaf plants can acquire water burns if they are sprinkled when full sun is falling upon them. Explain how this can be possible. *The water droplets act as lenses to concentrate sunlight on a small area on the leaf.*

7. Is the image formed on the retina of your eye erect or inverted? *It is inverted.*

8. Is the image formed on the retina of your eye smaller or larger than the object? *It is smaller.*

9. Discuss how different wavelengths of light refract. Give an example.
   Different wavelengths of light refract differently. Short wavelengths refract more than longer wavelengths. Examples include prisms and rainbows.

Material Safety Data Sheet (MSDS)

Chemical _____

   1. Hazard index: Health _____   Flammability _____   Reactivity _____

   2. Personal protection _____

   3. Warnings _____

       Target organs _____

       Storage or disposal instructions _____

   4. First aid _____

   5. Use _____

Chemical _____

   1. Hazard index: Health _____   Flammability _____   Reactivity _____

   2. Personal protection _____

   3. Warnings _____

       Target organs _____

       Storage or disposal instructions _____

   4. First aid _____

   5. Use _____

Chemical _____

   1. Hazard index: Health _____   Flammability _____   Reactivity _____

   2. Personal protection _____

   3. Warnings _____

       Target organs _____

       Storage or disposal instructions _____

   4. First aid _____

   5. Use _____

Chemical _____

   1. Hazard index: Health _____   Flammability _____   Reactivity _____

   2. Personal protection _____

   3. Warnings _____

       Target organs _____

       Storage or disposal instructions _____

   4. First aid _____

   5. Use _____

To the Teacher

Teaching Philosophy

The foremost aim of this activity manual is to help you reach your primary goal, to help your students become more Christlike. This goal is achieved in this science course by appealing to the whole student. There should be no artificial barriers between knowing and doing in a Christian school. In all areas of his life, the Christian student must realize that he should act upon what he knows to be true. Science can reveal to the student the wonders of God's creation. It can teach him how to make objective observations and analyze information. But you, the teacher, will teach him how to apply what he learns to his daily life by the way you teach and live.

Good scientific research is based on five principles that are emphasized in the investigations.

1. Human and instrumental error affect results. This is the reason that replication of experiments and data is necessary.

2. There is a difference between subjective and objective terms. Good science requires objectivity.

3. Research is a combination of observations and inferences.

4. Science rarely produces clear and absolute answers.

5. Science is self-criticizing. The scientific method is not so much a linear model as a circular one and leads to constant reevaluation of hypotheses.

The last point is perhaps the most important. The circularity of scientific procedure leads to better experiments and better research. It also leads to the development of higher-order thinking skills in your students, a critical need in this day of "fad" science. Public policy makers and politicians often use science in support of their ideas. Only those who are critical thinkers can discern between good and bad science.

Features

You will notice in each investigation of this laboratory manual questions that the student is directed to answer prior to the lab period, as well as discussion questions to be answered after the period is over. Requiring the students to turn in the pre-laboratory questions early will accomplish two goals. First, you will be sure that they have read the entire investigation. Some of the questions assigned assess the student's understanding of the introductory material. Other questions, however, deal with specific laboratory procedures, and the students will need to read the entire investigation in order to answer them. Second, you will be able to collect them before the lab, helping you to see whether the students understand the ideas that they will be investigating.

Many of the investigations in this laboratory manual can easily be performed at home or in a small school. Some use equipment readily available at home. Others can be performed with creative substitutions.

We have tried to streamline your preparation for each investigation by including a complete materials and equipment list at the beginning of each investigation as well as a comprehensive list at the back of the book. Extensive teacher's notes for each activity give directions for the preparation of any necessary solutions, alert you to any difficulties that you need to be aware of when performing the investigation, and give suggestions for substitutions that may be helpful for home schoolers and small schools.

Safety and Teacher Responsibility

Safety is an important consideration in any laboratory activity. Certain investigations in this manual require the use of chemicals that the students will not be familiar with. It is the responsibility of the teacher to ensure that these materials are handled safely. Each chemical will come labeled with certain safety information. Make sure that you are familiar with this information yourself before opening any chemical container. In addition, a Material Safety Data Sheet (MSDS) contains detailed safety information and should be obtained from the supplier for each chemical. Because students this age are often careless and because this may be their first real exposure to laboratory procedures, it is important to build into them the habit of considering and following the safety warnings associated with the chemicals and the equipment that they will be using. Indeed, some *teachers* have not developed good safety habits, and you must remember that your students will follow your example!

In accordance with this goal, one of the first investigations contains an exercise designed to get the students to notice the safety information by copying the information on the MSDS. Some teachers may wish to emphasize this to their students by having students follow this procedure with each new chemical as it is introduced in the investigations. Because class time is often limited and some chemicals are more dangerous than others, teachers may not wish to take class time for the students to fill out the information on every chemical. However, please remember that *you* must be aware of the dangers associated with the materials used in each investigation that you choose to perform. It is *your* responsibility to make sure the students are handling them safely. With proper handling, there is no reason to fear what you will be using.

For safety reasons, it is recommended that you store chemicals and lab equipment in a locked cabinet or a room that can be locked. Many Christian school classrooms are also used for other church-related activities. Easy access to laboratory materials could result in damage to your equipment and serious injury to curious, unsupervised children.

Propane, butane, or natural gas burners ("Bunsen" burners) are preferred for regular laboratory use. Alcohol burners are also available. However, alcohol burns with an almost invisible flame, and this characteristic has resulted in many laboratory accidents. Therefore, they are NOT recommended.

Because of substitutions in the recommended equipment or because of other unexplained factors, experiments do not always go as planned. You should become thoroughly familiar with the investigations before assigning them to the students and alert them to any changes that you will be making. It is also essential that you *perform* the investigations in advance of the lab period so that you will know what results to expect and what kind of assistance your students might need during the lab period.

Scheduling

This manual contains more activities than the average class can do in a school year. Most teachers will have to choose the activities that best suit their students, their facilities, their time, and their budgets. To help you schedule these activities, each chapter in the Teacher's Edition of *The Physical World* includes a planning guide. Be sure to consult these guides as you plan the activities for your class.

A decision that teachers commonly face is how much credit to give for laboratory activities. Most states require that 20 percent of the classroom time in upper level high-school science courses be devoted to hands-on activities. If your state has this requirement for this level course, the laboratory activities should compose about one-fifth of the students' final grades.

Following this section, you will find several tools that will help you prepare for the activities in this course. Alphabetized lists of the equipment and materials necessary to perform all of the activities in this lab manual will give you an idea of how your lab will need to be stocked before the beginning of the year. *The quantities in these lists are the maximum you will require for that item for any given exercise.* Following those lists, you will find a combined list of the materials and equipment needed for each lab. The list includes exercise numbers that show all items needed to prepare for and perform each investigation and demonstration. *The numbers of items in the combined list are per lab team unless otherwise stated.* See the teacher's notes for each exercise for possible substitutions and detailed requirements.

Obtaining Materials

You will need to submit your equipment and materials shopping list to your school administration early in the summer so that your orders can be processed in time for the beginning of the school year. It is wise to order supplies for the entire school year at the same time since some suppliers discount the prices of bulk orders. Discounts are also possible if you request a bid. Try to order hazardous chemicals from the same company at the same time. By shipping chemical orders together, you may be able to minimize shipping costs. As your supplies arrive and as you make local purchases, develop an inventory list that will help you keep track of your needs.

Basic laboratory equipment and supplies are available from many science supply companies. Because of legal restrictions, however, many of these companies will not ship chemicals to home schoolers. An order form is available from Bob Jones University Press to help you in ordering your science materials. Call BJU Press Customer Service at 800-845-5731 ext. 3300 to request a copy of the Science Materials Order Form.

Item	Size	Max #	Source	Lab	Remarks	Item	Size	Max #	Source	Lab	Remarks
Alligator clip	small	2	L	2B		Buzzer, DC or AC		1	S/L	19B	
				17B		Can, overflow		1	L	3D	
Apron, rubberized		*	S	9C	*one per student	Candle holder, optical bench		1	S	20C	
Balance, mass		1	S	3C		Cart, kinetic		1	S	14C	
				3D		Clamp, buret	(−)	1	S	9C	Optional
				15B		Clamp, knife-edge		4	S	14A	
Balance, spring	10 N	1	S	14B						14B	
Balance, spring	20 N	1	S	14C						15A	
Battery	1.5 V	4	L	17B	Optional	Clamp, test tube	(−)	1	S	4B	
Battery	6 V	3	L	2B		Compass, magnetic		5	S/L	17B	
				18B						18A	
Battery holder	1.5 V	4	S	17B	Optional	Conductivity apparatus		1	−	7	See 2B Investigation
Beaker	50 mL	10	S	5C						8D	for instructions.
				9C						17B	Optional
				11		Cylinder, metal, S.G.		1	S	3C	
Beaker	100 mL	8	S	4A						3D	
				5B		Dishpan	(−)	1	L	15A	
				5C		Electrolysis apparatus	(−)	1	S	9C	
Beaker	250 mL	3	S	1B		Eyedropper		8	S/L	3D	
				2A						9C	
				2B						11	
				3D						15A	
				4A						15B	
				7		Flask, Erlenmeyer	250 mL	1	S	16A	
				8D		Flask, Erlenmeyer	500 mL	1	S	15A	Large mouth
				10		Fork, dinner		2	L	13B	
				16A		Funnel	(−)	1	S	9C	Optional
				17B		Glasses, safety		1	S/L	6A	
Beaker	500 mL	3	S	5C		Graduated cylinder	10 mL	1	S	15B	
				10		Graduated cylinder	100 mL	1	S	2B	
Beaker	600 mL	2	S	4B						3D	
Beaker	1000 mL	2	S	15A						4A	
				16B						9C	
Board, terminal		1	L	17B		Graduated cylinder	500 mL	1	S	19B	Optional
Boyle's law apparatus	(−)	1	S	4B		Hanger, clothes		1	L	13B	
Brush, test tube		1	S	9C		Hot mitt		1	L	15A	
				15B		Illumination source		1	S/L	20A	
Burner, Bunsen		1	S	4A		Lamp base, miniature		4	S/L	2B	
				4B						17B	
				5C		Lens, convex		1	S	20C	
				6A		Lens holder, optical bench		1	S	20C	
				7		Light bulb, miniature	6 V	4	S/L	2B	
				9C						17B	
				10							
				15A							
				16A							
				16B							

Item	Size	Max #	Source	Lab	Remarks
Lighter, burner		1	S/L	4A	
				4B	
				5C	
				9C	
				10	
				16A	
				16B	
Line source tip, ripple tank		1	S/L	20A	
Lodestone		1	S	18A	Optional
Magnet, bar		2	S	5C	
				18A	
				18B	
Mallet, rubber		1	L	19B	Optional
Mass, metric	50 g	1	S	13B	Optional
Mass, metric, set		1	S	14A	
				14B	
				14C	
Metal (samples)	(−)	3	L/S	16B	
Microscope		1	S	5C	Optional
Mirror, plane	10 × 20 cm	1	S/L	20B	
Mortar and pestle	(−)	1	S	9C	
MSDS file			S/L	5A	
Multimeter		1	S/L	7B	Optional
				17B	Optional
Pan, shallow		1-2	L	2A	
Pencil w/ eraser		1	L	19B	
Pins, straight		1 box	L	20B	
Plank, wooden	1 m	1	L	14C	
Point source tips		2	S/L	20A	
Protractor		1	L	20B	
Rack, test tube		3	S	9C	
				11	
				15B	
Refraction plate, ripple tank		1	L	20A	
Ripple generator		1	S	20A	
Ripple tank w/legs		1	S	20A	
Rod, dowel	1/2 in.	1	L	15A	
				18B	
Rod, glass	1/2 in.	1	S	18B	
Rod, metal		1	S/L	17A	
Rod, plastic	1/2 in.	1	S/L	18B	
Rod, static, glass		1	S	17A	
Rod, static, plastic		1	S/L	17A	
Rod, stirring		2	S	4B	
				5C	
				9C	
				10	
				16B	

Item	Size	Max #	Source	Lab	Remarks
Rubber band	large	1	L	4A	
Ruler, metric	1 m	1	S	1B	1 per student (3C)
				2A	
				3C	
				4B	
				14A	
				14B	
				14C	
				15A	
				20C	
Ruler, plastic	12 in.	1	L	19B	
				20A	
Scoop, chemical	(−)	1	S	9C	
Screen holder, optical bench		1	S	20C	
Screen, optical bench		1	S	20C	
Slinky	long	1	L/S	19A	
Spectroscope, diff. grating		1	S	6A	1 per student (Optional)
Stopper, rubber, small		3	S	5C	Solid
		1	S	16A	1-hole fits flask
Stopwatch	(−)	1	L/S	19A	Optional
		2+		20A	
Support, optical bench		2	S	20C	
Support ring		1	S	17A	
Support stand, lever		1	S/L	14A	
				14B	
				15A	
Support stand, ring		1	S	9C	Optional
				17A	
Switch, knife		1	S/L	17B	
				18B	
Syringe, veterinary	50 cm^3	1	S/L	4B	Optional
Table, periodic		1	S	5A	
Tablespoon		1	L	8D	
				10	
Teaspoon			L	2B	
				4A	
Test tube	18 × 150 mm	6	S	11	
				9C	
				15B	
Thermometer	−10 to 110 °C	4	S/L	1B	
				3C	
				4B	
				10	
				16B	
Tongs, beaker		1	S	4B	
				7	
				10	
				16A	

Item	Size	Max #	Source	Lab	Remarks
Tongs, crucible		1	S	9C	
				16B	
Transformer, model train	(−)	1	L/s	17B	Optional
Tripod		1	S	4A	
				4B	
				5C	
				7	
				9C	
				10	
				16A	
				16B	
Tube, resonance, glass		1	S/L	19B	Optional
Tubing, glass	3 mm I.D.	1	S	16A	
Tuning fork, quality		1	S	19B	
Wash bottle	(−)	3	S	9C	Optional
				11	Optional
Wave barriers, ripple tank		3	S/L	20A	
Wire gauze w/ ceramic		1	S	4A	
				4B	
				5C	
				7	
				9C	
				10	
				16A	
				16B	

Materials for Laboratory Exercises by Item

Item	Size	Max Amt. Req.	Source	Lab	Remarks	Item	Size	Max Amt. Req.	Source	Lab	Remarks
Acid, hydrochloric		1 mL	S	11	12 *M*	Element—Cu		sample	S/L	5A	
Ammonia, household		40 mL	L	4A						8D	wire or sheet
				11		Element—Fe		sample	S/L	5A	
Ammonium nitrate		orig. container	S	1A		Element—Fe, filings		100 g	S	5C	
Bag, plastic		1	L	17A						18A	
Baking soda		30 cm^3	L	4A						18B	
				5B		Element—H$_2$		sample	L*	5A	*also from electrolysis
				8D							
Balloon	10 in.	1	L	15A		Element—Hg		sample	S	5A	
				17A		Element—I$_2$		sample	S	5A	
Bleach		45 mL	L	1A	original container					7	
				2B		Element—Mg		8 cm	S	5A	
Block, wooden	2 × 4 × 6 in. squared	1	L	1B						9C	
				3D		Element—N$_2$		sample	*	5A	* (air)
				13B		Element—Na		sample	S	5A	
				20B		Element—Ni		sample	S	5A	
Board, poster		3 sheets	L	19B		Element—O$_2$		sample	L*	5A	*also from electrolysis
Bolt, machine	1/2 × 3 in.	1	L	18B							
Bottle, beverage	2 L	1	L	15A		Element—Pb		sample	S/L	1A	original container
Bromothymol blue		as needed	S	11	Optional					5A	
Calcium chloride		15 cm^3	S	5B		Element—S		sample	S	5A	powdered
				6A						7	powdered
Can, beverage, aluminum		1	L	15A						9C	powdered
Candle		2	L	2A		Element—Sb		sample	S	5A	
				20C						7	
Cardboard, corrugated	30 × 40 cm	1	L	20B		Element—Si		sample	S	7	
Card stock		1	L	18A		Element—Sn		sample	S	5A	
Cereal, oat ring (Cheerios)		1	L	17A		Element—Zn		sample	S	5A	
Coal		lump	L	7				10 g		9C	powdered
Copper(II) chloride		1 cm^3	S	6A		Epsom salts		1 box	L	4A	
Copper(II) sulfate		50 g	S	9C	crystalline					5B	
		15 cm^3		5B		Fabric, silk	400 cm^2	1	L	17A	
Corn oil		5 mL	L	15B		Foil, aluminum		400 cm^2	L	4A	
Detergent		40 mL	L	11						5C	
Egg, hard-boiled		1	L	15A		Food coloring		1 bottle	L	15B	green
Element—Al		sample	S/L	5A						16A	
				7		Glycerol		5 mL	L/S	15B	
Element—Bi		sample	S	5A		Hair spray		orig. container	L	1A	
				7		Hose (rubber tubing)	>1 cm I.D.	>2 m	L/S	15A	
Element—C		sample	S/L	5A		Household cleanser		orig. container	L	1A	
		sample		7	graphite	Ice, crushed		1000 mL	L	4B	
Element—Ca		sample	S	5A						5C	
										10	
										16A	
						Juice, apple		50 mL	L	1B	

Item	Size	Max Amt. Req.	Source	Lab	Remarks
Juice, lemon		40 mL	L	11	
Juice, orange		75 mL	L	5C	
Lead(II) nitrate	0.5 M	1.66 g	S	9C	
Lead dioxide		15 cm³	S	5B	
Lithium chloride		1 cm³	S	6A	
M&Ms		1 bag	L	6B	Optional
Manganese chloride		1 cm³	S	6A	
Mass, unknown	<900 g	1	L	14A	
		1		14B	
Matches		book	L	2A	
				20C	
Mercury(II) chloride		15 cm³	S	1A	original container
				5B	
Metal, brass		1	S	8D	
Metal strips	15 cm	2	L/S	2B	
Milk		40 mL	L	11	
Mix, orange drink		30 cm³	L	8D	
Nail	6 d.	box	L	18B	
Nail, iron	10 d.	1	L	7	
				9C	Optional
Paint		orig. container	L	1A	
Paper clips	Large	1 box	L	15A	
				18A	
Paper, filter	11 cm	1	S	9C	Optional
Paper, graph		1 sheet	L	4B	
Paper, litmus	blue	1 vial	S	11	
Paper, litmus	red	1 vial	S	11	
Paper, pHydrion		1 pkg	S	11	
Paper, screen	large	1	L	20A	
Paper, sheet		1 sheet	L	1B	
				13B	legal-sized
				15A	
				17A	
				18A	
				18B	
				20B	
				20C	
Pencil, soft drawing		1	L	7	
Penny		40	L	1B	
				6B	40 total for this investigation
Pepper		30 cm³	L	1B	
Phenolphthalein indicator		as needed	S	11	Optional
Potassium chloride		1 cm³	S	6A	
Potassium chromate	0.5 M	0.97 g	S	9C	

Item	Size	Max Amt. Req.	Source	Lab	Remarks
Potassium hydroxide	0.1 M	2.8 g	S	9C	
Red cabbage		1/4 head	L	4A	
				11	
Rock		1	L	1B	
Rubber band			L	5C	
Salt, table		45 cm³	L	2B	
				4A	
				4B	
				5C	
				8D	
				10	
				17B	
Sand		15 cm³	L	5C	
Shaving cream		orig. container	L	1A	
Soda, carbonated, clear		40 mL	L	11	
Soda, cola		1 can	L	1B	
				8D	
				11	
Sodium chloride		30 cm³	L	1B	
				5B	
				6A	
Sodium fluoride		orig. container	S	1A	
Sodium hydroxide		2 g	S	11	
Splints, wooden		14	L	6A	
String		1 m	L	14C	
Strontium chloride		1 cm³	S	6A	
Styrofoam, cup	8 oz.	5	L	16A	
				16B	
Styrofoam, sheet	1 in. thick		L	13B	
Sugar		30 cm³	L	2B	
				4A	
				8D	
				17B	
Tape, masking		1 roll	L	13B	
				14C	
				15A	
				17B	
				18A	
				18B	
				20B	
				20C	
Tape, office	1 in.	dispenser	L	17A	
Thread		spool	L	3D	sewing
				13B	
				15A	
				17A	

Item	Size	Max Amt. Req.	Source	Lab	Remarks
Thumbtack		1	L	13B	
Toothpick, round		1	L	13B	
Vegetable oil	(−)	150 mL	L	8D	
Vinegar		40 mL	L	4A	
				5B	
				11	
Water, distilled		900 mL	L	2B	
				4A	
				5C	
				8D	
				9C	
				10	
Wire, copper		80 cm	L	7	uninsulated
				2B	insulated
				17B	insulated, 12-18 ga.
		200 cm		17B	insulated, 18-22 ga.
				18B	insulated, 18-22 ga.
Wool, steel		1 pad	L	17B	

Equipment and Materials by Laboratory Exercises

	Equipment				Materials				
Lab	Item	Size	#	Source	Item	Size	Amount	Source	Remarks
1A					Ammonium nitrate		orig. container	S	
					Bleach		orig. container	L	
					Element—Pb		orig. container	L/S	
					Hair spray		orig. container	L	These items are suggested, but others
					Household cleanser		orig. container	L	may be substituted. See Teacher's
					Mercury(II) chloride		orig. container	S	Notes for Investigation 1A.
					Paint		orig. container	L	
					Shaving cream		orig. container	L	
					Sodium fluoride		orig. container	S	
1B	Beaker	250 mL		S	Block, wooden		1	L	
	Ruler, metric	1 m	1	S	Juice, apple		50 mL	L	
	Thermometer	−15 to 110 °C		S/L	Paper, sheet		1	L	
					Penny		1	L	
					Pepper		30 cm^3	L	
					Rock		1	L	
					Soda, cola		1 can	L	
					Sodium chloride		30 cm^3	L	
2A	Beaker	250 mL	2	S	Candle		2	L	
	Pan, shallow		1-2	L	Matches			L	
	Ruler, metric	1 m	1	S					
2B	Alligator clip	small	2	L/S	Bleach		45 mL	L	
	Battery	6 V	1	L	Metal strip	15 cm	2	L/S	Most electrical components for
	Beaker	250 mL	2	S	Salt, table		15 cm^3	L	investigations in this manual can
	Graduated cylinder	100 mL	1	S	Sugar		15 cm^3	L	be obtained from local
	Lamp base, miniature		1	S/L	Water, distilled		705 mL	L	electronics stores, such as
	Light bulb, miniature	6 V	1	S/L	Wire, copper, insulated		80 cm	L	Radio Shack.
	Teaspoon			L					
3C	Balance, mass		1	S					
	Cylinder, metal, S.G.		1	S					
	Ruler, metric	12 in. or 1 m	1	S					Have one ruler per student.
	Thermometer	−10 to 110 °C	4	S/L					
3D	Balance, mass		1	S	Block, wooden		1	L	
	Beaker	250 mL	1	S	Thread, sewing		spool	L	
	Can, overflow		1	S/L					
	Cylinder, metal, S.G.		1	S					
	Eyedropper		1	S/L					
	Graduated cylinder	100 mL	1	S					
4A	Beaker	100 mL	2	S	Ammonia, household		15 mL	S	
	Beaker	250 mL	1	S	Baking soda		5 cm^3	L	
	Boyle's law apparatus		1	S	Epsom salts		1 box	L	
	Burner, Bunsen		1	S	Foil, aluminum		250 cm^2	L	
	Graduated cylinder	100 mL	1	S	Red cabbage		1/4 head	L	
	Lighter, burner		1	L/S	Salt, table		5 cm^3	L	
	Rubber band	large	1	L	Sugar		3 cm^3	L	
	Teaspoon		1	L	Vinegar		35 mL	L	
	Tripod		1	S	Water, distilled		500 mL	L	
	Wire gauze w/ ceramic		1	S					

Lab	Equipment Item	Size	#	Source	Materials Item	Size	Amount	Source	Remarks
4B	Beaker	600 mL	2	S	Ice, crushed		300 mL	L	
	Burner, Bunsen		1	S	Paper, graph		1 sheet	L	
	Clamp, test tube	(−)	1	S	Salt, table		15 cm³	L	
	Lighter, burner		1	L/S					
	Rod, stirring		1	S					
	Ruler, metric	1 m	1	S					
	Syringe, veterinary (Opt.)	50 cm³	1	S/L					
	Thermometer	−10 to 110 °C	2	S					
	Tongs, beaker		1	S					
	Tripod		1	S					
	Wire gauze w/ ceramic		1	S					
5A	Table, periodic		1	S	Element—Al		sample	S/L	Not all elements listed are required for this investigation—see Teacher's Notes for details.
	MSDS file		*	S/L	Element—Bi		sample	S	
					Element—C		sample	S/L	
					Element—Ca		sample	S	
					Element—Cu		sample	S/L	Those items with L for source may be represented by various hardware items of the appropriate alloy.
					Element—Fe		sample	S/L	
					Element—H₂		sample	**	
					Element—Hg		sample	S	
					Element—I₂		sample	S	
					Element—Mg		sample	S	Copies of MSDS information may be provided in lieu of the file itself.
					Element—N₂		sample	#	
					Element—Na		sample	S	
					Element—Ni		sample	S	
					Element—O₂		sample	**	**These gases may be obtained by electrolysis of water.
					Element—Pb		sample	S/L	
					Element—S		sample	S	
					Element—Sb		sample	S	#Nitrogen can be represented by a vial of air.
					Element—Sn		sample	S	
					Element—Zn		sample	S	
5B	Beaker	100 mL	8	S	Baking soda		15 cm³	L	
					Calcium chloride		15 cm³	S/L	
					Copper(II) sulfate		15 cm³	S	
					Epsom salt		15 cm³	L	Calcium chloride is one form of road salt.
					Lead dioxide		15 cm³	S	
					Mercury(II) chloride		15 cm³	S	
					Sodium chloride		15 cm³	L	
					Vinegar		25 mL	L	
5C	Beaker	50 mL	1	S	Element—Fe, filings		15 cm³	S	
	Beaker	100 mL	2	S	Foil, aluminum		400 cm²	L	
	Beaker	500 mL	1	S	Ice, crushed		100 mL	L	
	Burner, Bunsen		1	S	Juice, orange		75 mL	L	
	Magnet, bar		1	S	Rubber band	large	1	L	
	Microscope (Opt.)		1	S	Salt, table		15 cm³	L	
	Rod, stirring		1	S	Sand		15 cm³	L	
	Starter, burner		1	L/S					
	Tripod		1	S	Water, distilled		75 mL	L	
	Wire gauze, w/ ceramic		1	S					
6A	Burner, Bunsen		1	S	Calcium chloride		1 cm³	S/L	
	Glasses, safety		1	L/S	Copper(II) chloride		1 cm³	S	These materials are sufficient for a Teacher Demonstration.
	Spectroscope, diff. grating (Opt.)		*	S	Lithium chloride		1 cm³	S	
					Manganese chloride		1 cm³	S	
					Potassium chloride		1 cm³	S	* One spectroscope should be available for each lab team or student.
					Sodium chloride		1 cm³	L	
					Splint, wooden		14	L	
					Strontium chloride		1 cm³	S	

Equipment and Materials by Laboratory Exercises

Lab		Equipment					Materials				Remarks
	Item	**Size**	**#**	**Source**	**Item**	**Size**	**Amount**	**Source**		
6B					Penny		40 (total)	L		
					M&Ms (Opt)		1 bag	L		
7	Beaker	250 mL	1	S	Coal		lump	L		
	Burner, Bunsen		1	S	Element—Al		sample	S/L		
	Conductivity apparatus		1		Element—Bi		sample	S		
	Multimeter (Opt.)		1	S	Element—C, graphite		sample	S/L	The conductivity apparatus	
	Tongs, beaker		1	S	Element—I$_2$		sample	S	consists of parts assembled in	
	Tripod		1	S	Element—S, powdered		sample	S	Investigation 2B.	
	Wire gauze w/ ceramic		1	S	Element—Sb		sample	S		
					Element—Si		sample	S	The wire must be uninsulated.	
					Nail, iron	10 d.	1	L		
					Pencil, soft drawing		1	L		
					Wire, copper		40 cm	L		
8D	Beaker	250 mL	1	S	Baking soda		30 cm^3	L		
	Conductivity apparatus		1	L	Cola soda		150 mL	L		
	Tablespoon		1	L	Element—Cu, wire or sheet		1	L/S		
					Metal, brass		1	S/L	The conductivity apparatus	
					Mix, orange drink		30 cm^3	L	consists of parts assembled in	
					Salt, table		30 cm^3	L	Investigation 2B.	
					Sugar		30 cm^3	L		
					Vegetable oil	(—)	150 mL	L		
					Water, distilled		300 mL	L		
9C	Apron, rubberized		1	S	Copper(II) sulfate	1 M	49.9 g	S		
	Beaker	50 mL	3	S	Element—Mg, strip		4 cm	S		
	Brush, test tube		1	S	Element—S, powdered		5 g	S		
	Burner, Bunsen		1	S	Element—Zn, powdered		10 g	S		
	Clamp, buret (Opt.)		1	S	Lead(II) nitrate	0.5 M	1.66 g	S		
	Cylinder, graduated	100 mL	1	S	Nail, iron (Opt.)		5-6	L		
	Electrolysis apparatus		1	S	Paper, filter (Opt.)	11 cm	1	S		
	Eyedropper		2	S/L	Potassium chromate	0.5 M	0.97 g	S	These materials are sufficient for a	
	Funnel (Opt.)		1	S	Potassium hydroxide	0.1 M	2.8 g	S	teacher demonstration.	
	Lighter, burner		1	L/S	Water, distilled		750 mL	L		
	Mortar and pestle		1	S					The investigation has the option to	
	Rack, test tube		1	S					permit students to perform one	
	Rod, stirring		1	S					of the less hazardous steps. Be	
	Scoop, chemical		1	S					sure each student has an apron.	
	Support stand, ring (Opt.)		1	S						
	Test tube	18 × 150 mm	1	S						
	Tongs, crucible		1	S						
	Tripod		1	S						
	Washbottle (Opt.)		1	S						
	Wire gauze w/ ceramic		1	S						
10	Beaker	250 mL	2	S	Ice, crushed		1000 mL	L		
	Beaker	500 mL	3	S	Salt, table		45 cm^3	L		
	Burner, Bunsen		1	S	Water, distilled		900 mL	L		
	Lighter, burner		1	L/S						
	Rod, stirring		2	S						
	Tablespoon		1	L						
	Thermometer	−10 to 110 °C	2	S						
	Tongs, beaker		1	S						
	Tripod		1	S						
	Wire gauze w/ ceramic		1	S						

Lab	Equipment Item	Size	#	Source	Materials Item	Size	Amount	Source	Remarks
11	Beaker	50 mL	10	S	Acid, hydrochloric	12 *M*	10 mL	S	
	Eyedropper		8	S/L	Ammonia, household		40 mL	L	
	Rack, test tube		3	S	Bromothymol blue		as needed	S	
	Test tube	18 × 150 mm	6	S	Detergent, dishwashing		40 mL	L	The pHydrion paper may be
	Wash bottle (Opt.)		3	S	Juice, lemon		40 mL	L	substituted with any universal
					Milk		40 mL	L	indicator pH paper.
					Paper, litmus	blue	1 vial	S	
					Paper, litmus	red	1 vial	S	See Investigation 4A for
					Paper, pHydrion™		1 pkg	S	instructions on making the
					Phenolphthalein indicator				cabbage extract.
					(Opt.)		as needed	S	
					Red cabbage extract			L	Quantities listed are for the entire
					Soda, carbonated, clear		40 mL	L	class.
					Soda, cola		40 mL	L	
					Sodium hydroxide		2 g	S	
					Vinegar		40 mL	L	
13B	Block, wooden		1	L	Paper, sheet	legal	1 sheet	L	See the investigation to estimate
	Fork, dinner		2	L	Styrofoam, sheet	1 in. thick		L	dimensions of the wooden block.
	Hanger, clothes		1	L	Tape, masking			L	
	Mass, metric (Opt.)	50 g	1	S	Thread		1 m	L	Other materials are suggested in
					Thumbtack		1	L	the investigation Teacher's Notes.
					Toothpick, round		1	L	
14A	Clamp, knife-edge		3	S	Mass, unknown	<900 g	1	L	
	Mass, metric, set		1	S					
	Ruler, metric	1 m	1	S					
	Support stand, lever		1	S					
14B	Balance, spring	10 N		S	Mass, unknown	<900 g	1	L	
	Clamp, knife-edge		4	S					
	Mass, metric, set			S					
	Ruler, metric	1 m	1	S					
	Support stand, lever		1	S					
14C	Balance, spring	20 N	1	S	String		1 m	L	
	Cart, kinetic		1	S	Tape, masking		1 roll	L	
	Mass, metric, set		1	S					
	Plank, wooden	1 m	1	L					
	Ruler, metric	1 m	1	S					
15A	Beaker	1000 mL	1	S	Balloon	10 in.	1	L	
	Burner, Bunsen		1	S	Bottle, beverage	2 L	2	L	These materials are sufficient for a
	Clamp, knife-edge		1	S	Can, beverage, aluminum		1	L	teacher demonstration.
	Eyedropper		1	S/L	Egg, hard-boiled		1	L	
	Flask, Erlenmeyer	500 mL	1	S	Hose (rubber tubing)	>1 cm I.D.	>2 m	L/S	The flask should have a wide
	Hot mitt		1	L	Paper clip, large		1 box	L	enough mouth to accept allow
	Rod, dowel		1	L	Paper, sheet		1	L	an egg to pass under suction.
	Ruler, metric	1 m	1	S	Tape, masking		1 roll	L	
	Support stand, lever		1	S	Thread		1 roll	L	
15B	Balance, mass		1	S	Corn oil		5 mL	L	
	Brush, test tube		1	S	Food coloring	Green	1 bottle	L	
	Eye dropper		1	S/L	Glycerol		5 mL	L/S	
	Graduated cylinder	10 mL	1	S					
	Rack, test tube		1	S					
	Test tube	18 × 150 mm	3	S					

Equipment and Materials by Laboratory Exercises

Lab	Equipment				Materials				Remarks
	Item	Size	#	Source	Item	Size	Amount	Source	
16A	Beaker	250 mL	3	S	Food coloring		1 bottle	L	These materials are sufficient for a Teacher Demonstration.
	Burner, Bunsen		1	S	Ice, crushed		1 L	L	
	Flask, Erlenmeyer	250 mL	1	S	Styrofoam, cup	8 oz.	5	L	
	Lighter, burner		1	L/S					
	Stopper, rubber, 1-hole		1	S					
	Tripod		1	S					
	Tubing, glass	3 mm I.D.	1	S/L					
	Wire gauze w/ ceramic		1	S					
16B	Balance, mass		1	S	Styrofoam cup	8 oz.	3	L	Metal samples may include specific gravity cylinders required for other exercises as well as element samples obtained from science suppliers. Hardware components may also be used.
	Beaker	1000 mL	1	S					
	Burner, Bunsen		1	S					
	Lighter, burner		1	L/S					
	Metal sample (various)		3 (as needed)	L/S					
	Rod, stirring		1	S					
	Thermometer	−10 to 110 °C	1	S					
	Tongs, crucible		1	S					
	Tripod		1	S					
	Wire gauze w/ ceramic		1	S					
17A	Rod, metal		1	L	Bag, plastic		1	L	
	Rod, static, glass		1	S/L	Balloon		1	L	
	Rod, static, plastic		1	S/L	Cereal, oat ring (Cheerios)		1	L	
	Support ring		1	S	Fabric, silk	400 cm²	1	L	
	Supprt stand		1	S	Paper, sheet		1	L	
					Tape, office	1 in.	dispenser	L	
					Thread		1 spool	L	
17B	Alligator clip	small	2	L/S	Salt, table		30 g	L	The quantities shown are those required for one lab team to build all stations in sequence. See investigation if all stations will be set up simultaneously. The conductivity apparatus (optional) consists of parts assembled in Investigation 2B, which are also used for other stations in this investigation.
	Battery (Opt.)	1.5 V	4	L	Sugar		30 g	L	
	Battery holder (Opt.)	1.5 V	4	S	Tape, masking		1 roll	L	
	Beaker	250 mL	3	S	Wire, copper, insulated	18-22 ga.	2 m	L	
	Board, terminal		1	L	Wire, copper, insulated	12-16 ga.	20 cm	L	
	Compass, magnetic		1	L/S	Wool, steel		1 pad	L	
	Conductivity apparatus		1	L					
	Lamp base, miniature		4	L/S					
	Light bulb, miniature	6 VDC	4	L/S					
	Multimeter (Opt.)		1	S					
	Switch, knife		1	L/S					
	Transformer, model train (Opt.)		1	L/S					
18A	Compass, magnetic		5	S/L	Card stock		1	L	
	Lodestone (Opt.)		1	S	Element—Fe, filings		100 g	S	
	Magnet, bar		2	S	Paper clips		box	L	
					Paper, sheet		1	L	
					Tape, masking		1 roll	L	
18B	Battery	6 VDC	3	L	Bolt, machine	1/2 × 3 in.	1	L	
	Magnet, bar		2	S	Element—Fe, filings		100 g	S	
	Rod, dowel	1/2 in.	1	L	Nail	6 d.	box	L	
	Rod, glass	1/2 in.	1	L/S	Paper, sheet		1	L	
	Rod, plastic	1/2 in.	1	S/L	Tape, masking		1 roll	L	
	Switch, knife		1	L/S	Wire, copper, insulated	18-22 ga.	2 m	L	
19A	Slinky	long	1	L/S					This is a teacher demonstration. A long Slinky will stretch nearly 10 m.
	Stopwatch (Opt.)		1	L/S					

	Equipment				Materials				
Lab	Item	Size	#	Source	Item	Size	Amount	Source	Remarks
19B	Buzzer, DC or AC		1	L/S	Board, poster		3 sheets	L	
	Graduated cylinder (Opt.)	500 mL	1	S					These materials are sufficient for a teacher's demonstration.
	Mallet, rubber (Opt.)		1	L					
	Pencil w/ eraser		1	L					
	Ruler, plastic	12 in.	1	L					It is important to obtain a quality tuning fork that will produce pure sound.
	Tube, resonance, glass (Opt.)		1	S					
	Tuning fork		1	S					
20A	Illumination source		1	S/L	Paper, screen	large	1	L	
	Line source tip, ripple tank		1	S/L					These materials are sufficient for a teacher's demonstration.
	Point source tips, ripple tank		2	S/L					
	Refraction plate, ripple tank		1	L/S					
	Ripple generator		1	S					A ripple tank purchased from a science equipment supplier is ideal, but a home-built one would be serviceable.
	Ripple tank w/ legs		1	S					
	Ruler, metric	12 in.	1	L					
	Stopwatch		1	L/S					
	Wave barriers, ripple tank		3	S/L					
20B	Mirror, plane	10 × 20 cm	1	S/L	Block, wooden, squared	2 × 4 × 6 in.	1	L	Mirrors should be first-surface for best results.
	Pins, straight		1 box	L	Cardboard, corrugated	30 × 40 cm	1	L	
	Protractor		1	L	Paper, sheet		1	L	
					Tape, masking		1 roll	L	Round-headed pins work well.
20C	Candle holder, optical bench		1	S	Candle		1	L	
	Lens, convex		1	S	Paper sheet		book	L	
	Lens holder, optical bench		1	S	Matches		1	L	One optical bench per team is ideal. Minimum requirements are a lens, a candle, and a meter stick.
	Ruler, metric	1 m	1	S	Tape, masking		1 roll	L	
	Screen holder, optical bench		1	S					
	Screen, optical bench		1	S					
	Support, optical bench		2	S					